Feas, Famine

Feast of Famine

A PHYSICIAN'S PERSONAL STRUGGLE TO OVERCOME ANOREXIA NERVOSA

Joan M. Johnston, M.D.

RPI Publishing, Inc.
San Diego

Recovery Publications, Inc.
1201 Knoxville Street
San Diego, CA 92110-3718
(619) 275-1350

Library of Congress Cataloging-in-Publication Data
Johnston, Joan, 1949–
Feast of famine : a physician's personal struggle to overcome
anorexia nervosa / Joan Johns[t]on.
p.   cm.
Includes bibliographical references.
ISBN 0-941405-26-5 (pbk.)
1. Johnston, Joan, 1949–   . 2. Anorexia nervosa—Patients—
United States—Biography.   I. Title.
RC552.A5J64   1992
362.1'9685'2620092—dc20
[B]   93-10620
                                             CIP

Acknowledgments

So many individuals have contributed either directly or indirectly to the creation of this book that it is difficult to know where to begin in thanking them.

In some sort of chronological order, I am inexpressibly grateful to all of those who knew me through the famine and refused to abandon me to the Lie. To my parents, Marjorie and Hans. To my siblings, Adele, Betty, Tim, and my brother who prefers to remain unnamed. To my faithful friends, Madeleine Sabourin, Ian and Betty Gorman, and Mary Ellen and Gordon Haggerty. To my ex-husband and loyal friend, Eric Thomson. And to those who have preceded me into death: my grandparents, Hans and Martha; my stepfather, Archie McLeod; and my messenger from God, Ernie Runions.

I thank also those of you who share the feast with me now. My husband, Peter, whose patience and loving support have made this work possible, and whose expertise has unraveled the mysteries of my SE/30 on more than one occasion. My beautiful sons, Ben, David, and Chris, who have waited with a gracious tolerance far in advance of their years for *Maman* to be finished with this work. My soul-sisters, friends, and patients who have played such a pivotal role in the unfolding of my ideas; particularly Mary Beth McCurdy, Karen A., Karen Blair, Jennifer, Monica, Paula, Barbara, Pat Kopyn, Bill M., Karen Lynch, Murray Dorin, Joanne Moen, and Rick Lundeen. All my giving friends at A.A. and Al-Anon who have encouraged my creative gifts. And, of course, my precious confidante and partner, June Kerr, without whose cheerful and capable presence overseeing my office I would no longer have a medical practice.

I am deeply grateful also to those men and women of letters who have unknowingly catalyzed my transformation into writer. To

Scott Peck, the first inspiration on my journey. To Matthew Fox, that Spirit-filled man of God who has influenced me so profoundly. To Anne Wilson Schaef, a woman whom I long to meet and learn more from in the future. And to Clarissa Pinkola Estés, whose poetry takes my breath away.

Thanks are due also to those who have taken risks on my behalf. To Carol Kostynuk, who started it all at Kananaskis last year. To Perry Segal, who was willing to try something new on his ward this year. To my publishers Valerie Deilgat, Ron Halvorson, and Bob Manley, who saw something worth accepting where others had rejected. And to my gifted editor, Jan Johnson, who has been unbelievably patient as she taught me how to transform a manuscript into a book.

Special mention must be made of Lana Ohler-Madsen and Henry Madsen, whose assistance with the research for part seven saved me many days of work, and who gave me invaluable feedback that helped to clarify my ideas.

Finally, and most importantly, I am eternally grateful to the One who laid the banquet at which I continue to feast.

The Lord looks on those who revere him,

on those who hope in his love,

to rescue their souls from death,

to keep them alive in famine.

Psalm 33:18–19

To BEN, DAVID, and CHRIS,

the three greatest miracles in my life;

PETER, who made them possible,

and my loving parents:

my father, HANS, who would have been there

had it been possible,

and my mother, MARJORIE BOWMAN MCLEOD,

who saw it all.

Contents

P r e f a c e

The story that follows is true. It is the factual account of a young woman's fourteen-year battle against a deadly illness. The disease that afflicted her has currently reached epidemic proportions in the Western world and exacts a tragic and frightening toll in the lives of its young victims. It has a mortality rate higher than most infectious diseases, results in more wasted years of productive life than lung cancer, and is less treatable than heart disease and leukemia. It brings untold suffering, not only to those directly afflicted, but also to every member of their families, and its course is measured not in months but in years and decades.

It is a paradoxical and seemingly incomprehensible illness: to the outside observer, to the families involved, to the victims themselves, and to their therapists. And it is this incomprehensible quality that lies at the root of the abysmal failure rate of every treatment used to date. Theories about the disease abound, as numerous as the thinkers and researchers who have formulated them. But despite some advancement in understanding of the condition, the treatments derived from this knowledge have as yet effected little change in the outcome for those afflicted. In the recent words of a leading researcher, "The number of different treatments which have been used reflect the helplessness and confusion which has characterized and still characterizes the treatment of [these] patients."[1]

This book will take the reader on a fascinating and, I hope, illuminating journey through the twisting and baffling maze of this disease, from its onset to its conclusion in what most therapists will regard as a remarkable and atypical recovery. Because the author viewed it in the same way, she saw no purpose in telling the story until nine years after its fortunate conclusion. Of what use could it possibly be to others? There are a large number of books published about real individuals who have experienced extraordinary recoveries from one condition or another. Why clutter up the shelves with one more?

But that situation has changed, and the story can now do far more than titillate the reader. In parts six and seven will be found a map, a blueprint for adding a new dimension to the therapy of the sick and suffering victims of this disease. And it is the author's fervent prayer that the blueprint, derived from this victim's exodus from the wasteland of her illness, may provide new hope for others trapped in the same ghastly torment, for their families, and for their therapists.

The disease is called anorexia nervosa.

The story is mine.

Some of the names and identifying details of individuals in this book have been changed to protect their privacy. However, I wish to acknowledge my gratitude to those persons—my family, my ex-husband, my dearest friends—who kindly allowed me to use their true names in the writing of this story. My desire to do so was urgent and inexplicable, even to myself, yet I am fully aware that they, too, might have wished to maintain their privacy had I not begged for their permission to shatter it.

I am also sincerely grateful to Mae Runions who, following her husband's untimely death, and in his absence, has permitted me to use his true name in this work as well. May it serve as a posthumous tribute to the integrity of one of the greatest men I have ever known.

Part One

In the Beginning

For He knows how we are formed;

He remembers that we are dust.

PSALM 103:14

C h a p t e r 1

"You're getting a little broad across the beam there, girl. You'd better watch out," my mother observed with a friendly pat on the rump as she passed behind me washing dishes at the kitchen sink. The comment sounded innocent enough, and neither of us knew that Sunday evening in September that it would trigger a chain of events that would decimate our lives.

"Do you think so? Maybe I'd better weigh myself." I had been eating more since moving into the university residence four weeks earlier. Years of watching Mom stretch her pennies to feed all of us had taught me to eat everything placed in front of me. Nothing edible had ever gone to waste in our home, and consequently I was overwhelmed by the enormous quantities of food available in the university cafeteria. I dutifully consumed everything I was "allowed" on my meal ticket.

After finishing the dishes, I went into the bedroom to pack up my books and clean laundry, preparatory to returning to campus after a weekend at home. I surveyed myself critically in the full-length mirror and had no choice but to admit that my mother was right. My bottom was bigger than it had been the last time I looked, my thighs thicker, my stomach bulging into a distinct paunch. My breasts were still small, unfortunately, so I was beginning to resemble a barrel. My gaze traveled up to my head ... Not bad ... It had a pleasing shape, the thick chestnut hair possessed a natural wave, and the features that stared back at me were passable. The bone structure beneath the pudginess was definitely good: the chin strong like my father's and the high cheekbones, straight nose, and broad forehead strikingly like my mother's. My eyes were also hers: large and set exactly the right distance apart and of an unusual color, green with tiny flecks of gold in them. If you ignored the poor complexion—and acne scars could be concealed with makeup—my face was decidedly attractive. I grinned at my reflection, but the grin faded as I looked down once again and saw my blouse and pants straining at the seams.

I opened the closet, pulled out the scale, stepped on, and was appalled to discover that it registered 136 pounds, a full 15 pounds heavier than when I had last weighed myself three months before. I had never been this heavy in my life and knew that my five-foot-three-inch frame, despite its heavy bone structure, should not be carrying this much weight. Part of it had been gained during the summer while the family was on vacation in California. We all ate too much during that month away from home, the pleasures of eating mingling with the exhilaration we experienced while discovering the marvels of the western states.

But I was nineteen years old, just beginning my first year of medical school, excruciatingly self-conscious, and the realization that I was now twenty pounds overweight was a considerable blow to my already shaky self-esteem.

"I'm going on a diet, Mom ... tomorrow," I declared as I finished packing my bag. "And I think I'd better dig out that calisthenics book with the pink cover and start doing exercises again, too. I haven't done them for two years, but I'm sure the book is around here somewhere." I rummaged through my chest of drawers and found the item in question.

"Good luck with your diet, Joan," Mom said as she kissed me good-bye an hour later in front of Pembina Hall. She had driven me back to campus as usual, not wanting me on the streets waiting for buses after dark. Already by 1968 the streets were not safe at night for a woman alone, even in Edmonton.

For the first time in my life I was away from home, engaged in a wonderful adventure. Pembina Hall was the female graduate student residence, and although I was not technically a graduate student, I had obtained special permission from the Dean of Women to live there. I wanted a quiet atmosphere in which to study, having not the slightest inclination to become embroiled in the frivolities that reputedly went on day and night in the undergraduate residences.

Frivolity had been conspicuously absent from my own life for many, many years. Shortly after my seventh birthday my mother had dispassionately informed me that Daddy would not be living with us anymore. I would never forget the unnatural calm in her voice as she introduced the word *separation* to my vocabulary, a word that quickly assumed a terrifying, mysterious connotation in my childish mind. Whatever agonies my parents had endured in arriving at this momentous decision were carefully concealed as Mom enlisted my understanding and support.

I had known for a long time that something was wrong in our household, that Mommy and Daddy were not a cohesive unit, and I would retain no clear memories of the two of them together during my early childhood. The startling contrasts between my parents were legion and involved every level of their beings. My mother had the intense fiery blood of her French-Canadian mother coursing through her veins; my father treated life as a game in reaction to the grim battle for physical survival that his impoverished immigrant parents had been compelled to make it. She, a devout Roman Catholic, educated and literate, had been expelled from a nunnery at the age of nineteen when her nerves collapsed; he, the atheistic son of agnostics, had sailed laughing through his military service trusting Lady Luck to protect him from Hitler's cohort. She was one of five children and valued above all else the treasure of family; he was the only son of Swiss peasants, spent his first thirteen years as an only child, and sought first and foremost an escape from his critical and domineering father. She centered all her energies on home and children; he much preferred to roam with his drinking buddies, seeking adventure.

Their marriage, like many wartime unions, had been a precipitate one, contracted in a fantasy time without insight into underlying motivations. It rapidly degenerated into a wasteland of noncommunication and broken dreams, from which my father fled by way of alcohol and work. Reared on an Alberta homestead during the Great Depression, he had received little formal schooling, yet his keen mind, mathematical genius, and spirit of adventure had resulted in his becoming a self-made man, an entrepreneur like his father. To us children, it seemed as though Daddy was perpetually away as he pursued one new business venture after another. He was never a presence in our lives but rather drifted in and out like a visitor. He did not drink at home, so my memories are not of drunkenness but of inexplicable absences and mysterious telephone calls that left my mother alternately shrouded in nebulous anxiety and seething in tight-lipped rage. In later years I would understand their marital problems and view them with compassion. But as a small child, all I knew was the desolation of lying in bed at night, listening to them arguing in the kitchen after they thought we were asleep.

And so they separated. Because marital breakdown was a rare event in 1956, there were no books written about the subject and no common wisdom to guide my parents. In particular, little was known about the impact of separation and divorce on children. In planning for the future, my parents were therefore left to their own devices—principally their common sense. My father accurately judged that Mom would do a better job of raising us than he ever could, so he went away. No court battle ensued, no dispute over custody or child support or visiting rights. He simply dropped out of our lives, as both my parents judged this would be less disruptive and confusing for us. He moved to another province, started a second family, and for the duration of my childhood all further contact with him was reduced to a few brief hours once or twice a year, a rare letter, and a parcel that arrived faithfully every Christmas.

My mother was a tough and independent woman, having been rendered motherless at the age of fourteen and shortly thereafter ejected from her home by the proverbial wicked stepmother. This undoubtedly accounted for some of her current strength, which blossomed in the face of fresh adversity and challenge. She quickly plotted a realistic plan of action for assuming the role of single parent to five children between the ages of three months and ten years, immediately began working outside the home to support us, and within a year had been accepted into a teacher training program at the University of Alberta, located in the provincial capital of Edmonton, a hundred miles distant from our small hometown of Edson.

Advancing her education necessitated breaking up the family for a year, as the cramped basement suite she had rented near the campus would accommodate only herself and one or two children. As eldest daughter I was selected to live with her and the baby in Edmonton and was cast into the role of principal helpmate to my mother, a role that filled the next ten years of my life.

During her second pregnancy my mother had begged the Virgin for a daughter, vowing to name the child in her honor if the request were granted. When I sprang from the womb in unison with the lilacs of April, she joyfully fulfilled the promise by calling me Joan Mary. "Joan" did not connote the valor and self-actualization of Joan of Arc but rather the privileged social position of the richest girl in her hometown, the envied only daughter of the town's doctor. From infancy I was encouraged to see myself as one specially favored, dressed in flounces and ribbons as the budget permitted, and at the same time taught to sit quietly with knees together and hands folded in my lap and to do as I was told like a good little girl.

My inborn nature allowed me to fit readily into this mold, so by the time of my parents' separation I was an obedient "model child," anxious to please my elders. I earnestly cultivated the virtues of reliability, precocious acceptance of domestic responsibility, unwavering self-discipline, and compulsive attention to detail, and received as my reward the praise and admiration of every grown-up I encountered. I never revealed outward evidence of such disturbing emotions as anger, hatred, and fear. These simmered far beneath the surface, generating such shame from my recognition of them that eventually I learned to deny to myself the reality of their existence. Good girls did not get mad. Good girls did not hate anyone. And although good girls might be afraid, they were careful to conceal it from everyone.

Fortunately this denial did not extend to my innate intellectual abilities. On the contrary, I consistently received rich rewards of maternal praise for my scholastic achievements, which were many. I had a natural inclination for academics, teaching myself to read by the age of three, and reading voraciously for the entirety of my childhood. I loved school, sensing that the secrets of the universe could be learned there, excelled at every subject, and my fertile imagination exploded throughout my school years. If ever I were bored during the lesson, I would close my eyes, soar to a faraway land, and participate in any number of fabulous adventures there, all the time listening with one ear to the teacher in case I were called upon to answer a question. From first grade I rose to the top of the class, and in 1958 and 1959, to my great delight, was accelerated through grades four and five, reinforcing my secret conviction that I was a special creation of God, his principal gift to the world in 1949.

This attitude predictably led to increasing rejection by my peers which was reinforced by my parents' separation. Coming from "a broken home" set me apart from my classmates in a way I did not like one bit, and I constructed elaborate fantasies in my mind centering on my absent father. My social isolation deepened in 1960 when the family moved permanently to Edmonton. Transplanted to a new environment at the age of eleven, just entering puberty and aware of my new status as "a young woman," I was painfully self-conscious about my somewhat chubby body, terrified of boys, and awed by the sophisticated ways of my female classmates in junior high school. My safest defense was to retreat to the sidelines where I could concentrate compulsively on my studies, secretly gloat over my superior academic position, and convince myself that I was far too busy and far too grown up to bother with such silly adolescent foolishness as clothes and boyfriends and dates. Besides, I had no dreams of becoming a wife and mother, as I was by now comprehensively disgusted with looking after younger children and rejected such a role for myself.

Instead I resolved to have a career. I was in high school from 1963–1966 and eagerly absorbed the party line being proclaimed by the women's libbers, who were rapidly gaining ascendancy. Always uncomfortable with my own sexuality, I was ready prey for the militant advocates of women's equality. From early childhood I had hoped to become a nurse. The idea of sponging a fevered brow or bringing relief to someone in pain had held a peculiar attraction for me for as long as I could remember. Doubtless the glamour of the role as portrayed in such children's books as *Sue Barton, Student Nurse* appealed to me. On another level, largely unconscious, perhaps I also wanted to be in a position of power over others. For despite my scholastic achievements, in the deepest recesses of my being lay a monstrous lack of self-confidence and a haunting conviction that I was, in fact, insignificant and powerless, particularly when compared with my mother.

Yet I was afraid of any job requiring too much initiative or decision making. What if I made a mistake? I believed as a child that I preferred taking orders. Except when answering straightforward questions in class, I kept my mouth firmly closed most of the time as I was always afraid of saying or doing the wrong thing, especially in front of my peers. I was obsessed with the need to be perfect, but lacked the maturity to see the futility of allowing myself to remain thus motivated. I could never be perfect enough to satisfy myself because I knew what a sinful, selfish, hypocritical prig I really was. I could only hope that I would not be found out. I constantly sensed that I was deceiving everyone around me into thinking that I was a good girl, leaving me in lonely possession of the secret knowledge of what a despicable creature I really was.

One's childhood years truly are filled with pain. Why is it that as an adult one recalls only the carefree times and completely forgets the agony of growing up, of budding self-discovery and self-flagellation? I am certain that it was not merely my strict Catholic upbringing that caused my torment, although it certainly contributed to the rigid conscience and impossible ideals that ruled my spirit for too many years.

I recall one of the most terrible periods in my life when I was thirteen and had just passed through puberty. I was filled with all manner of dark urges, which I was convinced were too evil to bring into the light of day. So I suffered alone, believing myself unique in my preoccupation with my body. I became so scrupulous that I could not take a bath without believing that I had committed a mortal sin merely by washing my breasts. On countless occasions I was convinced that I was doomed to eternal damnation, would slink into the confessional, and accuse myself of sins of "impurity." This agony lasted for about a year, until a priest who was a close friend of the family somehow sensed my problem, took me aside one day, and gently explained that I was not the great sinner I believed myself to be, that God wanted me to be filled with his love and his peace, not riddled by guilt. After that I gradually stopped brooding over my actions; the inner debate over whether I had or had not sinned in any particular situation died a natural death as my faith matured slightly.

Thus did my high school years pass. The first time I ever questioned whether I should become a nurse after graduation was in eleventh grade; I was blessed with one of the best teachers I have ever known. She did not merely *teach* English literature but rather breathed life into it, leading me to fall in love with Shakespeare, Blake, Coleridge, Byron. I started to consider taking an arts degree, knowing that my grades were high enough to earn scholarships and honor prizes sufficient to pay for any amount of university education I desired. My mother fueled this new ambition with all her ingenuity, for she thought it nothing short of tragic that I wanted to be a nurse. Such a waste of such an intellect! She began to talk about medicine, pointing out that the University of Alberta had earned a reputation as one of the four best medical schools in Canada. At first I flatly refused to consider it. My stomach churned whenever I thought of all that responsibility, all the decisions a doctor has to make. Never, never could I develop the assertiveness needed to fill such an authoritative role, nor did I want to.

But I was growing up. I began to look at my plans with a little more common sense. After all, what could one do with a degree in English literature? Write? Possibly. I was showing some talent in that direction, had produced some poetry of sufficient merit for a school publication, and was writing a regular column for a small Catholic newspaper with province-wide distribution. Teach? That held no attraction for me. In fact the idea of standing in front of a class, talking without a script and, worse still, maintaining discipline, paralyzed me with fear. Public speaking was never easy for me; even delivering the valedictory at my high school graduation took more courage than I knew I possessed.

And so the idea of going to medical school began to take root in my mind. Maybe I *could* do it. After all, my television heroes Ben Casey and Dr. Kildare had done it. I would have at least seven years in which to develop the requisite skills before I would have to take any ultimate responsibility. And besides—I could always change my mind. In the end I compromised: I applied for admission to the Faculty of Arts rather than Science for my pre-med years. That way I could take some English options in addition to the sciences required for entry to medicine.

Those first two years of university were possibly the happiest of my life. I was still innocent enough to believe in my ideals for a better world and had acquired enough confidence to believe that I was part of a generation that would change the world, as I had bravely promised in my valedictory. My younger sisters had by now assumed a greater portion of the domestic responsibility that I had carried for so many years, leaving me with ample time in which to study and even occasionally to goof off. I adored my Latin professor, went to her home for informal evening tutorials where she regaled us with tales from classical mythology, and I even began to take serious notice of the opposite sex.

Although I still rejected the idea of motherhood, I had for many years indulged in vivid daydreams of falling in love with Prince Charming and living happily ever after. At the time I failed to recognize the significance of the fact that the prince in my dreams always bore a remarkable likeness to my father. I had been hopelessly in love with one or two of my teachers in high school but had almost never dated, and now at university I longed to be invited out on a date, despite the fact that I hadn't the faintest inkling of how to act on such an occasion.

Principally I continued to concentrate on my studies, and all my effort was rewarded as at the end of my two years pre-med I received a most flattering letter from the Dean of Arts suggesting that I reconsider my career plans. He encouraged me to enroll in an Honors

English program, not wanting to surrender to another faculty the student with the highest grades in his for the past two years.

In the spring of 1968 Pierre Elliott Trudeau entered the political arena and took most of the country, including our home, by storm. An intellectual! An idealist! Not a run-of-the-mill politician. The females in our house fell in love with him, beginning with my mother. She joined the Liberal Party and all of us worked on the election campaign of our local candidate, wearing big Trudeau decals pinned to our clothing and knocking on doors to distribute campaign leaflets. My youngest sister, Betty, was the prettiest of us all, a shapely exuberant redhead, and at fourteen was the right age to be selected to wear an orange mini-skirt and wave a pom-pom at campaign rallies. We were all bitterly disappointed when our candidate was defeated in the June election, but the experience of working on a common project had united the family in a fresh way.

That summer Mom took us on a vacation to California. We still had very little money, but that had never prevented us from having fun. We drove through the western states, camping along the way, and stayed with distant relations in San Francisco and Los Angeles. The Flower Children had reached their zenith, and as we toured Haight-Ashbury I fantasized that I was one with the barefoot, dreamy-eyed (I didn't know they were stoned) young people lining the streets. Disneyland was a fairy tale come true, and the fact that I was nineteen didn't stop me from enjoying it to the full. I still have a picture of the four youngest Eiseners arranged around a figure of Frankenstein at Disneyland, the three girls continuing to flaunt Trudeau buttons. I had no inkling at the time that that was to be the final carefree period of my life, the close of my childhood, the last time I would ever truly enjoy anything for countless years to come.

Chapter 2

"*Guess what, Mom,* I've already lost six pounds!"

It was a weekend toward the end of October, a month since I had returned to residence that Sunday night pledging to go on a diet.

"That's wonderful, Joan," my mother said warmly. "You're doing better than Adele and I are doing at Weight Watchers. Keep it up!"

"Don't worry, I intend to," I replied with fervor. "My clothes are starting to fit me again and it feels great."

I recall feeling very pleased that at last I was doing something better than my mother. As long as I could remember, Mom had been on one diet or another or talking about starting one. She had been markedly obese for at least ten years by that time, and my sister Adele was showing signs of following in her footsteps, a serious problem for a sixteen-year-old. It was that which had induced Mom to take her to Weight Watchers and attend herself as well, now that she at last had enough money to fund a reducing program.

We had all grown up filling our bellies with the wrong foods. Cheap starches and sugars were the staple of our diet, supplemented by a minimum of meat and costly fruits and vegetables. But we enjoyed our food, and I had never been concerned about excess poundage seriously enough to deprive myself of the things I liked to eat. Furthermore I led a sedentary existence, having no athletic prowess and preferring to keep my clumsy body off the playing field where I was vulnerable to the ridicule of my schoolmates.

But now I became obsessed. I applied the rigid self-discipline I had always used in my chores and studies to the task of shedding pounds. Initially I acted sensibly. I was taking my meals in the university cafeteria, so the selection was rather limited, but somehow I knew roughly what foods I should avoid and which ones I should cut down in quantity. After classes I would do twenty minutes of vigorous calisthenics in my room before going for dinner, no matter how tired or hungry I was. I became accustomed to feeling permanently hungry all day long and throughout the five or six hours of study that filled my evenings.

And every Saturday morning I weighed myself on the scale in the residence laundry room when no one else was around. What a thrill to see the pounds drop away! I felt a marvelous new sense of power. All my life I had heard people moan about how hard it was to lose weight, yet here was I, doing it on my first attempt. I felt as though I were the perfect dieter, just as I had always strived to be the perfect child, perfect student, perfect daughter. I began to live for the moment each week when I stepped on the scale and felt that rush of pleasure. I never wavered. As in every other sphere of my life, having applied my determination to the task, I would not let go.

At some point in those first few months of dieting my nutritional practices became somewhat more bizarre. I became more restrictive at breakfast: eliminating the fruit, putting water on my cereal instead of milk. I decreased my intake at noon and began to treat myself at dinnertime as my reward. In residence there was unlimited access to ice cream, a food I had loved since childhood when such an expensive treat was a rare delight. So I began eating smaller portions of meat and vegetables (having long since eliminated all starches from my diet) and consuming an enormous serving of ice cream instead.

I'll never forget one particular evening in December in the crowded cafeteria, finding a seat for myself at one of the long tables. Seated opposite me was a nun who also lived in residence, a hawklike woman whom I knew to possess a sarcastic tongue, although I had never before been its target. Her gaze traveled from my tray to my face in puzzlement.

"Why are you only eating dessert?" she said curiously.

"Well, I'm on a diet and …" I began, but got no further.

She erupted into scornful laughter, attracting the attention of everyone seated nearby. Then, regaining her control with some difficulty and ignoring my blush of embarrassment, she proceeded to offer her unsolicited views on the subject. "You'll never lose weight eating that way, girl."

Adhering to my usual practice in such a situation, I smiled and made no comment. Somehow I managed to eat my meal without choking on the hard knot of anger in my throat, judging that it would appear rude of me to move my tray elsewhere. The single thought filling my mind throughout the meal was, *I'll show you whether I can lose weight or not!* I tried to avoid the woman for the remainder of that year. Even now the recollection of that incident arouses a faint echo of anger within me. Powerful evidence attesting to the folly of suppressing such strong emotions. They never go away.

By Christmas that year my weight had dropped by eighteen pounds and I delighted in buying some new clothes to fit my new figure. By this time the loss was noticeable to my classmates and acquaintances in residence, and I received many favorable comments on my improved appearance. I felt truly attractive, perhaps for the first time in my life, and self-confident enough to begin attending our class parties with my only close friend, Mary Ellen. These affairs involved a good deal of heavy drinking, crude talk, some mildly outrageous behavior, and plenty of good fun. Parties like these were part of the tradition of med school, and we were all working hard to follow the script. I began drinking at these parties, a little too much on occasion if I didn't have to drive home. Somehow I didn't worry about the calories in the alcohol I imbibed, but simply ate less on the days of the parties. I enjoyed the feeling of being part of the group for the first time since early childhood. Perhaps at nineteen I was entering adolescence.

I recall one particular Saturday night, coming home very late from one of these parties. It must have been 3 A.M. when Mary Ellen dropped me off and I stumbled into the house. My mother was waiting up in the living room and was furious. "If you're going to stay out till all hours, Joan, you can damned well stay at residence on weekends. That way I won't have to sit up worrying about you!"

I recall feeling through my alcoholic haze a mild sense of pleasure to be doing something disapproved of for the first time in my life. The next morning, of course, I was properly repentant and promised to be more considerate in the future.

These parties were a normal and necessary outlet for us because first-year medicine is a difficult one, designed to weed out the students who will not survive the rigors ahead. The competition was fierce, the pressure high at all times, and I was finding it difficult to have only pure sciences to study. Although I had invariably excelled at subjects requiring rote memorization, nonetheless I found most of them very dull. Where was the glamor that had attracted me to medicine? Where was the patient? Our cadaver in anatomy class hardly qualified. I grew a trifle disenchanted with everything and wondered whether I had made a mistake in starting medicine. At times I fantasized about running away from it all, taking only my guitar and the poetry I was still writing in my spare time, and hitchhiking across Canada.

But I had never in my life quit in the middle of something I had started, and I was not about to do that now. Instead, in February I went to the faculty's student advisor and told her about my misgivings. Demonstrating the wisdom of her experience, she arranged for my professors to excuse me from classes for two days during the following week so that I might observe the physicians at the Family Clinic at the University Hospital. I followed them around from morning till evening and was utterly enthralled. I watched them interview and examine patients, reach a diagnosis, and prescribe treatment, all the while talking to me as though I were a colleague familiar with what they were doing. I made rounds with them and even scrubbed in on an emergency cesarean section one night, the first surgical procedure and the first birth I had ever observed.

I was hooked. I decided then and there to become a family doctor. The following week I returned to classes starry-eyed and never again faltered in my path. If what I had seen was the end result of these boring classes, then bring them on! I worked harder than ever and completed the year with the third highest standing in our class of 105 students, bitterly disappointed to have been surpassed by two classmates, both male, and resolved to do better the following year.

But I continued to socialize as well as study. In January I met Ian Gorman, a young graduate student from Prince Edward Island who was doing his master's degree in mathematics, and from our first meeting in the cafeteria we experienced an immediate mutual attraction. I quickly appreciated that he was a true genius, the most rational thinker I had ever met, and was fascinated by his brilliant mind. Peering at me from behind his thick spectacles, he could expound for hours on some obscure concept in philosophy or economics, generally leaving me with eyes glazed halfway through his discourse. His eccentricity also held immense appeal. Of short stature and with an unprepossessing boylike appearance, he was a man utterly oblivious to dress, food, and social niceties. It simply never occurred to him that he should care about what other people thought of him.

He had a close chum in the graduate program, an East Indian man who began to join us for dinner and occasional evening strolls around campus, occasions for vital and stimulating conversation. In February our little circle was expanded by the addition of two other young men, also foreign graduate students, and we became the self-styled "Fearsome Five," a motley crew indeed. I was in my glory during those early months of 1969. I truly felt like a rose among thorns and adored having four men to escort me to the residence socials.

I have so many memories of our time together that I can scarcely believe the association was so brief. At the beginning of May, Ian returned to P.E.I. to be married, but with plans to return in September, bringing his new wife with him. It was the end of term and the others also dispersed to summer jobs, but not before all four attended my twentieth birthday party on April twenty-eighth. I still have a photograph of the five of us sitting in our living room, me perched on the floor in front of the sofa with the four men arranged about me. To this day it evokes warm and vibrant feelings whenever I look at it.

At the end of May, Mom and I drove to Calgary for a Liberal Party fund-raising banquet. The drive afforded an opportunity for three hours of togetherness, an experience we had not enjoyed for many months. During a lull in the conversation, I watched the lush and gently rolling countryside of southern Alberta passing by outside the car and reflected on the rich blessings in my life. My thoughts were interrupted suddenly by my mother's voice.

"Joan, don't you think you've lost enough weight now?"

"Well, maybe," I said evasively, "but I think I'd like to get down to a hundred and five pounds. I'm a hundred and eight at the moment. I sure don't want to put it back on."

"I think you're fine now, just the way you are. Actually, your collar bones and ribs are starting to stick out a little," Mom observed, her voice edged with concern.

I set my mouth in a taut line and made no reply to this. I had made up my mind to be slender and was not going to let her or anyone else tell me what I should weigh or what I should eat. I had given no thought to what I would do when I lost enough weight. In fact, as the pounds were shed, I had set my goal weight progressively lower. For the first time in my life I was "petite," an adjective I had heard applied only to other girls of my stature, whereas I had always been merely "short." I loved buying size seven clothing and being too small to wear my cousin's hand-me-downs, which had been the mainstay of my wardrobe since I was three years old.

I had not considered the possibility that it was unhealthy to be below normal weight. My periods had occurred with clocklike regularity every twenty-eight days since I was twelve years old, so I was alarmed when my March period failed to appear. I had always taken my body for granted, as only the healthy young are able to do. Never in those days did I consider the possibility that my rigid dieting was a form of physical self-abuse, that it was a stress capable of disturbing my body's normal functions. So when I failed to menstruate, I did what any normal girl would do. I went to a doctor.

I still recall vividly my visit to Student Health. Neither I nor the doctors I consulted connected my lack of menstruation with my weight loss. I find their oversight curious in retrospect; not even the gynecologist I was referred to questioned me about weight loss. Perhaps she assumed that I was not underweight at 112 pounds. Or, more likely, in those days little was known about the connection between body weight and menstruation.

The gynecologist was a large matronly woman with a face like a basset hound. She studied me over the rims of her spectacles, then brusquely demanded, "Are you pregnant?"

I was shocked and highly incensed by this suggestion. In 1969 premarital sex was still frowned upon. Couldn't she see that I wasn't "that sort of girl"? Today I would have made a witty reply, but at that time all I could do was blush fiercely, then solemnly assure her that I was still a virgin. She asked a few more questions before asking me to undress for the examination. I was terrified as well as humiliated by the procedure and can still recall the excruciating pain when she attempted to insert a speculum into my vagina. I had tried using tampons only once in my life, about five years earlier, and had finally given up in despair, concluding that there must be some mystery about the anatomy down there that I had not yet solved.

"In the first place, young lady, you appear to have a narrowing of the vaginal opening that may well have to be surgically corrected before you are married." (I appreciated this belated tribute to my virtue.) She paused, fixing me once again with her eagle eye. "But that has nothing to do with why you've missed your period. That sort of thing happens in normal girls all the time, particularly during times of stress. I'm sure your periods will resume soon, but I want to give you some medication anyway, more or less as a therapeutic trial."

Her muddied diagnostic thinking amuses me now, but at the time it did not strike me as paradoxical that I was being given some pills to correct a phenomenon that she considered normal. Neither of us dreamed that I would not spontaneously menstruate again until more than fourteen years later.

She gave me a prescription for desiccated thyroid pills to take for two months, a treatment I now know to have been hopelessly outmoded as well as useless even then. But over the centuries menstruation has been shrouded in mystery in the human mind, and that particular treatment is only one of a variety of weird and wonderful nostrums that have been used to correct menstrual disturbances.

None of them really worked, which is perhaps the reason for their multiplicity.

My periods did not resume, but during a follow-up visit in May the doctor once again assured me that everything was fine, that I had only to wait patiently, and that in the meantime I was to enjoy my freedom. I had carefully conveyed this message to my mother, sensing the need to convince her that I was still healthy. But she remained unconvinced. To her, and probably also to me, had I been able to admit it, it was just not natural to stop menstruating, and this conviction may have been part of the reason for her appeal to me that day in the car en route to Calgary.

"You know you've never weighed less than a hundred and fifteen pounds since you've grown up, Joan. Remember you've got my heavy bone structure even if you are only five foot three. You're getting too thin and I think it's time to stop," she said decisively. I noticed that her knuckles on the steering wheel were white.

But I don't want your bone structure, I thought. I wanted to look like those models in the magazines and on television. Plenty of them were ten or even twenty pounds below their theoretically "ideal" weights.

I retreated into silence, my habitual response to any disagreement with my mother, but I recall thinking that perhaps it was time to stop dieting so rigidly. However when we attended the banquet that evening, my stomach churned as we lined up for the buffet. I couldn't do it! If I ate a baked potato or a roll tonight, how could I ever turn one down again? Everyone would expect me to eat potatoes and rolls forever, and then I would get fat again. No, it was far simpler to be consistent: "I never eat bread with my meals" ... "I never eat desserts" ... "I don't like potatoes" ... "I like my salad without dressing." These were simple rules. Never mind that they were lies. I would turn them into truths by sheer act of will. They neatly fielded offers of food I did not want. And besides, they helped me too: With rules like these fixed in my mind I did not have to bother making any decisions at mealtimes. Perhaps they made eating a little boring, but at least they would keep me slim.

Such were the thoughts that tumbled around in my mind that night. In the end I ate a plain tossed salad and well-broiled steak, carefully trimming off all the fat, and watched everyone else consume the beautiful desserts. As usual, I imagined their taste and at the same time experienced the peculiar pleasure I always derived from feeling hollow inside, from knowing that I had denied myself those fattening goodies, from affirming that I had the power to steadfastly do that and leave the table hungry.

In retrospect, I am not sure if I knew then that my dieting was becoming highly abnormal. I rather think I did not. But my mother knew and was daily growing more concerned as she was unable to comprehend my recalcitrant behavior. To this day I am not certain of how it came about that I became obsessed with weight control. How did the normal dieting become a disease? But I do understand why it happened and when. The "why" is found in my earlier life, in the vulnerable personality of the perfect little girl, all unpleasant emotions carefully contained, who was compelled to prove her worth to a menacing and unpredictable world, and in the losses that destiny brought her. The "when" forms the next part of my story and occupies the summer of 1969: an overseas vacation out from under the watchful eye of my mother.

Part Two

Descent into Darkness

He who digs a pit may fall into it.

ECCLESIASTES *10:8*

Chapter 3

"Have a wonderful time, you two! Write often, Joan."

With a final wave to my mother, I boarded the plane to begin a six-week trip to Great Britain, a once-in-a-lifetime opportunity afforded me by the generosity of Florence Campbell, a longtime friend of the family and my first grade teacher from Edson. Because we would be visiting her friends and relations there, my sole expense would be the charter-class airfare.

All of my life I had longed to visit Great Britain, the setting for many of the books I had read and the dreams I had dreamed since my consciousness emerged from the void. And although Mrs. C., as we affectionately nicknamed Florence, was forty years my senior, I was not worried about being her companion. I had been eagerly anticipating the trip for months, and I marvel now at how I had blissfully ignored my blossoming eating disorder. I gave absolutely no consideration to the possibility that my nutritional practices might create some difficulties while I was abroad. As it happened, the entire disorder crystallized during those six weeks.

I was too excited as our plane took off that evening to be disturbed by the thick letter that my Filipino friend from the university had thrust into my hand a few hours before. After the close of the university term, I had dated him once or twice, not knowing how to refuse his persistent invitations, to let him know that he was but a minor star in the constellation of admirers I had coquettishly encouraged during the past months, and that I held no deep feelings for him. But, after a dance one night in June when he made a few tentative romantic overtures, I felt both embarrassed and guilty for encouraging him and firmly put an end to the relationship. In the letter he poured out his heartbreak and his longing that relations might be different between us, but I was incapable of understanding these feelings and experienced only amazement as I read his words. I folded up the letter the same way I folded up most of my emotions in those days, into a neat little two-dimensional package with sharp square edges, shoved it into my bag as I pushed it from my mind, and concentrated on the great adventure ahead.

Florence was a large blonde woman with a deeply lined face, ready smile, inquisitive blue eyes, and a deep booming voice. She adored the art of conversation and was interested in any subject mentioned, so the nine-hour plane trip passed surprisingly quickly.

Our vacation began auspiciously enough. We landed at Gatwick and took a train up to London, where we were met at Victoria Station by a friend of Mrs. C.'s, Ann Spencer. We were whisked by taxi to Liverpool Street Station, while I sat openmouthed, struggling to absorb everything. It all seemed like a dream: the bustle of Piccadilly at midday, the shrill clamor of English voices, the ancient train with individual compartments opening onto the platform, the smoke and fumes and dirt of the most exciting city in the world, the squalor of the East End, the traffic in Trafalgar Square, the majesty of the Houses of Parliament and Westminster Abbey, Big Ben. Everything was happening too fast, and I wanted to jump up and shout, "Slow down! Give me time to breathe."

Of course I did nothing of the kind. Instead I sat in the taxi with my nose pressed to the glass and experienced a most peculiar affinity for the kaleidoscope passing before me. I felt as though I had come home. Everything was strange, yet at the same time hauntingly, evocatively familiar. The glorious jumble of my emotions overwhelmed me that day, and I made a vow to return to this fairy-tale city, a vow that I have kept many times, experiencing on each occasion a profound feeling of belonging there.

As our train lurched out of Liverpool Street Station and headed northeast for Suffolk, the calm and peace of rural England enveloped us, and my mind slowed down at last, allowing me to appreciate Mrs. Spencer, a brisk little white-haired Englishwoman with a warm and charming manner. Her husband, Edward, reminded me of a big St. Bernard dog, solid, silent, and welcoming when he met us at the station in the market town nearest their village and drove us to their home, the most amazing dwelling-place I had ever seen. It was a thatched-roof cottage dating from Tudor times with its half-timbering and original thick stone walls and floors intact.

I could scarcely believe that people still lived in five-hundred-year-old buildings, I who came from a land where public policy appears to demand that every structure more than fifty years of age be demolished to make room for the new. And what startled me even more was the way the Spencers seemed to take their way of life so much for granted, as though people everywhere lived this way. I wanted them to understand what striking contrasts existed between their life and that of North Americans. I wanted them to know what treasures surrounded them in their home, their village with its thousand-year-old church, their Roman roads.

And so I passed that first day in England in an enchanted daze, so exhilarated that I was jarred out of my normal behavior sufficiently to eat the evening meal presented to us upon our arrival, even though it consisted of foods I generally shunned. Then in a state of disoriented exhaustion induced by jet lag, I staggered up a steep staircase to the upper story, fell into bed, and dropped immediately into a deep and dreamless sleep.

I awoke the next morning to the song of larks and the delicate scent of roses drifting in on a fresh dew-laden breeze through the tiny gable window by my bed. I arose, did my morning calisthenics, and descended for breakfast. That day my dietary habits reasserted themselves. I informed Mrs. Spencer that normally I took only black coffee for breakfast and repeated several times how much I loved salads made with fresh garden vegetables. In this way I managed to obtain two salads a day, supplemented by a small serving of the meat she prepared. I steadfastly refused starches and desserts in my usual fashion and recall being very hungry most of the time. However, it was when we went to Scotland four days later that the situation became immeasurably worse.

I have long considered it a major flaw in my nature that my moods are strongly influenced by the weather. Perhaps this characteristic is generally shared by individuals of cyclothymic temperament, one facet of the personality that may fall victim to anorexia. In any event as our train rolled into Glasgow at 7:00 A.M. on July fifth, my spirits sagged to reflect the heavy gray clouds that hung low over the city, weeping a steady drizzle. The pools of water standing in the streets and in low-lying grassy areas attested to the fact that it had been raining for a long time. We did not know at the time that this was a fitting overture to the weather for the next six weeks.

Mrs. C.'s brother, Angus McTaggart, and his wife, Mary, welcomed us with open arms at the station. A jolly rotund pair whose warmth was of the same generous proportions as their figures, they whisked us home, deposited us in front of the fire in their dreary tenement, gave us tea to drive the chill from our bones, then put us to bed for a few hours. I woke up at mid-afternoon much refreshed. But, on waking, and over the next few days in their home, I began to realize the magnitude of my predicament.

Our hosts were typical Scots: open, down-to-earth, and hospitable people. And their hospitality found expression much of the time in the offer of food and drink. I found myself constantly being exhorted to eat. They were appalled by my gaunt figure and blunt in their observations that I needed to "put some meat on my bones," "fatten myself up a bit." They could not understand why I persistently refused virtually everything they offered.

For my part, I became increasingly self-conscious about my stringent dietary practices, felt guilty about insulting my hosts by rejecting their offerings, yet felt helpless to do anything about it. The preceding nine months of rigid self-discipline had certainly worked well: I had successfully conditioned myself to experience a physical aversion to a long list of Forbidden Foods. I became panic-stricken as I watched the meals being prepared and served:

Meat cooked in gravy! Butter on the vegetables! Chops being fried! Ham and bacon rather than beef! Teatime meals consisting almost entirely of bread, scones, and biscuits with butter and jams! What was I to do? I discovered that salads were rarely found on a Scottish table, at least in the city. Fresh fruit and vegetables were expensive luxuries beyond the means of the average working-class Glaswegian.

Observing the nutritional practices of my hosts, I understood why 90 percent of the people I met were obese. In fact, Angus and Mary were just plain fat! I became obsessed with the irrational fear that I would grow fat again, too, if I relaxed my self-discipline for even one moment. For although I felt physically ill at the sight and taste of most of my Forbidden Foods, there were certain of them that I craved. I longed to sink my teeth into some of those beautiful breads, cakes, and biscuits. But I feared that if I gave my hosts an inkling about my secret cravings, they would ply me with these foods all the time, and I would then have no excuse to refuse them. Nor any willpower. No, it was much better to issue blanket policies that began with, "Thank you, but I don't like..." It was much better to lie.

I scarcely remember now how I survived those days. I do recall taking long walks through the streets of Glasgow to escape from the unremitting exhortations to eat. Of course I enjoyed seeing the wonders of the city as well, but much of the time I was so hungry I could think of little else but food. I was still relentlessly pursuing the goal weight of one hundred pounds that I had arbitrarily set for myself in June. There was something mystical about that number. Perhaps one hundred represented perfection, as in 100 percent. I had bought a calorie counter booklet many months before, but now I began to spend longer periods perusing it, indeed memorizing it, as though I could enjoy fattening foods by staring at their names on a page. Similarly I spent hours gazing at food during my solitary walks: in the farmers' market stalls on the streets, in bakeries and confectioneries, even in grocery stores. I began to buy fresh fruit to supplement my meagre intake at mealtime. Occasionally I would treat myself to ice cream while I was out—how good that felt to actually quell the hunger pangs temporarily.

Yes, I was hungry. In this sense *anorexia* is a misnomer, for I had been ravenously, desperately, savagely hungry for months. For the entire duration of my starvation. I believe that it was the hunger that caused my intense preoccupation with food, a primitive survival mechanism found in all living creatures. Have you ever observed the behavior of a starving animal? Searching out food at any cost assumes the highest priority. Yet I would never have admitted the hunger to a living soul at the time and eventually I succeeded in denying it even to myself.

Back at the McTaggarts' I ate unbuttered brown bread, boiled eggs, whatever plain vegetables and meat I could obtain, gingersnaps (my book listed their caloric content as only thirty-five calories each), and drank gallons of tea and coffee to occupy myself while the others finished their hearty meals. Poor Mrs. C. soon became acutely embarrassed by my behavior and even tried to speak to me about it one day. "You know, Joan, I don't particularly like some of the food they give us here either, but I always take a little bit just to be polite. I always figure it won't kill me ..."

I was submerged by a wave of guilt over the distress I was causing her, but I also felt profoundly isolated with a huge gulf between us. How could I communicate my fears to her in a way that she would understand? Because I knew them to be irrational, I did not even try.

Nor did the situation improve when we moved during the following week to Greenock to stay with Mrs. C.'s other brother and his wife. Instead I sent yet another family into turmoil as they cast about to find something that I would eat. And I walked more rain-drenched streets day after day. And I watched my weight hover on the 100-pound mark, then drop below it. Oh happy day! I rejoiced because I felt that now I had a buffer zone. If I remained below my goal weight, it wouldn't matter if tomorrow I lost control of myself and gorged on some delectable food, or if I were forced by circumstance to eat something fattening at mealtime.

But that "tomorrow" never arrived. Instead I was becoming a master of excuses. "I'm not hungry" ... "I don't like alcohol's effect on my brain" ... "I don't have a sweet tooth" ... "I never eat between meals" … "I can't face food before noon." The quick lies were coming so automatically now that one part of my mind began to believe them. I also learned that it is possible to spend a good deal of time rearranging the food on one's plate, and that if one groups it artistically at the close of the meal it does not appear that so much is being left.

I did enjoy myself as much as it was possible to do in my state of semistarvation. I found the Scottish people delightfully open and uncomplicated in their approach to life. As individuals they were, almost without exception, kind and generous, and I actually envied their nature. Why couldn't I be satisfied with the simple things that satisfied them? Why did I yearn for something more? Why was I feeling bored with their daily routine? And above all, why was I so terribly preoccupied with food all the time?

Indeed I was beginning to realize that something was wrong inside my head, but as quickly as that thought came to consciousness, I pushed it back below the surface. To admit that something was wrong would mean that I would have to correct it, and if I did that, I would begin to eat again, enjoy food again, and then I would get fat again!

And so the vicious cycle continued. I am certain that my new friends never suspected how much inner turmoil I suffered. I had managed to convince them that I was "a lovely girl," and everyone appeared to like me. I kept wondering why, knowing how disgracefully I was behaving as a guest in their homes. Once again, as so often before, I felt as though I were hoodwinking everyone about my character, leaving me isolated with the awful truth about my real nature.

Everyone expressed their concern that I must be bored by the constant company of "old folks" and said that I should be out meeting young people my own age, enjoying myself in the evenings like normal twenty-year-old girls, not sitting by the fire listening to their stories. I secretly knew that was ridiculous. I felt that I had been born old, that I had been predestined never to feel an affinity for adolescent pursuits.

But then suddenly, in the fourth week of our vacation, my hosts' wish for me was granted. It came like a bolt of lightning, utterly unforeseen, and it fractured the foundation of me.

Chapter 4

"This island is incredible! It belongs in a history book. I never imagined that a place like this still existed on earth."

We had just arrived in Islay, one of the Inner Hebrides, after a day-long journey from Glasgow, up through the wilderness of the Highlands by car and onward by steamer from the west coast of Scotland. I stared in awe at this austere land, at its windswept barren hills, rugged coastline, and rocky fields dotted with sheep, at its one-lane roads and tiny villages with wonderful unpronounceable Gaelic names. The scattered farms were composed of stone buildings huddled together as if for protection against the elements, which constantly challenged them. But the inhabitants of this island were just as friendly as the people I had met on the mainland. Perhaps their warmth was a defense against the menace of the land in which they eked out their existence. We had a full demonstration of their hospitality when we attended a *ceilidh* in the village near the farm where we were staying with Mrs. C.'s cousin Jean McInerny.

The *ceilidh* is a wonderful Gaelic tradition. All the villagers and farmers from the surrounding countryside gather for an evening of impromptu entertainment: music and dancing and performances by anyone present with artistic abilities. It is astonishing just how much talent is to be found in such a small and isolated group of people. The local women supply food and nonalcoholic beverages, and the men leave the hall at regular intervals for stronger fare outside.

"Please miss, might I have some milk for my tea? ... Miss? ..."

These words, uttered in an unfamiliar English accent, distracted me from the musician who was on the stage at the moment. I looked to my right and discovered a young man attempting in vain to attract the attention of a girl who was serving tea a short distance away. I immediately added my voice to his, with the result that we caught her attention and he obtained his milk.

"Thank you," he said, looking straight into my eyes.

I experienced a most peculiar jolting sensation in my chest. I made some inane reply before returning my eyes to the stage, astonished to discover that my pulse rate had just doubled. I was certain that the noise of my heart beating and the heat suddenly emanating from my body would attract his attention again at any moment. But it did not, and I was able to study him—if it is possible to study someone out of the corner of one's eye—throughout the remainder of the performance.

He was blonde and blue eyed with a long, narrow face and straight, aristocratic nose. His gaze upon me, though brief and somewhat reserved, had been shockingly direct and penetrating. I have no recollection of the remainder of the program that night. When the audience arose to push back their chairs in preparation for the dancing, I was both dismayed and relieved to find that I had been separated from this disturbing person. However, I could not stop myself from scanning the room for him, and I soon spotted his striking figure clad all in black standing about thirty feet away from me.

But what is this? ... No, it can't be ... Surely he isn't coming toward me? Oh God, he is! I forced my gaze to the opposite corner of the room, clenched my hands together to stop their trembling, and willed my heart to slow down. It refused to cooperate, and I could feel the flush on my cheeks as I heard his voice above me.

"Hello, again! Would you mind if I joined you?"

Trapped! There was no way out. I had to reply.

"Of course not. Do sit down." I scarcely recognized the strangled croak coming from my mouth. I was only aware of his face, of his beautifully tall athletic frame, of his eyes. *Oh God, those eyes!*

He sat down beside me, apparently relaxed, and began chatting. Despite the interior earthquake that had taken place, I somehow managed to respond coherently and evidently even succeeded in amusing him, for we talked continuously for the next two hours. I learned that his name was Paul Tavistock, that he was on holiday in Islay with his family from Stoke-on-Trent, and that he was nineteen and studying architecture at the University of Manchester. Unfortunately his vacation was to end in two days' time. He showed intense interest in my background, and I regaled him with stories about Canada, a land he longed to visit. Our conversation ranged over a myriad of topics, and we discovered many common interests and similar personal characteristics.

I lost all track of time and even forgot where I was, until I suddenly remembered that I had come to the *ceilidh* with Mrs. C. and Jean and that they had planned to leave early. I looked about and observed them standing near the door. My spirits sank as I realized this wondrous interlude must end.

"I'm afraid I'm going to have to leave now," I said, turning back to Paul. When I saw the dismay on his face I was overjoyed.

"I wonder if perhaps ..." he faltered. "That is, if you would like ... Do you suppose I might see you again tomorrow afternoon?" he concluded in a rush.

My reply was a foregone conclusion. Our eyes connected, and we smiled simultaneously as my heart repeated its earlier performance. I then led him across the room to introduce him to my companions, and Jean gave him directions for finding her farm the next day. He walked us out to the car, by some clever maneuver succeeding in taking hold of my hand.

We stopped by the car and turned to face one another again. "Good night, Joan," he said softly, the words a kiss.

I lay awake that night for hours, seeing his face and feeling his touch and hearing his voice, and all through the next day I could think of nothing but him. Would he come? Or had I just served as a novel diversion for him the night before? Not knowing what time he might turn up, I remained near the cottage and yard all day, for fear of missing him. The hours dragged by, and by four o'clock I could tolerate the waiting no longer. I walked the two miles from the farm down to the main road and back. Still no sign of him. Could I possibly have dreamed the whole thing?

I had abandoned all hope of seeing him again when we sat down to tea at six o'clock. The tea table was situated in the sitting room of the cottage, behind a large window that overlooked the yard and road in front of the farm. I thought I was hallucinating when at six thirty I looked up and saw a small car come to a halt in front of the gate. Paul unfolded himself from the driver's seat, opened the gate, and strode purposefully up to the front door. Jean admitted him to the cottage and gave him a cup of tea, and he chatted politely with the women, in masterful command of the situation while I sat like a mindless idiot, tongue-tied and stupid, and heard not a single word of their conversation.

Finally he set down his cup, rose from his seat, and smiled at me. "Would you like to go out for a drive, Joan?"

I emerged from my daze as he drove, very fast, the short distance from the farm to the western shore of the island, where I had earlier discovered a precious jewel of a beach, completely isolated from the main road and from all passersby. Apparently he had explored this side of the island, too. We left the car and began to stroll along the beach, and when he took my hand, there returned a glimmer of the rapport we had established the night before.

We removed our shoes and socks and scrambled up onto the rocks, where we sat for a long time watching the sun drop like a bloodied coin into the sea and absorbing the sound of waves, wind, and seagulls. We talked quietly and our conversation turned to more personal matters. Presently he put his arm around me, looked down into my eyes, and kissed me. I was utterly terrified, and he quickly drew back without comment.

After a time he said, "Shall we walk down the shore a little? I found a beautiful spot last week when I was here exploring. We would be more sheltered from the wind down there."

I allowed him to take my hand and we climbed down. The sand felt warm on our feet as we walked along to his hideaway, the barrier of my fear still palpable between us. A short time later—I don't know how he sensed the time was right—he drew me gently into his arms again and, without speaking, searched my eyes for what seemed an eternity. I saw in his expression a naked appeal for trust, and this time I found myself moving toward him, my mouth finding his with a passion I had never dreamed I possessed. My walls crumbled in an instant as I surrendered and dissolved into him.

Is there any joy on earth comparable to the joy of one's first kiss? Like the moment of birth it can be experienced but once and never again recaptured. It went on forever, that kiss. I was utterly lost as our spirits took wing and soared through an open place of freedom and of light. I remember thinking that heaven must be exactly like this.

Some time later we surfaced, gasping for air. But now the barriers were down and stayed down. We talked and kissed, hugged and kissed, watched the moonrise and first star's appearance and kissed. We played like little children in the sand and kissed, laughed and teased and wept and kissed. Six hours passed, but it could have been six minutes or six days to me, for time had ceased to exist.

"You know, Paul," I said haltingly, "I've never felt for anyone what I'm feeling for you right now. I didn't know I was capable of feeling this way. I ... I wish I could make love with you." The words spoken, I continued with increasing boldness, caution swept aside by newborn passion. "I want to give you everything I am. I want to be close to you, skin to skin. I want your body to be my body, and mine to be yours ... I know it's not possible, I know we just met and we don't really know each other yet, but that's the way I feel."

He looked at me, smiled, traced the line of my cheek gently with his forefinger, and said, "Oh, Joan, you and I have known each other for a thousand years. But you're right. We can't sleep together, not here, not yet." He regarded me intently. "Be careful, Joan. You're a good girl ... Please be careful. There are a lot of men who would take advantage of a situation like this. You don't have to be afraid of me, because I've already learned my lesson." He went on to tell me about an ex-girlfriend named Moira and about their year-long affair, which had recently ended. "It wasn't worth the price I paid," he said finally.

We were silent for a long while. "You know, I still don't know whether I really loved her or not," he mused, "but I guess I didn't, because what I feel for you is something completely different."

The night grew cold as the stars emerged one by one, and we held each other closer still, striving desperately to ward off the inevitable. "Tomorrow noon I leave Islay," he said, "and just think:

It might only have been beginning, you and I. We could have had something good together, something beautiful."

The waves crashing on the rocks punctuated this statement with high drama, and the tragedy of it all overwhelmed me. I started to cry, and his arms tightened around me, his mouth kissing away my tears.

"Don't cry," he said with a sudden grin. "Just remember, one seat different and I might have spent last night talking to my dad! We might never have met." After a moment he murmured, almost to himself, "I'm so lucky."

We lay entwined in one another's arms and stared at the sky above, its ebony dome now pierced by a hundred million stars. It reminded me of eternity, and beneath it I felt both insignificant and, with Paul's heart beating next to mine, infinitely powerful.

"You know, they don't make girls like you in England," he whispered.

"And I've never known anyone like you in Canada."

He looked at me and his eyes twinkled. "How would you like to live in Greenland?" And we both laughed.

Finally we were forced to recognize that we were shivering uncontrollably from the cold, and even kissing would not stop it. Reluctantly we arose from the sand and retraced our steps through grass heavy with dew to the car. He drove slowly back to the farm, where we made our farewells, exchanging addresses and agreeing to remain in touch with one another.

"You never know: Life is so strange and unpredictable ... our paths might cross again," he said as we embraced for the last time. I climbed out of the car, waved, then stood watching his taillights until they disappeared and I could hear nothing but the chirrup of frogs in the night.

I thought that I must surely drown in the sea of pain and loss that engulfed me. Six hours in paradise! And this was the price I must pay for it. Had it been worth it? My heart cried out, *Yes, yes, a thousand times yes!* as I wiped away my tears and turned toward the cottage.

The next two weeks were flat and tasteless for me. I went through the motions of living and even managed to smile and talk and appear to be enjoying myself, carefully concealing the terrible aching emptiness within. Would this pain ever lessen? I took long solitary walks by the sea and sat for hours staring out at the waves reexperiencing that most beautiful night of my life.

However the pain did diminish, and gradually I began to think about other things, in particular about how homesick I was. In early August we returned to Glasgow, where I found a letter from Mary Ellen waiting for me. In it she announced that she was engaged to Gordon Haggerty, a very fine young man she had met six months before. They were planning to marry in May of 1970, at the end of our second year of medicine, and she wanted me to be her maid of honor. I felt oddly unmoved by her happiness. I remember thinking, *Why on earth would she want to get married? We are going to be doctors!*

These thoughts did not strike me as incongruent with my own feelings for Paul still fresh in my mind. Paul was a beautiful fantasy, a fairy-tale prince who had swept me off my feet and might do so again in some distant time and place. Gordon was an ordinary man, and real men merely got in the way of one's goals. I never pictured Paul in the context of marriage, except perhaps in a dreamy faraway idyllic fashion. Gordon would actually be there with Mary Ellen, taking up space in her bedroom, interrupting her studies, demanding her attention, using her toothpaste. I thought her very foolish indeed.

Finally August fourteenth arrived, the day of our return to Canada. I said good-bye to all my new friends and promised to return to enjoy their hospitality once again. As the plane took off, I watched the earth shrink with a curious mixture of emotions. What a holiday it had been! I felt as though I had changed irrevocably in a number of ways and was not at all sure that I liked the changes. Life felt dangerously out of my control, both in the growing obsession in my mind with food and fat and in the earthshattering experience of falling in love. As the clouds obscured the islands below, my mind raced ahead to Canada. I thought of the coming year and considered how to make everything safe once again.

Chapter 5

"My God, Joan, you've lost more weight!" My mother's voice was filled with dismay as she caught her first glimpse of me at the airport.

I hadn't anticipated this reaction. I'm not sure now how I could have thought that she would fail to notice a drop of another six pounds in my weight. Poor Mrs. C. looked distraught and explained defensively how I had eaten during the past six weeks. I felt a sudden wave of pity for her, as I hadn't realized until now that she was blaming herself for my nutritional practices.

That night Mom came to my room, sat down, and spoke very seriously of her concern for my health.

"Please don't worry, Mom. I'm fine. I feel great! I'm a hundred pounds now," I said brightly, mentally crossing my fingers as I uttered this lie, telling myself that I would be a hundred, after all, if I weighed with my clothes on instead of naked. "That's my goal weight, and I'll stop losing now. I promise!"

I wasn't lying about everything. I really did feel great. I was bubbling with energy, unable to sleep beyond 5:00 or 6:00 A.M. any day, and was almost manic in my behavior around the house for the next few weeks. I did increase my caloric intake to avoid further weight loss, but I did not widen the severely restricted range of foods on my Permitted Foods list. I simply ate more of them. The only time I broke my rigid laws was when we drove past a Dairy Queen. I craved soft ice cream, and Mom began to use this in an attempt to get me to eat more. If we were out in the car she would deliberately detour by a Dairy Queen and offer to treat me, knowing full well that I could not resist indulging in a large ice cream cone. I derived an intense physical pleasure from allowing the creamy smoothness to fill my mouth and slither down my throat. But alas, it was always too soon over, leaving me to deal with a nagging sense of guilt. For the rest of the day I would frantically count and recount the calories I had consumed, calculating how I could skimp on another meal so as not to exceed the magic allotted number.

By this time I had fully committed my calorie book to memory, and had developed an internal cash register that kept a running tally of every calorie that crossed my lips. I never ate ice cream at home, feeling that it was safer to restrict this indulgence to the Dairy Queen, since it was not immediately available. If I began eating ice cream at home, I was afraid my mother would buy gallons of it, and I would not be able to stop myself from consuming it until every carton was empty.

Social events away from home became increasingly problematic. It seemed to me that everything in our society was centered around food. People were forever pushing it at you, and 90 percent of what they offered was Forbidden Food. I dreaded the inevitable response when I turned something down: the coaxing, the comments on my gaunt appearance, the inability of everyone to comprehend my fears. So I avoided invitations whenever possible and developed a few new tricks to deal with the problem if I did have to go out. Certain foods lended themselves to easy disposal, so I would accept them, then wrap them up in my napkin or stuff them in a pocket when nobody was looking my way. Later I would excuse myself, go to the bathroom and flush them down the toilet. Drinks could often be poured into nearby plants, and I later wondered how many plants began to sicken after I had been to visit.

Thus I maintained my weight at ninety-eight pounds. I weighed myself surreptitiously every morning, stripped, just before I performed my daily routine of exercises, and panicked if I was even one-half pound above ninety-eight. I always stated that I weighed a hundred pounds, when asked, somehow rationalizing away my two-pound buffer zone. My mother's concern continued to run high, but she quickly realized that every attempt to force me to eat was counterproductive, resulting only in a stubborn set to my jaw and a silent withdrawal from the fray, so gradually she said less and less about my diet.

Other people were less reticent, however, in particular my paternal grandparents in Edson, who for some time now had been bewildered by my peculiar diet, my uncompromising refusal of all the delicious treats I had enjoyed as a child, and my gaunt figure. Though I loved them dearly, I began to dread our visits with them because Grandma always said, "You're so thin, Joan. Why don't you eat more?" And Grandpa, when he embraced me, would poke his fingers into my chest wall and remark, "You're starving, girl; I can count all your ribs. Why don't you put some meat on those bones?"

This made me intensely uncomfortable, conflicting with my own delusion that my body was now attractive, and I had no reply for them, so would merely smile and change the subject. Mom knew me so well that she sensed my anxiety and realized that it only caused me to eat less, so at home a conspiracy of silence began to surround the whole issue. I imagine Mom felt that as long as I lost no more weight she might as well resign herself to the situation.

She did, however, take me to her own gynecologist because of my prolonged amenorrhea. He assured us that nothing was wrong with my body and that my periods would resume again on their own. He did make reference to my weight loss as being implicated, the first time any doctor had done so, but he didn't seem to think there was anything wrong beyond simple overzealous dieting. He, too, urged me to "put on a few pounds." This advice I took to heart as much as everyone else's. My mind was made up. I liked being thin.

In the meantime I threw myself into the second year of my medical studies with my customary intensity. I was living at home that year, as Mom had obtained a sabbatical leave from her teaching position in order to attend university full time, so she and I and Adele drove to the campus together in the mornings. Ambitious as ever,

Mom planned to do all the course work for her master's degree and most of the research for her thesis as well in that one year.

I grew increasingly distant from my classmates and stopped attending the class parties. I had become a teetotaler anyway (far too many empty calories in liquor) and I was always embarrassed about turning down the food at social gatherings, so it seemed far easier to just stay home. I told myself that parties were silly nonsense, that I had more important business to attend to. I even began isolating myself from Mary Ellen. I was still incapable of understanding the total commitment she had made to nurturing her relationship with Gordon, and consequently I sensed that we had less in common than in the past.

I allowed myself few diversions from my routine. Once a month I wrote a long letter to Paul, to which he always responded. How easy it was to keep the fantasy alive on paper as these letters became increasingly passionate. We both evidently loved the English language, enjoyed constructing extravagant poetic descriptions of all that we had felt for each other that night on the beach in Islay, and usually ended on a poignant note bemoaning the tragedy of our separation. I once concluded a letter with a quotation I had learned in high school: "Of all the words from tongue or pen, the saddest are 'It might have been'." I was thrilled by my role in this drama of star-crossed lovers and fell asleep every night dreaming of Paul and imagining our next meeting, for I was growing certain that we were destined to meet again.

In the meantime I had a very real Roy Patterson to contend with, a friend of Gordon's whom I had met the previous spring on a blind date. Roy was a kind, reliable, even-tempered, if somewhat unimaginative young man whom I found comfortable to have around. I had at first encouraged his attentions, simply because I still enjoyed feeling attractive to the opposite sex. Now in the autumn, I was having trouble discouraging him. My family thought him wonderful and teased me about his painfully obvious devotion to me. This enraged me because I did not feel physically attracted to him and was as usual finding it difficult to deal with a flesh-and-blood man. It was so much more satisfying to dream about Paul and imagine myself committed to him. After all, he was a safe five thousand miles away. I became increasingly alarmed as I watched Roy's feelings for me grow more serious, and I hated the thought that I was using him merely to validate my femininity. Yet I didn't know how to tell him these things, so instead I began to make excuses for not seeing him.

He got the message. He stopped calling, and the next time I saw him was in May, 1970, at Mary Ellen and Gordon's wedding. We were thrown together by the fact that we were serving as the principal attendants in the wedding party, but our exchanges were somewhat strained, and it was a relief when the weekend came to an end. Roy tried to approach me for an explanation of my sudden coolness, but I would not give him a chance. There was only sadness in his eyes when he said good-bye, increasing my burden of guilt. I sensed that I had handled the entire affair very badly but was too ashamed to share my feelings with anyone and work out how I could have managed it differently. It was much easier to forget the whole thing and retreat to my fictional romance with Paul. To run away. My habitual response to pain.

During the spring of that same year, I made a most shocking discovery in my psychiatry textbook. In the chapter on psychosomatic medicine I came across a brief section entitled "Anorexia Nervosa," my first encounter with this rare entity. As I read it through I grew more and more appalled, for the author was describing *me!* I read on in horrified fascination, unable to take my eyes from the page:

> The patient is usually a young, unmarried girl of good ... intelligence, whose behaviour in other respects has hitherto been impeccable. She is usually a conscientious type with a high moral code and a flair for doing good. ... The condition is usually seen in ... a family situation where the child conflicts with the mother. ... The home environment is usually very sympathetic but ineffective in dealing with the problem. ... Refusal of food is invariably accompanied by all forms of subterfuge to get rid of it and these patients can become most expert in disposing of food. ... The patient has an air of brightness and

sparkle and appears energetic, going to work and showing her usual zest and enthusiasm. ... Some become almost delusional, insisting that they are overweight. ... Others develop food fads. ... There is gross emaciation. ... A fine lanugo-like hair covers the body. ... Amenorrhea is almost universal. ... The illness can be dangerous and ... the mortality rate can reach 20 per cent.

My horror turned to terror as the text continued, describing treatment of this bizarre malady:

In hospital, the ... patient has usually demonstrated her capacity to resist the usual forms of psychotherapy and is presenting the doctor with a deteriorating physical state which can prove fatal. ... Immediate tube-feeding has been advocated. ... Strict nursing supervision with an attitude of benevolent neutrality is a good policy. ... Overoptimism is the cardinal error in treatment and the patient should be nursed in bed, ... taken to and from the toilet and allowed to sit up only under supervision. The aim should be to get the patient to replace not less than six kilos before there is any relaxation. ... Frequent follow-up is essential. ... Like alcoholism, one lapse is invariably the precursor of rapid deterioration and it should not be ignored. ... A new treatment combined the use of large doses of chlorpromazine ... with modified insulin treatment carried to the point of sweating and drowsiness. ... Leucotomy has also been advised. ... It is very tempting to try the short-cuts and teach the patient a lesson. ... These patients can summon almost superhuman reserves to combat those who are trying to save their lives.[1]

I slammed the book shut and sat for a long time feeling prickly all over, listening to the blood pounding in my ears. I could not believe it. I would not believe it. There must be some mistake. I was not sick! I was just a normal girl watching my weight. I was not crazy! I would not have my behavior labeled as a disease. If one had a disease one went to a doctor to be cured. I didn't want to be cured!

Getting cured from this so-called disease meant being forced to gain weight. I would not do it! I would not let anyone make me fat again! Not after the struggle I had gone through to become slim and attractive for the first time in my life.

My mind was made up. I firmly displaced this new information from my conscious mind and refused to allow myself to think about it. I worked hard at repressing this knowledge for the next few weeks and months, and gradually I came to believe my own lie ... most of the time.

In the meantime the university year drew to a close and I began to look forward to enjoying one of the rewards of my effort: the honor of participating in a six-week "summer externship" program at a hospital near Providence, Rhode Island. I could not have predicted what further trauma lay in store for me that summer, nor how much deeper I had yet to descend into hell. For I had failed as yet to see the consistent connection between going away from home, from my mother, from all that was real and familiar, and the downward acceleration of my disease. I was additionally unable to recognize how my tragic isolation from others itself aggravated the very obsessions that had engendered it.

Chapter 6

I left Edmonton on July first, 1970, the same day that I had arrived in Britain one year earlier, and arrived at the airport in Providence brimming with enthusiasm for my great adventure. I was twenty-one years old and proud of my new sophistication. I felt myself quite the world traveler, able to do things independently now. I made my way to the suburban hospital and reported to the administrator's office. I was warmly greeted, shown to my quarters, and introduced to the four other recipients of the externship award: a girl from France, a young man from St. Louis, Missouri, and two boys from Glasgow.

The five of us got on very well together. The other students were pleasant and good-natured, and the Scottish lads were both blessed with a delightful sense of humor. There was never a dull moment when they were around, and I could have had a lot of fun that summer had I been capable of it. Unfortunately by this time my capacity to relax and enjoy myself had been all but completely eroded by the rigid, neurotic lifestyle I had cultivated over the past two years. Of course, I was too sick to admit or even to recognize this at the time. All I knew was that I was unhappy and lonely.

Mealtimes were as difficult as ever, so I would often find excuses for not joining the others in the cafeteria. I took long solitary walks in the evenings, telling myself desperately that I was enjoying the summer. Even the hospital failed to give me the pleasure I had hoped for as I discovered it was not the exciting place I had dreamed about. Instead of idealistic, enthusiastic doctors and nurses making life and death decisions, I saw ordinary men and women carrying out a monotonous routine of activity, watching the clock with lifeless eyes, with little evidence of real caring anywhere to be found. Another bubble burst. Another dream shattered.

So I retreated from my surroundings in body and spirit, comforting myself by spending long hours in my room, reading medical books and munching on gingersnaps. I needed something to fill the void left by my skimpy meals, and gingersnaps were so low in calories that I could eat a large number of them, prolonging the pleasure over a couple of hours, without exceeding my daily calorie allotment. Breaking them into small pieces, placing one morsel at a time in my mouth, savoring the spice and the sweetness and the crunch, all became the highlight of my lonely days. I discovered a little grocery store nearby on one of my walks and became a regular customer, although the single item I repeatedly purchased must have raised the eyebrows of the owner. I was too self-absorbed to notice.

I also found solace in writing to Paul. In fact, in the desolate reaches of my mind, removed from home and all that was familiar, my infatuation with him grew stronger until it, too, became an obsession. I began thinking about him in every waking hour and passionate images of us together filled my troubled dreams. The fantasy that we were meant for each other, that our destiny was to be together again, assumed massive proportions. I received a letter from him three weeks after my arrival in Rhode Island, written in his customary intimate tone. He was in Manchester for six weeks attending summer school and he too was lonely.

Then a brilliant idea occurred to me. Why not fly to England to see him? As soon as this thought formed, my mind was flooded with images of the two of us together, strolling hand in hand through the city streets, sharing intimate dinners in dimly lit restaurants (with me eating normal meals somehow), our eyes meeting above the candle conveying unspoken messages of love. In my loneliness I longed for that kind of intimacy. I gave no thought to such practical details as where I would stay and what would happen once we got beyond the kisses and embraces. Somehow that would all work out. I thought only about the logistics of getting to Manchester.

I called the airlines to enquire about fares and schedules. I had enough money in the bank at home, saved from my summer job in May and June, to pay for my airfare. Mom could wire the funds to me. I would be excused from the final two weeks of my externship somehow. That would give us the entire month of August together.

But first things first: Would Paul want me to come? I wrote, outlining my proposal to him, and anxiously awaited his reply. Finally his letter arrived, giving his consent to the scheme, although couched in a guarded tone that I chose to ignore. Now all that remained was to call Mom to ask for the money. In my deluded state I actually believed that she would be happy for me. I had written to her a few days before, telling her of my plans, thinking it best not to take her completely by surprise.

As long as I live I'll remember my mother's voice over the phone that night, filled with an emotion that I had never heard before. I cannot find an adjective that adequately describes it. "Distraught" is too mild.

"My God, Joan, are you crazy? You can't just throw yourself at this boy! What are you going to do over there for a whole month? Use your head! ..."

Poor Mom. I have only compassion for her now. Her beloved child, the model daughter who had never before stepped out of line, was about to rush headlong into a situation where angels would fear to tread. She knew from the vantage point of her maturity that I was doomed to be hurt, perhaps irreparably, if I carried out this insane scheme.

But compassion is an adult response, and I was an infant emotionally. I grew pale as I listened to Mom's voice, feeling the pain of her disapproval, but at the same time I set my jaw stubbornly. I had never done anything impulsive in my life before, and I was going to do this! I felt maligned and misunderstood as I heard Mom brand me a scarlet woman, a cheap floozy, a shameless hussy—I interpolated into her speech these colorful epithets extracted from romantic novels I had read—and gave free rein to my sense of the dramatic.

Weeping, I interrupted the monologue. "I'm sorry, Mom, but whether you like it or not, this is something I have to do. I'm going! Now will you send me the money or do I have to get it some other way?"

There was a long pause, then an immense sorrow in her voice as she bowed to the inevitable and surrendered me to my fate. "I'll send it. But just remember, you're making your bed and you're going to have to lie in it."

It amazes me now to think that I hadn't the faintest idea of what she was talking about.

Chapter 7

I arrived in Manchester on Sunday morning in the first week of August, and as the plane taxied toward the terminal I found that all my bravado had suddenly evaporated. What on earth was I doing here? But I summoned up every ounce of courage I possessed and marched into the Arrivals area. With apprehension I scanned the sea of faces for the one I had seen in my dreams every night for a year. There he was! He made his way toward me, and when he greeted me very casually with a quick peck on the cheek, I realized that he was as nervous as I was.

He made some meaningless enquiry about my flight to which I made some equally meaningless reply. Then we stood regarding one another, utterly at a loss for words, as the panic-stricken thought crossed my mind, *What are we ever going to talk about for a whole month?* This boy was a complete stranger to me. Could this possibly be the author of those passionate love letters that had been the light of my existence for the past year? Where was the easy rapport we had found so quickly in Islay the previous summer? Suddenly the task of getting to know this person seemed monumental, and I wasn't at all sure that it was a task I wanted. The enormity of my folly dawned upon me.

But I was here, and there was no way out, so I decided to drink the cup I had poured. I braced my shoulders and my determination, and initiated the conversation. As we found my bags and made our way to the bus stop, we talked about Paul's studies, the university, the city, my visit in Rhode Island, his family, my family, and so forth. I learned that he had booked a room for me in the women's residence on campus for the next two weeks while he finished his course. He had obviously been thinking more practically than I had. After that he wanted me to go home with him to Stoke-on-Trent for the remainder of the month. He said that he had told his family I was coming, and that they would be pleased to have me as their guest.

Gradually, as we began to relax, the situation appeared less impossible to me. When we arrived at the university campus, he took me to his quarters in the men's residence, settled me in his room, then proceeded down the hall to prepare a light lunch in the common kitchen. Food! I had given no thought to how I would eat once I was here, because in my dreams I saw myself living happily ever after, in a state of nirvana where surely no one ever thought about food. Now I was faced with the reality of having to share meals with Paul, and I sensed that I would have little choice in the menu. What was I to do?

"I'm afraid I'm a bit strapped for money, Joan, so I don't eat very much," Paul said apologetically as he returned with some buttered bread and cheese and two big mugs of steaming coffee, to which he had already added liberal quantities of milk and sugar.

"Oh, Paul, I'm sorry. I take my coffee black."

He looked at me and grinned. "You'd better drink it this way ... You won't get much else!"

To my own amazement I drank it that way. The sweetness was strange to me, but not unpleasant. I nibbled on a bit of the food before we lay down together on top of his bed, both of us exhausted from lack of sleep. We embraced and kissed then, and for a brief moment I was transported back to the beach in Islay. But when Paul started to unbutton my blouse I returned to the present with a jolt. I grabbed his hand, not knowing what to say or do. Amazingly, I was completely unprepared to deal with this aspect of the situation.

"Please, Paul, I'm just not ready for this yet. Please don't ask me to explain," I pleaded.

He acquiesced easily enough and simply held me until we both fell asleep. We awoke refreshed several hours later and, as the day was still warm and sunny, decided to go for a walk.

"You're going to have to amuse yourself while I'm in classes on weekdays for the next two weeks, Joan," he warned.

"I certainly won't have any problem doing that," I assured him. "I love walking, and I love new cities. Two weeks won't be long enough for me to do all the exploring I would like!"

We stopped at a fish-and-chips shop, and Paul ordered two servings of chips without even asking if I liked them. He handed them to me in their newspaper wrapping and proceeded to pour salt and vinegar on his own. I inhaled their tantalizing aroma and amazed myself for a second time that day by actually eating them. This was most definitely a Forbidden Food, but I was weak with hunger and there was no prospect of getting anything else in the foreseeable future. The chips were delicious, the first I had tasted in two years, but I felt very guilty. However, I consoled myself that this was a day for new things and reminded myself that I might as well get used to changing my old habits, because it looked like this wasn't the last change I would be forced to make.

I was right. That evening Paul took me down to the Students' Union Building, or "the Union" as it was dubbed by the students. He ordered a pint of beer for himself, then turned to me. "And what would you like, Joan?"

"Gosh," I said uncertainly, "I'm not sure. I certainly don't like beer. What else do they have?"

"If you don't have a taste for beer, try some cider," he decided. "A half-pint for the lady, please," he said to the bartender.

I enjoyed it immensely and felt a lovely glow steal over me as we sat there, Paul chatting with his friends after introducing me. He had several more pints of beer and I had another half-pint of cider before we made our way back to the residence. It was dark by this time and my bags were still in Paul's room.

He looked at me somewhat uncertainly, "How about staying here tonight, Joan? We'll find your room tomorrow."

I was mildly intoxicated, sufficient to release my inhibitions. I looked at him bleakly for a long empty moment, then burst into tears.

His face immediately filled with concern. "Joan, Joan, whatever is the matter? Stop crying, please! Tell me what's the matter."

"Oh, Paul," I wailed, "I didn't know how to tell you this before, but I'm afraid I can't sleep with you. I can't sleep with anyone. I don't know how to say this, but I ... I have a congenital narrowing of the entrance to my vagina. I found out about it a little more than a year ago. The doctor says I'll need surgery before I can ever have intercourse. I see now that I shouldn't have come, but I wanted to see you so desperately. Can you ever forgive me?" I lifted my tear-stained face to look at him directly.

He enfolded me in his arms, held me close, and gently wiped away my tears. "It doesn't matter, Joan," he said tenderly. "We don't have to make love. Don't be afraid. I would never do anything to hurt you. But we can still hold one another all night. I would like to do that. Would you?"

Despite my misgivings, I let him undress me, then watched as he took off his own clothes. I was terrified; even the alcohol did not help. I had not seen a naked male body since I was five years old and had walked into the bathroom to discover my father urinating in the toilet. My fear was just as great now as it had been then. I was also filled with the absolute certainty that I was committing "a grave wrong," as my catechism had phrased it and my conscience had absorbed it.

But I felt helpless to alter what was happening. Paul drew me into his bed, put his arms around me, whispered sweet things in my ear, then fell asleep. It felt so good to lie there naked in his arms, to feel his heart beating against my breast, to move with the rise and fall of his steady breathing. I loved these novel physical sensations, felt myself aroused and tingling, and whispered a prayer as I fell asleep: *Oh God, this can't possibly be evil, can it? How could anything so beautiful and right be wrong? Please help me. Please show me what to do.*

I awoke in the early morning to the thin light of a summer dawn. For a moment I was disoriented in the strange room until I remembered where I was. I looked over at Paul's sleeping profile and experienced a bewildering mixture of emotions: tenderness, possessiveness, fierce pride, erotic desire, and then, overriding everything else, pure unadulterated panic. I tried to sort through these feelings, but only became more and more confused, and eventually slipped back into a troubled sleep.

When I awoke again, Paul was up, fully dressed, and standing over me with a mug of coffee. "It's about time you woke up, sleepy-head," he laughed. "Here's your coffee. I have to dash or I'll be late for class, but I'll meet you at the Union at noon for lunch. Here's a key to lock up on your way out ... Have fun." And with a quick kiss he was gone.

Filled with sudden enthusiasm I hopped out of bed, found a robe, and made my way to the washroom. I stood at the mirror for a long time, searching my face for some outward sign of the wondrous trans-formation that had occurred within. I felt as though I had stepped over a threshold, irrevocably and forever. Was it possible that such a passage could leave no visible mark on my face? I carried myself with pride as I attracted a few male glances in the hall on my way back to Paul's room, reveling in this glorious sense of my own femininity.

I spent the morning exploring my surroundings, then walked to the Union cafeteria to meet Paul. He was in high spirits but maintained the casual air with which he had first greeted me the day before. We filled our trays as he commented, "The food's not very good here, but it's cheap, so I make this the main meal of the day."

There was no choice in the menu. I was handed a plate with a gray amorphous mass on it, which I heard someone label shepherd's pie, alongside some overcooked pale canned peas. I stared at my plate for a moment, then took a deep breath, picked up my fork and ate most of the meal. I was faint with hunger and saw no alternative at the moment except to eat these Forbidden Foods. Paul returned to class, and I wandered about the streets for the afternoon, striving desperately to keep my optimism from crumbling, telling myself over and over again that everything was OK, that I was having the time of my life playing out this drama. I thought it incredible that a mere thirty hours had passed since I had arrived in England. It felt like a lifetime.

The next two days trickled by in much the same manner. We found my room in the women's residence, but its empty unfamiliar-ity felt so threatening that I slept with Paul once again. On Tuesday evening we took a bus to the suburbs to visit the Applebys, a warm and gracious couple who were friends of his parents, and I found it a relief to talk with someone other than Paul for an evening.

On Wednesday morning something snapped within me. I was feeling unbearably fragmented by the drastic changes that had occurred in every aspect of my life in the past three days, and I could maintain my façade no longer. I admitted the fact that the whole affair was not the fairy-tale adventure I had anticipated and forced myself to face squarely what was troubling me.

First and foremost was a terrible guilt over my sexual activity. In my heart I was appalled by how easily I had abandoned the moral principles I had always so loudly proclaimed. *How easy it is to be virtuous when one has never been tempted*, I thought ruefully. I could rationalize away my actions no longer. I knew that I must change my behavior but trembled as I tried to imagine how I would do it. That morning I found a Catholic church, went in, and prayed desperately for forgiveness and guidance. Since that first night in Paul's arms, I had been afraid to pray again. I knew that if I turned to God, I would have to admit that I was sinning, and that would obligate me to alter my behavior.

At the same time, the craving for my familiar ritual foods became intolerable. I surrendered to what I believed was inevitable and bought some ice cream. When I joined Paul for lunch I had only tea, telling him that I was not hungry, and thereafter excused myself from lunch most days. I purchased some fruit and gingersnaps that afternoon and concealed them in my room at the university. I moved all my belongings out of Paul's quarters and in the evening told him that I felt it best that I not sleep with him anymore. He looked surprised, but accepted my decision without comment. I began refusing most of the Forbidden Foods I was offered, and most evenings I drank nothing when we went to the pub. Paul must have wondered what I was living on, but he demanded no explanation.

It is highly significant that this reversion to my pathological eating rituals occurred *simultaneously* with my emotional withdrawal from Paul. The reader might even see what I could not see at the time, that my anorexia served as the vehicle for my terrified retreat from an unknown future. It provided the bricks and mortar for the fortress I needed to make myself invulnerable.

I thought of a way to recover another part of my lost identity. I had passed the Manchester Royal Infirmary many times on my long walks. On Thursday morning I donned my most respectable clothes, marched in the front entrance of the ancient building, and asked to see the director in charge of medical students. I introduced myself, told him I was visiting Manchester for two weeks, and asked if it would be possible for me to join in with the other students for a few days, so that I could learn a little about how the British medical system worked. He welcomed me graciously, and so for the next few days I assumed my comfortable medical student role once again. It felt good to join the entourage behind the senior registrar and consultants on morning rounds, to ask questions and participate in case discussions afterward, to attend outpatient clinics in the afternoon, to think about medicine and begin to live it once again. It was so much easier than being a lover. So much safer.

Thus was I gradually restored to the old familiar Joan I thought I knew so well. Yet something had changed, something I could not yet label. Paul and I continued to interact on a superficial level, but a subtle shift had occurred in our relationship. I had distanced myself and thereafter abandoned any real attempt to connect with him, although I continued to go through the motions at times and even convinced myself that I still cared for him as I had before. I was not ready to admit that I was incapable of true intimacy. I did not yet see that the secrecy and lies of anorexia *always* prevent authentic intimacy.

Early Sunday evening, Paul suggested that we telephone his family in Stoke-on-Trent to make arrangements for his father to drive up and collect us the following weekend.

"But first I have a confession to make," he said sheepishly. "I just didn't know how to tell my mom and dad that I had a girl coming from Canada to stay with me for two weeks. So I told them you were a boy! They think I have someone named John here with me right now, and that I met him in Islay last year. Now I have to figure out how to break the truth to them. Any ideas?"

I was at first taken aback, then amused by his story. We laughed heartily before crowding into a phone booth to place the call. He held the receiver so that I could listen too, anticipating a very funny exchange. It all seemed like a childish game, a huge practical joke. Until we heard his mother's voice over the line.

Her initial response to his greeting was a strange pause, then a tone cold and hard as steel, which sliced through me like a knife. "Just what do you think you're about, Paul? What are you trying to do to us? Gwen Appleby rang us last night for a chat and mentioned this girl you have living with you. How do you think I felt when I had to tell her we knew nothing about it? I've had enough of your lies. I told you that before. Well, this time you have gone too far. Who is this girl anyway? What kind of a girl would ..."

At this juncture Paul recovered abruptly from his paralysis, pulled the receiver away from my ear and held it against his own, so that I could hear no more. I was stunned and heard little of what he said to his mother over the next few minutes as he attempted to soothe her, apparently without much success. As I stood there I was transported two weeks back in time to my telephone conversation with my own mother. *Oh Mom,* I cried silently, *you knew, didn't you? You were so right and I was so wrong! What on earth am I going to do now?*

Tears streamed down my cheeks, and I could not control my sobs as Paul hung up the phone. He put his arms around me. "Please don't cry, Joan ... It's going to be all right ... We'll figure something out."

But I was bereft and unable to dispel a shattering sense of catastrophe from my mind. I could find nothing to say to Paul and eventually excused myself and went to my room. I slept very little that night, tossing about in bed as I attempted to formulate a plan of action. I knew I could never face Paul's parents now; it was out of the question for me to go down with him to Stoke-on-Trent. But my airline reservation could not be altered, as I had obtained a "no-changes-allowed" ticket. Perhaps I could stay on here at the university alone for another two weeks? Or find a bed-and-breakfast somewhere? Or even scrape together enough money for train fare to Scotland and pay a surprise visit to my acquaintances there? One idea after another whirled through my mind until I eventually drifted into an uneasy sleep as dawn brushed the eastern sky.

That evening Paul devised a plan of his own. We went back to the Applebys and had a long frank discussion with them. They seemed to like me—although I couldn't imagine why—and were sympathetic to our predicament, assuring me again and again that Paul's parents would also like me and accept me with open arms as soon as the misunderstanding was cleared away. Then they called the Tavistocks and arranged to meet them for drinks the next evening in a small town midway between Manchester and Stoke-on-Trent. I felt a glimmer of hope that perhaps everything would work out in the end.

And it did. In fact, Paul's mother rang up the day after the rendezvous and asked to speak to me. I could not believe that this warm melodious voice was coming from the same person I had heard on Sunday.

"I'm terribly sorry you've been hurt by all this mix-up, Joan ... may I call you Joan? ... But I'm certain you can understand how we felt. Sons! We do want you to feel welcome here. We are very much looking forward to your visit, and we shan't hear of you canceling it now ..."

I stammered out some reply, accepted her invitation, and shortly afterward handed the receiver back to Paul. I was jubilant, as was he when he hung up the phone. We embraced one another, then went down to the Union for a drink to celebrate.

But despite this moment of togetherness, it was painfully evident that everything had changed between us. Looking back, I regret that we both lacked the maturity to communicate what we were feeling at the time. Such an opportunity for growth was missed. We could have learned a great deal from the experience, had we only talked about it openly. But I had rebuilt my walls by this time, and the experiences of the past three days had solidly fortified them. I sealed myself up, fully armored, in my own deluded consciousness and retreated from any further authentic contact with Paul. I became so insensitive to him that I can scarcely recall what occurred between us during those final days in Manchester and during the two weeks in Stoke-on-Trent.

With one notable exception.

Chapter 8

The tense estrangement between Paul and me found welcome termination the following weekend when his father arrived in Manchester. Charles Tavistock was a big man, tall and heavily built, with a surprisingly gentle face and serene manner. Although a man of few words, his eyes and smile were perpetually warm, and I relaxed with him at once. He said not a word about the misunderstanding of the previous weekend. Instead he asked about me, my background, and about Canada. When he conversed with Paul, I sensed a profound communion that flowed like a river between them, swift and deep and largely silent.

My hope for the next two weeks was further strengthened when we arrived at Stoke-on-Trent and met Paul's mother and his younger sister. I fell in love with Mrs. Tavistock, a beautiful vivacious brunette with a heart-shaped face, delicate features, and intelligent gray eyes. She reminded me of my own mother in her dynamic, self-possessed, capable manner, yet she demonstrated even greater warmth and sensitivity to those around her. She obviously ran the household, but without displacing her husband as its head. Her love for her children, and particularly for her only son, was so evident as to be almost palpable even to an outsider, and I wondered how Paul coped with it. But he obviously did, for I quickly saw that his relationship with his mother was even closer than that with his father.

True to her promise the family welcomed me with open arms, and I quickly found my niche in the household. I got through the first meal somehow, then managed to install myself in the kitchen to do the "washing-up," overriding my hostess's protests. I convinced her that I would only be comfortable if allowed to help around the house for the next two weeks, so she acquiesced gracefully.

The time passed quickly enough. I spent hours conversing with Mrs. Tavistock and grew to know her much better than I knew her son. Mealtimes were a problem as usual, but the Tavistocks were too polite to question my peculiar tastes. Instead they provided the vegetables and fruits I claimed to like so much and never pressed me to eat a food I refused. I secretly supplemented my meagre intake with gingersnaps, but I stopped eating ice cream, as I was afraid of taking in too many calories. I found a scale and was surprised—and delighted—to discover that I had lost four pounds since my arrival in England. I still had control over something in my life.

For deep inside I felt very much out of control of my relationship—or lack thereof—with Paul. The fairy-tale prince had long since vanished from my mind, and I had been afraid as always to become involved with a real man. So I continued on what I saw as the safest course: isolation. We did very little together as a couple. He did take me out once or twice alone, but principally I restricted my contact with him to family outings: sightseeing, drives around the countryside, visiting friends. His mother was understandably curious about the nature of our relationship and even tactfully broached it with me one day. I immediately assumed a cool clinical tone and gave her the careful story that I was constructing in my mind to explain away the whole affair.

"Paul and I were infatuated with each other last summer," I said with the utmost control, all emotion contained, determinedly feigning nonchalance. "Now we find that we are not all that compatible. We still like each other very much, but we just want to be friends."

It sounded tidy and perfectly logical in my own ears, and I was quite satisfied with this explanation. Mrs. Tavistock gave me a long inscrutable look and then began talking to me about Paul on a different level, much as she would to a close friend, or to a doctor.

Unfortunately my neat little fabrication failed to hold up to Paul's challenge. He generally left me alone in my solitary fortress during those weeks in Stoke, and I thought as I neared the end of my stay that I might escape untouched. On the few occasions when we were alone together, I felt as though I were holding my breath, praying that he wouldn't attempt to trespass on my privacy again. But it was not to be so.

In retrospect, I realize he must have been hurt and bewildered by my rejection over the preceding weeks, by my silent withdrawal without any explanation for why I had changed. I was unaware of this at the time, because I absolutely refused to open myself up to him again. But he needed something from me, an explanation for my aloofness, or at the very least some sort of recognition of his existence. When it was not forthcoming, the tension mounted. Finally the volcano erupted, on the very eve of my departure.

On that evening Paul invited me to go for a drink as our final outing together. In the car en route to his favorite pub I proceeded to maintain my usual polite distance, chatting in a friendly and super-ficial manner. But Paul would not have it so.

"We're meeting some people tonight, Joan. Actually, they're all girls, old friends of mine from secondary school. One of them is Moira ... You may remember my mentioning her last summer," he added with a sidelong glance.

Of course I remembered, as I would remember for all time every word he had spoken to me that night a century before in Islay. I suddenly felt a chill suspicion that he was engineering something, that he was setting me up in some way. I did not have to wonder about it long, for he went on immediately.

"Oh, by the way," he said with studied casualness as he pulled into the parking lot, "my friends think you have only been here for two weeks. They don't know about the time we spent together in Manchester, and I would be grateful if you would back up my story."

It was a test. I know that now. He needed proof that there was still some trust between us, that the special attraction he had origi-nally experienced for me was no figment of his imagination. He wanted to know that I was a friend, that we could share a secret and stand united in it against an outside world. Looking back, I marvel at my stupidity, at my blind refusal to see him for what he was: a kind and essentially good but insecure young man searching, like myself, for validation of his being and for meaning in the adolescent chaos of his existence. Now I have compassion. But at the time I would allow myself no such vision. I was far too absorbed in myself, in my own enormous struggle to bind together the pieces of my sick and fragile ego. To see him as he was instead of how I wanted him to be would have been itself a form of commitment. And commitment is risky and dangerous. Commitment can get you hurt. Commitment requires emotional adulthood. So I opted for the easy route: judgment. It was very comfortable to allow myself to grow angry with him, to cast him as a villain maliciously placing me in an untenable position, and to seek revenge.

Inside the pub we found his friends immediately and sat down. He introduced me and we started chatting. They were friendly enough, and I felt no particular strain in conversing with the girl with whom he had been physically intimate for an entire year. I had by now thoroughly stifled any capacity I might have had to relate to him as a lover. Yet I needed to maintain my own myth that I did care for him: It was part of the new fairy tale I intended to carry back with me to Canada. So I tried desperately to conjure up the feelings that a wounded girlfriend might be experiencing at that moment, and as usual even began to believe in my role as the evening wore on.

Moira was anything but stupid, and she sensed that Paul was playing some game. When he left the table for a few minutes, she turned to me and asked point-blank when I had arrived in England. My response was immediate. I was playing the virtuous maiden that night, so I told her the truth, sparing not so much as a fleeting thought to any loyalty I might owe Paul. I was secretly delighted by the anger that congealed on her face at my words.

"That deceitful sod! ... that rotten effing s.o.b.! ... I might have known ..." She interrupted this tirade of expletives and her expression became pensive. "Listen, Joan, I think it's time to teach him a lesson. Will you help me?" I nodded without hesitation and wonder now why I didn't have a vision of thirty pieces of silver crossing the table.

When Paul returned with another round of drinks Moira's face was blank. But she cleverly steered the conversation around to his final two weeks in Manchester, then asked him some casual question about what I had done on such-and-such a day. Paul feigned a perfect air of innocence.

"But Joan wasn't in Manchester," he said easily. "She only arrived in England a couple weeks ago. Didn't I tell you that before?"

Moira was also a consummate actress. Her face assumed a puzzled expression. "Well, that's very strange. I thought Joan just finished telling me she's been here for a month, that she spent the first two weeks alone with you in Manchester ... Didn't you, Joan?"

All eyes swiveled in my direction. I experienced a sick sensation as I awakened and realized that this was not as much fun as I had anticipated. Wasn't revenge supposed to be sweet? Then what was this bitter taste in my mouth? Why did I feel suddenly that the tables had been turned on me? I looked at Paul and glanced quickly away, unable to bear the naked hurt I saw revealed there, the pain of ultimate loss he was enduring at my betrayal. I looked at Moira and recognized in her eyes a wickedly triumphant gloating over the pair of us. I felt suddenly dirty. I wanted to turn the clock back ten minutes and play the whole scene again.

But life doesn't work that way. I was learning that actions have consequences, that what is done cannot be undone. I now had to say something, so I vainly tried to muster up my vanished sense of self-righteousness. I turned to Paul with an effort. "I'm sorry, Paul, but I'm not going to lie for you," I said primly.

That sounded good. Now why can't I feel that I did the right thing?

A few minutes later we left the pub. Paul drove very fast, in silence, in a direction I didn't recognize. I don't think he was aware either of where he was going. He pulled the car to a halt on a quiet street, then sat staring straight ahead. I wanted to dissolve, to escape any way I could. But there was no way out, so I decided the best tactic was to take the offensive. After all, Paul was the villain, I reminded myself. I was the injured party, truthful and pure.

"Paul, if you're going to continue telling lies you're going to keep getting yourself in trouble, you know. I don't know what else you expect." I sounded like his mother.

His body recoiled at these words as if I had slapped him across the face. He sat for a moment in stunned disbelief, then suddenly smashed the steering wheel with the side of his clenched fist with a violence that startled me. When he turned toward me I shrank back from the rage and contempt that blazed from his eyes.

"Listen, you conceited, hypocritical, self-centered bitch," he spat at me. "Don't talk to me about lies. Why did you come here anyway? You've just been *using* me for the last month. You know bloody well you came wanting to get laid! Then you tell me you can't ... Well, you're the biggest fraud I've ever seen, the worst slut I've ever known ... At least the others were honest about what they wanted. You can't even be honest with yourself ... Go ahead and cry. You're good at that." He paused for breath and his tone altered somewhat. "The greatest irony about all this is that I honestly didn't care about not fucking you. Do you really think I invited you here for your *body*? You'll never turn any man on with it. All I ever wanted was your friendship ... So why did you go away?"

His words were burning embers in my ears. I knew he was telling the truth. I was rotten to the core. I deserved everything he had said and more. I sat there speechless, trembling and weeping silently, a torrent of tears cascading down my cheeks. Something was crumbling within me, disintegrating and flowing away in those tears, something unidentifiable, and I knew I would never recover it. At his remarks about my body I experienced a physical blow much as one must feel from a bullet in the chest. Ultimate devastation.

At last he ran out of words, then sat for a long time watching me weep. When he spoke again his fury had fully dissipated. There was only a depleted sorrow in his voice as he repeated that final question, "Oh, Joan, why did you go away?"

The words hung between us, but I still had no reply.

"Oh, Joan, my poor little girl!" My mother's words echoed Paul's, but their tone was light years away from his as she clung to me at the airport and wept with abandon. "Whatever has happened to you?"

I was exhausted from the weeks of turmoil and the as yet incalculable emotional loss I had endured, and I'm certain it must have showed on my face, in the dark smudges beneath my eyes—the legacy of too many sleepless nights—and in the way my clothes hung on me, looser than ever before. But I smiled brightly, insisted that I was fine and would tell her all about it later.

During the long journey home I had relived the past four weeks over and over again, struggling to make some sense out of what had occurred, to transform it into a memory that I could live with. In the end I ignored the really important lessons that I now see: the missed opportunity for open communication between two human beings, the mutual distancing that invariably results from silent retreat, the inevitable negative personal growth and interpersonal destruction that are the fruit born from the seeds of denial and deception, the shattering of relationship that occurs when physical intimacy is allowed to precede deep spiritual connection and commitment. Instead I retreated further into delusion and assembled another fantasy. Only this one was labeled not *The Star-Crossed Lovers* but rather *The Disaster*. I tied it all up into a neat package, carefully devoid of any emotion, and shared this brief tale with anyone who asked, including my mother.

"It was a disaster ... He wasn't Prince Charming after all." I pretended that I was able to laugh at myself, the sophisticate amused at the demise of her own naïve illusions. "But I had a good time ... lots of fun ... He has a really nice family ..."

Only once did I ever give Mom a hint about what had really transpired. But her sympathy was more than I could bear; her alignment with me, casting Paul as the villain of the piece, was intolerable, serving as it did to reawaken my guilt over the truth of who had hurt whom, so I terminated the discussion and never again shared my true feelings with anyone. I thought it much better to forget them. But I ended the summer with one firm resolution: Never, never again would I allow myself to care for anyone. It wasn't worth the pain. I would become a doctor. I didn't need anybody. To hell with relationships. To hell with men.

Chapter 9

I threw myself back into my medical studies with renewed vigor. It was an enormous relief to fill my mind with thoughts of diseases and drugs and, at last, The Patient. Finally we spent time on the hospital wards, learned how to interview and examine patients, and practiced these things on real people. Gradually I overcame my instinctive fear of talking to patients and painstakingly began to acquire some clinical skills.

I'll never forget one of the first patients assigned to me, a middle-aged man recovering from surgery for a chronic bowel disorder called diverticulosis. It took me three hours to interview and examine him, but the poor man never lost patience with me. I then spent two hours in the library researching his disease, which was new to me, followed by another three hours writing up my report. My thoroughness was rewarded by high praise from my preceptor the following day, encouraging me to continue this comprehensive attention to detail, both in my clinical work and in my studies.

I allowed nothing to conflict with my work for the next two years, no distractions or other demands on my time. If my classmates had considered me a loner before, they must have labeled me a recluse during this final phase of our training. I virtually never left the house except to attend classes during the week and to go to church on Sundays.

I socialized not at all, but buried myself in my room in the evenings and on weekends, poring over my books, relentlessly memorizing vast amounts of technical material. My bizarre eating habits had crystallized now and were more unhealthy than ever before. Breakfast was still black coffee, lunch a cheese-and-tomato sandwich—from which I now discarded the bread—and an apple, and dinner a salad and minute portion of lean meat. Then in the evening as I studied I would consume precisely two dozen ginger-snaps, crumb by crumb, stretched out over about two hours to help pass the time over my books. I carefully allotted myself sufficient calories to stabilize my weight at ninety-three pounds.

I bought my cookies in large economy-sized bags and hoarded them in my bedroom closet, always ensuring that I had an extra unopened package available in addition to the one I was using at the moment. I never offered to share my soul food with the rest of the family and in fact became frantic one day when I discovered my sister helping herself to a cookie. The family knew about my peculiar addiction and occasionally made jokes about it, which I did my best to ignore.

My mother's grave concern over my eating habits found expression on occasion, but I maintained a fortress of passive resistance that she found impregnable. I refused to see a doctor, claiming to be in excellent health, and indeed I never had a sick day in almost two years. I told her that my weight was stable and that I ate gingersnaps because I liked them. When she discovered once more that any pressure she exerted on me to change resulted only in my eating less of other foods, she again fell silent. But her vigilance never faltered, and I was constantly aware of her watching me. I ate dinner only to satisfy her, then escaped to my hideaway to eat my comfort food in private.

Periodically I was assailed by terrible loneliness, as a true glimpse of what I was doing with my life penetrated my consciousness. These attacks would often come when my neurotic habits interfered with something I truly wanted to do. For instance, when my beloved grandparents from Edson came to visit for an evening or weekend and I would have liked to talk with them until bedtime,

I still felt compelled to seclude myself after dinner for two or three hours, with the excuse that I had to study. Then, sitting alone in my room, a gingersnap clutched in my hand, listening to the murmur of voices from downstairs, one part of me knew the awful truth: My object was no longer to study, but to eat my cookies. I heard Grandma say, "Joan works so hard, Marge, can't she take a night off once in a while?" and felt wave after wave of guilt and shame, mixed with a growing sense of powerlessness to alter my own behavior. At such times I would catch a fleeting glimpse of myself trapped forever in this ritual form of secret eating.

But the aboriginal loneliness resulting from this vision was intolerable, so I dealt with it in the same way I had dealt with every other painful awareness in my life: I pushed it out of my mind. I would not think about it, by sheer force of will. I was just studying. I was OK. And I returned to my books, forcing everything else from my mind except the words on the page in front of me and the soothing background effect of the gingersnaps melting in my mouth and sliding down my throat.

On very rare occasions I now lost control of myself and binged on a Forbidden Food: usually ice cream, which I had now added to my off-limits list because of its caloric density. These urges generally assailed me in the middle of a sleepless night. Like an automaton I crept downstairs, stole a spoon from the kitchen, then slunk into the basement, removed the ice cream from the freezer, and started eating. Mom always bought it in large pails, so I knew I could eat a lot without it being noticed. This knowledge gave me no pleasure, because for some obscure reason I felt compelled to eat as much as I dared, almost to the point of discovery. I experienced no pleasure in this eating, as every bite was accompanied by terrible self-loathing. But I seemed incapable of stopping myself. Spoonful after spoonful went into my mouth as I watched the level of the ice cream drop in the container. I could not stop eating until I was uncomfortably full, almost to the point of being sick. Then I returned to my bed and lay in a sea of discomfort, physical and mental, as I berated myself for my weakness. The next day I exercised harder and eliminated a few items from my diet in reparation for my sin.

This entire two-year period was punctuated by only one episode of comic relief. On a Wednesday morning early in May, 1972, one week before my final exams, I awakened with a stomachache. It was not at all like the crampy abdominal pains I had experienced periodically for the past three years during periods of stress, which I had come to call my "gutaches." This was a deep, nauseating, unremitting pain, severe enough to keep me in bed that day. At the time I was a student intern (fourth-year medical student) on surgery at the General Hospital. By noon I was still unable to find a position of comfort, so I called Mom at her school to come home and take me to the doctor.

Our family doctor met us in the emergency room. Shortly before he arrived I rushed into the washroom with diarrhea. He examined me, found nothing tender in my abdomen, checked my blood, then agreed with my own diagnosis of intestinal "flu." He prescribed an antispasmodic drug to relieve the cramps and sent me home.

For the next three days I lay on the sofa at home, taking the medication every four hours to ease the pain, and sipping on water and juices. I could bear the thought of nothing else in my stomach. By Friday night I was worse, and the medication no longer brought any relief. I felt very warm, lightheaded, and oddly disoriented as I lay on the sofa with my knees drawn up, trying to remain absolutely still so as not to stir up the pain in my lower abdomen. Mom had gone out with friends for dinner after school and thus did not arrive home until after nine o'clock. I was relieved when I heard the car door slam and her footsteps in the hall.

"Good grief, Joan, you look awful! ... You're burning up with fever! ... I'm taking you back to the hospital, right now."

I was almost delirious by this time and scarcely remember moaning my reply. "Oh Mom, I can't go to the hospital. It just hurts too much to move. I can't stand the thought of riding in the car."

At this juncture she wasted no further time. My brother Tim picked me up bodily and carried me to the car, and I lay back against the seat, clutching my right side. Throughout the trip all I was aware of was the fiery stab of pain deep in the right lower quadrant of my abdomen every time the car jolted. The bell chimed suddenly in my mind, even through my febrile haze.

"Oh no, I've got rebound tenderness. That means peritoneal irritation. I must have appendicitis! Oh no! What about my exams next week?"

Three hours and four doctors later, my diagnosis was confirmed on the operating table. I later learned that my appendix was draped over the pelvic brim, thus accounting for the atypical symptoms, and was on the point of perforation when my abdomen was opened. Even today it seems ludicrous to me that a fourth-year student, one week away from completing her medical training, about to be unleashed on an unsuspecting public, could lie around for three days with appendicitis without making the diagnosis.

This was my first surgical procedure since a tonsillectomy at age five, and it was a true revelation to see things from the other side of the bed. The first twenty-four hours was like a nightmare as I kept surfacing from my drugged sleep to be overwhelmed by the most excruciating physical pain I had ever known. I caught glimpses of faces swimming above me: Mom, other family members, Daddy (where did he come from?), nurses; but I was unable to form a coherent sentence. The nurses somehow knew what I needed even before I asked, and were always right there with another injection of narcotic. After a few minutes the pain in my abdomen would mercifully begin to recede, like a tide, and I would drift away on a fluffy pink cloud, absolutely weightless, into another opium dream.

I left the hospital on the third postoperative day and wrote my final exams two days later. The Dean of Medicine heard of my plight and insisted that I write my exams in his office rather than in the examination hall. So for two days I made my way there, was seated in a comfortable armchair at a large desk, instructed to move around as much as I liked, assured that I could have extra time if I needed it, and was served coffee throughout by his secretary. I have always joked that this preferential treatment accounted for my superior performance: In customary fashion, I topped the class on every paper and scored in the ninety-ninth percentile on the national phase of the examinations.

My success story was marred by one unpleasant incident. On the first morning of the exams, Mom suggested that I eat breakfast for a change. She knew I had lost three more pounds during my illness and was still debilitated from the surgery. Out of long habit I declined, claiming not to be hungry, and returned to my room to do what few calisthenics I could still manage. A few minutes later I heard a tap on the door, and Mom walked in carrying a tray, more distraught than she had appeared in many months.

"Joan, I can't bear this stupidity any longer," she said as she set down the tray, her voice tight, her eyes brimming. "You know damned well that you need something in your stomach to write eight hours of exams today. I've done my best to help you these past four years, but I'm at the end of my rope. You've got to make your own choices from now on and live with them. Here's some breakfast. You can eat it or not. You're on your own."

Without waiting for my response she left the room, leaving me to cope with the turbulent flood of my emotions. I despised myself for bringing such grief to the person I loved most in the world. I was angry at her for disturbing my fragile serenity on such a critical morning. And, above all, I felt an overwhelming hopelessness as I stared at the meal, knowing that I would be unable to eat it, despite knowing rationally that I should do so. Like the helpless puppet of some terrible demon, I carried the food into the bathroom and flushed it down the toilet. As I watched it swirl away I thought of what a relief it would be to escape from home the next month when I started my internship in Halifax. I would be alone at last to eat as I chose, with absolutely no one to bug me. No one trying to control me. No one inducing guilt in me.

June first, 1972, the day of my convocation, dawned bright and clear. It was a day to remember. A day to contemplate the threshold on which I stood. I awakened early and went with my mother to early Mass to offer thanksgiving for all past blessings before attending the annual faculty breakfast honoring the graduating class. Sitting in the elegant country club dining room, shifting the food around on my plate, I felt intensely uncomfortable, like a stranger among these hundred men and women, my classmates, who had been my constant companions for the past four years. For I truly was a stranger.

Speeches were made and the awards presented following the meal, and I was in my glory as I was called forward to receive two gold medals: one for the highest overall academic standing, and one for surgery. Surgery! That was a surprise. I had no flair whatsoever for its technical aspects and no burning desire to elbow my way in at the operating table and wrest the scalpel from the surgeon's hand. But I had mastered the theory perfectly, having memorized the textbooks from cover to cover. And, equally important from the standpoint of grades, I had learned to render excellent pre- and post-operative care to my assigned patients, and always worked tirelessly on the wards, something that the attending physicians noticed and rewarded through their evaluations of my performance.

Accepting those accolades from the Dean, I truly felt that I had reached the culmination of my dream. This feeling persisted as I later led the class onto the stage, wearing the black robe and scarlet ribbon of my profession, and bowed before the Chancellor to receive my M.D., *cum laude*. I actually believed in myself that day, in the fictional character I had worked so hard to create. My mother donned her academic gown from the previous year, when she had earned her master's degree in education, and we posed together for photographs outside the auditorium. Like mother, like daughter. A real success story, everyone said. And we all believed it, all the family and friends who had congregated for the occasion.

"Congratulations, honey, I'm sure proud of you." My father kissed and embraced me as he uttered these words, and I knew he meant them. Mom had suggested that we invite him to attend the celebrations, too, for, after all, he *was* my father. So he flew in from Inuvik for the occasion, bringing his second wife with him. He brought an extravagant gift for me, a beautiful handmade sealskin parka with white fox trim, and he announced that he was taking me and my brothers and sisters out for dinner and dancing in the evening after my convocation.

As I sat in the noisy smoke-filled banquet room and gazed across the table at this strange man, I felt as though I were in a dream.

I was five and six years old again and delighted to be Daddy's little princess. I was seven and eight and crying myself to sleep every night, lost and bewildered by his desertion, wondering what I had done to make him leave me. I was nine and ten and eleven and had not stopped writing letters to him regularly, had not given up my hope that the prince would return one day and kiss away the aching void within. I was twelve and thirteen and fourteen and all hope had died a lingering painful death, and I had very deliberately forced him from my mind, determined to forget the pain.

And now he was here, and I smiled and talked and even flirted with him, this handsome charming stranger. I was as yet utterly devoid of insight, completely incapable of viewing him compassionately as a loving and well-meaning man who had done his very best to minimize the trauma his children had to experience when his relationship with their mother collapsed, as it was doomed to do from its inception; as an ordinary human being who had fallen victim to circumstance as all of us do. Instead I gazed at him across the table and at the lavish gift he had brought, and my heart gave a long and anguished cry. *Oh, Daddy, where were you when I needed you?*

And I looked at him and smiled.

Chapter 10

〰️〰️〰️ *"Oh, Joan, please take care of yourself."* My mother made a deep visual connection, and I tore my eyes away with difficulty. We both knew what she meant. "Phone home anytime you like. Reverse the charges, okay?"

Tears flowed freely as we embraced and said these final good-byes. I realize now she was struggling with the very real possibility that she might never see me alive again. I jumped into my little green Datsun, started the engine and, with one last wave, was gone. I was suddenly terrified of a future that stretched out before me like an unlit corridor before a wanderer without a torch. But there was no turning back now. All my earthly belongings were packed in this car, I was twenty-three years old, a graduate physician for the past forty-eight hours, and I should be capable of making my way in the world. *Stand on your own two feet. Stand on your own two feet.* The words played and replayed in my mind like a mantra as I pointed the car eastward and took to the open road.

And gradually, as the miles ticked off, I relaxed and began to anticipate the exciting adventure that lay ahead. Dalhousie University! That prestigious institution had accepted me into their two-year family practice residency program, one of the few such accredited programs in Canada at the time. The first year was to be a rotating internship during which I would be posted at five different hospitals around the Maritime provinces, in keeping with the traditional Dalhousie belief that variety enriches the minds of its students. My first assignment was to the Halifax Infirmary, and that was my destination now. However, I had more than two weeks to get there, which allowed time for stopovers along the way to visit with aunts and uncles in Winnipeg, Toronto, and Montreal.

Today I stand in awe of the stamina I possessed in those days and of my courage in undertaking such a journey alone. Was it youth that allowed me to perform thus in the face of such devastating physical and mental sickness? Or was it only the disease itself, the powerful denial that operated at every level of my psyche? Driving five hundred miles a day seemed effortless, and I enjoyed the solitude as well as the changing scenery through which I passed. My disease had not yet advanced to the stage where all authentic pleasure vanishes. My financial resources were severely limited, so most nights I pitched my pup tent in campgrounds along the highway and slept in it to save money. My diet consisted of the familiar gingersnaps, fruit, and ice cream from Dairy Queens along the way.

The country east of Montreal was new to me, and I was enthralled by the quiet beauty of the countryside and the quaint villages along the St. Lawrence. I left the main highway so that I could absorb the atmosphere of rural Quebec as I meandered along, reveling in the history that enveloped me. Despite my leisurely pace, I reached New Brunswick on the eighth day of driving. I still had ample time to take a side trip to Prince Edward Island, so I phoned ahead to Ian and Betty Gorman in Charlottetown to give them my whereabouts and obtain information about the ferries.

Prince Edward Island was a dream, a wonderful garden land reminiscent of England in the density of its population, in the cultivation of every available acre. This too was a land with a past, with ghosts lurking around every corner and, as a western Canadian, I appreciated them. Ian and Betty were overjoyed to see me and embraced me warmly as I alighted from the car. We had not seen each other for more than a year, since they had left Edmonton, and we sat up talking for most of that first night.

I stayed with them for several days, delaying my departure for Halifax until the last possible moment, having never felt so welcome at anyone's home in my entire life. Because they were wholly relaxed about having a houseguest, I was able to relax as well. I had fretted beforehand about meals, but Betty quickly learned my tastes and quietly provided the food I wanted, and neither of them said a word when I refused such delicacies as Betty's famous chili and her chocolate brownies. They accepted me wholeheartedly and without reservation, exactly as I was. They were the perfect hosts, providing constant but unobtrusive attention to my needs, appearing to have nothing else to do but savor my presence for those few days, always maintaining a casual air that kept me at my ease. I was surprised to find that I hated to leave their home at the end of my stay, as I had not truly enjoyed being anyone's guest since my bizarre eating habits had developed three years previously. During those days together we came to know one another better than ever before, and as I drove away I realized that I had two very precious friends in Ian and Betty, the kind one finds rarely in a lifetime.

But Halifax lay ahead, and it was to there that my attention now turned. I located the Halifax Infirmary, presented myself to the medical director, and was assigned a room in the interns' quarters. My first rotation was to be two months on internal medicine, additionally covering psychiatry and emergency at night. At 8:00 the next morning I was on the wards, proudly displaying my new white uniform, my stethoscope, and my very own beeper.

Thus began the most grueling year of my life. It was still traditional in 1972 for interns to be overworked and underpaid. We expected it, and the attending medical staff ensured that we got what we expected. There was no end to the work, starting with early morning rounds and ending with midnight admissions from the emergency room.

"There's a new admission in Seven Bed One, Dr. Eisener. Congestive failure. A patient of Dr. Michaels. He wants you to call him after you do the history and check the X-rays ... Oh, would you mind restarting the I.V. in Five Bed Three first? It just went interstitial and she's due for meds at midnight." ... "Dr. Eisener, come quickly! Mrs. Farley is having a transfusion reaction!" ... "Code Red, Station Fourteen, Code Red, Station Fourteen!" ... "Would you come and talk to the family of Mr. Wyatt, Dr. Eisener? They don't understand his condition. Only be careful about what you say: You know how Dr. Hopkinson is!" ... "Don't go too far away tonight, Dr. Eisener, there are I.V. meds due at one, two, and four and they're all drugs we're not 'covered' to give." ... "Dr. Eisener, would you come and do a blood culture in Eight Bed Two? She just spiked a temp of 39.5 and Dr. Watson ordered blood cultures stat if it went over 39." ... "Would you come and check Mr. Jones before you go for supper, Dr. Eisener? It seems he's been having chest pain for hours, but the day staff didn't call anyone to see him." ... "There's a new admission—" ... "There's an I.V. to start in—" ... "Would you check—" ... "We don't like his color." ... "Dr. Eisener, report to emergency, STAT!"

I had never worked so hard physically in my entire life. My legs permanently ached, my lower back was one screaming knot of pain. I existed in a state of chronic fatigue that even ten hours of sleep on my nights off could not relieve. In September I moved to the Victoria General Hospital for two months on general surgery, and it was there that I began sleeping in my clothes when I was on call, which was every second night. It was bad enough to have to drag my wounded body out of bed at 3:00 A.M. to see a new patient with appendicitis, but to have to get dressed before going to emergency was simply beyond my power. Some nights I even left my shoes on when I crawled between the sheets.

Despite the physical toll, however, I did learn a great deal about caring for patients. My clinical skills sharpened, I learned to assess patients and situations quickly, I lost my fear of making decisions. My technical abilities improved dramatically, and I began to acquire a bedside manner that enabled me to deal successfully with most people. By an enormous effort of will I concealed my fatigue and appeared to work with enthusiasm and energy most of the time, without ever complaining. For this reason I got along well with the nurses. The attending staff also appreciated the intelligence and meticulous attention to detail that I applied to diagnostic and therapeutic problems. I was frequently enlisted to make case presentations on the wards and at Grand Rounds, and received high praise for all my efforts.

This positive feedback was all that sustained me most of the time, because secretly I was dreadfully unhappy and lonely, and I often wondered how I would survive a whole year of this existence. My world had become bounded by the hospital wards and my bedroom, relieved occasionally by an evening walk through nearby streets or a weekend drive around the city or to the Annapolis Valley. It was an unreal existence, an unhealthy one, and, for me, a deadly one.

For I was slowly starving. In the midst of my preoccupation with medicine, my obsession with food and weight also became more intense and more distorted. The more rational I was on the wards, the more irrational my eating behavior became. The only solace from my backbreaking work was to hide in my room and eat as I read the current medical journals and reviewed my textbooks. To do this I could usually steal away at noon and suppertime and between tasks in the evening.

My gingersnaps tasted so good to my starving body that I began eating three dozen of them every day, constituting 80 percent of the carefully controlled calories I allowed myself. I knew that I needed protein also, so as a token to balanced nutrition I cooked half a pound of liver or fish every weekend, divided it into seven plastic containers, and stored it in the refrigerator in the interns' kitchen. I would consume one ounce every day with a bit of shredded lettuce or canned green beans on top. That meal disposed of my vegetable requirement, too, yet at a total "cost" of only one hundred calories. Additionally, in the evening I ingested two apples.

Such was my daily diet for the entire year. With one exception: On Saturdays, if I was not on call, I would drive to a nearby shopping mall, purchase a pint of ice cream, then sit in the car and eat it while reading a medical book. That was my Big Splurge, but I carefully reduced my cookie intake and omitted my meat on those days to allow for the extra calories. Needless to say I lost weight, but it was so gradual, about a pound every month, that I was able to trick myself into denying the loss. For I weighed myself daily, and whenever I saw the reading drop slightly, I explained it away: "I'm sure I had a larger bowel movement today," or, "It's just a fluid shift: It doesn't mean anything." The month-to-month readings I ignored.

In retrospect, the most remarkable thing about the year, and possibly the saddest, is the fact that no one at any time appeared to notice my illness. I was constantly surrounded by doctors and nurses, working shoulder-to-shoulder with intelligent and dedicated healers, but not once did one of them approach me to ask if anything was wrong. I appeared gaunt and emaciated at ninety pounds when I arrived in Halifax in June, and I was a grotesque living skeleton at seventy-eight pounds when I departed the following May. But no one noticed. Thus does medicine take care of its own. *Physician, heal thyself* ...

Yet I cannot affix much blame outside of myself, for neither did I invite anyone's approach. On the contrary, I rebuffed any tentative offers of friendship that were made. I wanted no complications in my life. To work, sleep, eat, and read was all that I could handle. And the frequent moves from hospital to hospital, with their attendant change in the interns and staff with whom I worked, discouraged any enduring relationships.

Ian and Betty journeyed to Halifax twice to see me, however, and it was on the occasion of their weekend visits that I had difficulty maintaining the denial of my illness. For they aroused such conflict in me. One part of me loved them dearly and wanted to be with them, but another part objected vehemently to the disturbance in my routine. In the silent reaches of my soul I scorned and detested that second part of me, but in the end I surrendered to it. I pretended that I had to work in the morning and asked them to pick me up at the hospital after lunch, thus avoiding two meals with them and allowing me to eat my gingersnaps before they arrived. Then at dinnertime I would feign a "gutache" or pretend I was not hungry and order only a salad in the restaurant to which they took me. I was wholly ensnared in my web of deceit. In my prison. In my own private hell.

I made only one feeble attempt to escape my isolation and reach out to another human being. Eliot Chapman was an intern at the hospital in Saint John, New Brunswick, when I transferred there in November for a three-month rotation through outpatients, gynecology, and urology. He was a soft-spoken, gentle, and sensitive individual, an American, and he seemed attracted to me for some obscure reason I could not imagine. Buried as I was within a shroud of malnutrition, in the tomb that encased my emotions by this time, it was impossible for me to genuinely connect with and care for anyone, but Eliot's attentions weakly penetrated my barriers. Perhaps the pain of my isolation was growing intolerable, or perhaps the recognition he paid me was simply welcome proof that I was still alive. Whatever the reason, I responded minimally to his overtures. We had coffee together a few times and spent many of our free hours in conversation.

I was further buoyed up at this time by the four-day Christmas vacation ahead and with it a flying trip home that I had planned at the eleventh hour. I was desperately homesick and had managed to save enough money out of my small salary to pay for the trip. I wanted to appear healthy and happy to everyone at home, congruent with the image that I was struggling to maintain of the successful, independent young physician. What better way to convince my family that everything was fine than to go home with news of a new boyfriend? I bought a new baby-blue angora dress for the trip, as everything I possessed was hanging loosely on my eighty-four pound frame. It was the smallest dress I ever owned, a size four, and it did fit me. I reasoned that nobody would notice my weight loss if my clothes fit properly. I accepted Eliot's offer to drive me to the airport and kissed him good-bye in high spirits.

I can scarcely recall my three days at home. I remember traveling a lot and sleeping very little. We drove to Edson in a snowstorm to spend Christmas Day with my grandparents. I don't remember many comments about my weight. Perhaps everyone was too deeply shocked to say anything. I followed the script I had written for myself and actually believed that everyone was convinced by my performance.

Eliot picked me up at the airport when I returned, and as we drove back to the hospital he asked me to go out for dinner that evening. I declined, claiming to be too tired, but in actual fact I badly needed my gingersnaps. I was suffering a true withdrawal reaction after three days without them and could think of nothing but the anticipation of their spicy taste and sweetness; of the way they crunched in my mouth; of their soothing and nurturing movement from there to my hollow stomach; of the two heavenly hours, the center of my day, the highlight of my existence, that it required to eat them. No human companionship could begin to rival the glorious and predictable pleasure I derived from those cookies.

My refusal set the pattern for the remainder of our interaction. He called a few days later and asked me to go skating, but I found another excuse, this time marginally true: I was always cold, so I hated outdoor activities. I did not tell him that the physical effort involved was simply too much for my weakened body and that the emotional effort of dating was utterly beyond my power. He invited me to go out on several more occasions, but I made excuses every time. I had decided that any involvement with him would upset my routine. I barely had enough time now to eat and read. How could I work a boyfriend into my schedule? And besides, I knew how dangerous it was to let any man get too close. Men were unpredictable. Intimacy was a risky business. *Remember what happened the last time you tried that.* Better to stick to cookies. Better to stay in control.

Finally his calls stopped, and then I began to feel guilty. He was a very good man, we had a lot in common, and we could have been friends. What sort of a pathetic excuse for a human being was I to reject him? On the morning of my departure from St. John I stared at the phone in my room, filled with a vague discomfort about leaving without talking to him. I hadn't spoken to him for a week, and we would probably never meet again in our lives. I felt compelled to acknowledge the friendship he had extended to me. So I picked up the phone with a trembling hand.

"Hi, Eliot! It's Joan," I said breezily. "I'm just ready to leave for Charlottetown, and I wanted to say good-bye. How are you doing?"

There was a long blank silence at the other end of the line. I felt my face flush and braced myself for his response. I'll never forget it.

"Well, Joan, it seems as though you're always saying 'good-bye.' When are you going to start saying 'hello'?" The words were a poignant observation, not an accusation.

I hadn't expected to be confronted in this manner, and I was angry at him for not playing my game of Everything's OK. He was forcing me to look at myself squarely and admit the truth. Well, I wouldn't do it! After stammering some inadequate response I hung up the phone as quickly as possible, then leapt into the car and headed for P.E.I., forcing yet another painful incident from my conscious mind.

February and March were spent at the P.E.I. Hospital doing obstetrics. It was a small hospital with a friendly family atmosphere, and I would have enjoyed it the most of all my rotations, had I been able to enjoy anything in those dark days. I was the sole intern on the ob/gyn service, so was on call every day and night, seven days a week, for the entire two months. My comprehensive exhaustion reached a peak during this time, and it was not caused merely by lack of sleep.

Everything in my life had somehow become an enormous effort. All energy and spontaneity had died. I plodded along from one day to the next, dragging my weary body around the wards and counting off the days until this terrible year would end. Even my love for obstetrics could not dispel my fatigue. I began to have difficulty falling asleep for the first time in my life and occasionally begged a sleeping pill from the night nurse on duty in the case room. Sometimes I even found my appetite truly blunted, also a new experience. I ate my gingersnaps out of habit, although they frequently tasted like sawdust in my mouth. All joy had gone from my life. I had forgotten how to laugh.

I was also by now incapable of responding to Ian and Betty's frequent calls and invitations to visit them. I was riddled with guilt for continually making excuses to them. But somehow the monumental task of smiling at them and pretending to be enjoying myself seemed beyond my capacity. And so I lied, and hated myself for doing so. "I'd love to get together, but we've got three women in labor tonight." … "I'd really like to come over for dinner, but I was up all last night and just have to get some sleep." … "I just can't come over this afternoon. Sunday is so busy on gynecology: I've got six pre-op histories to do."

Had I encountered a patient with this constellation of signs and symptoms, I would have made the diagnosis without hesitation: depression. But I refused to see it in myself. The recognition of illness necessitates a search for treatment and cure, an obligation to change, and I was still too terrified to change one single item of my behavior. Even the pain of my existence could not overcome my fear.

And so the winter faded into spring and I returned to Halifax for my final two months on pediatrics. For the first time in years I fell ill with a bad cold and was dismayed to find myself too weak to get out of bed. I missed two days of work, then dragged myself back onto the wards. I could barely climb stairs anymore but refused to consider the possibility that my weakness was due to the terrible atrophy of my muscles. I ignored the fact that the scale now hovered at seventy-nine pounds when I stepped on it.

However I did make one intelligent decision that month. Perhaps it was due to some primitive instinct for self-preservation, perhaps to divine intervention. But whatever the reason, I decided to give up my original plan of staying at Dalhousie for two years. I told myself, and the family practice program director, that my decision was motivated by homesickness. I would return to Alberta at the end of May, having completed my rotating internship, fully qualified to apply for a license to practice medicine. The director graciously accepted my resignation from his program with glowing praise for my performance over the past year. Not a word was spoken about my ghastly physical appearance.

I wrote home to announce my change of plans and immediately received a phone call from Mom supporting my decision. I was so buoyed up by the prospect of any escape from my prison that I was able to complete the last six weeks of my rotation with something resembling enthusiasm. I counted off the days to the end of May and once again, as so often before in my life, lapsed into magical thinking: Everything would be just fine, once I was safely home again. I would behave normally. I would be happy.

I had no way of knowing that I had not yet reached the bottom of the pit.

Chapter 11

I left Halifax at the end of May, 1973, in high spirits, full of light and hope. I headed west by a circuitous route in order to see some of New England. During the four days before I reached Toronto an unexpected change occurred within me. The solitary drive, the deep silence of expansive sky and primeval forest, the monotonous ribbon of highway stretching out before me, gave me time to think, time to pray. Something I had not done for months. Somehow I found the courage to face myself for the first time, to look honestly at my life as it had evolved over the previous five years. *Anorexia nervosa.* I said the words to myself without flinching. I admitted my illness. And I was surprised by the calm and peace that this simple admission brought to my soul. What had I been afraid of? Why had I been too terrified to face my condition before? I knew not why, but I did know that along with the recognition of the disease came a deep yearning to escape from its deadly clutches.

Oh God, have mercy on me, for I am alone and afflicted. Do not abandon to the depths below the one you love, but let your face shine on your servant. Look not upon my sins but upon my faith, and have pity on me. Deliver me from this darkness. The prayer welled up, unbidden, from my deepest center. And slowly the glimmer of light at the end of the tunnel grew brighter and a new plan took shape in my mind.

By the time I reached Toronto, where I stayed for three days, my spirits were abnormally elated. I was filled with energy and a new zest for living, waking up every morning at 5:00, unable to return to sleep, my mind buzzing with thoughts and plans and a ceaseless running communication with my God. I sensed that I was to be delivered from my illness, although there was little concrete evidence as yet in my eating behavior. But I followed through on the idea that had occurred to me during the journey. I found the phone number of the Sisters of Service, called it, and received an invitation to visit their motherhouse in Toronto.

The Sisters of Service had long occupied a special place in my heart, since they were the nuns who operated the hospital at Edson where I was born. They had taught me catechism and had always attracted me by their authentic goodness and simple life. Their order had been founded in the twentieth century specifically for the purpose of ministering to the needs of rural western Canadians, and they were unlike most of the older traditional orders of nuns, not only in their modern dress but also in their attitudes. When as a schoolgirl I had dreamed about becoming a nun, as all good little Catholic girls do, it was to the Sisters of Service that I was drawn.

Now I was being drawn to them again and went to their convent on a lovely June evening full of joyous anticipation. I was not disappointed by the warm reception I was given, but by the response I received when I informed the superior that I felt a call to join the community. Looking back now, I think she handled my overture very wisely. She said not a word about my skeletal appearance but was instead open and encouraging. At the conclusion of our lengthy conversation, she cautioned me that one must be very sure of the call, and of one's motives, before entering a religious order. She suggested that I return home and spend the next few months in reflection and prayer, and that I correspond regularly with their formation mistress.

I left Toronto confident that I was on the right track, but vaguely disappointed that I had not been accepted immediately with open arms and given a date to return and begin my training as a nun. I recognize my folly now, of course: My "call" to the religious life was yet another manifestation of my familiar penchant for fantasy. I longed for an escape from the prison of my neurosis and could think of no better route than to become a nun. I would have to live in community, following orders, unable to select my own food or to seclude myself from others. I would be *compelled* to live like a normal human being once again. I could give away my free will to my superiors, and they would be my police, forcing me to be good. What a motive! On the purer side, I also truly wanted to remain as connected with God as I was at that moment, and I saw becoming a nun as the surest way to do this, the straightest path to heaven.

All across the prairies I continued to meditate and pray. I knew what my next step must be and, with high drama, as I crossed the Alberta border I carried out this step. I halted at the first waste disposal stop after the border, stepped out of the car and threw all my gingersnaps into the barrel. I felt immeasurably lighter and somehow cleansed as I proceeded on to Edmonton.

I shall remember to my deathbed my mother's expression when I walked through the doorway that June afternoon. She looked upon the dying seventy-eight pound shell of her beloved daughter, into the smiling brilliant eyes of the infant she had brought forth in such joyful anticipation twenty-four years before, then without a single word took me in her arms and wept. I knew what she was thinking.

I sat down at the dinner table with my family, heaped potatoes and gravy and stuffing on my plate along with the turkey, and ate them, the first time I had tasted such foods in almost five years. Adele and Tim stared at me in openmouthed disbelief. I smiled at them and raved about Mom's cooking with genuine enthusiasm.

"Everything's going to be OK, Mom. I know I've been sick these past few years, but I'm OK now. I'm going to put on some weight and just relax for a little while. I'll go and see Dr. Hardy, too, and maybe I'll ask him to refer me to a psychiatrist … just in case." It was the day after my return home, and we were having a private discussion in my room. Then I shared with her my plan to become a nun. She said very little.

Perhaps she knew that the change in me was too good to be true. Too easy. Too much like magic. And she was right, of course, as I quickly discovered over the next few days. My familiar cravings returned in full force along with my fears of Forbidden Foods, and I surrendered to my urges one by one. However, I substituted ice cream for my gingersnaps, began eating more meat and vegetables, and increased my total caloric intake a little. But when I rapidly gained two pounds I panicked, terrified that I would be unable to stop the gain. I cut back once more.

In the meantime I saw our family doctor, an enormous step for me, since this was the first time I had admitted my disease to another. I masked my anxiety by taking charge of the interview and remaining very cool and clinical as I informed him that I had anorexia nervosa. I maintained this cerebral approach as I described the problem to him, carefully suppressing all visible sign of emotion.

"... So that's the story, Dr. Hardy," I said levelly. "But I think everything's going to be OK. I'm eating again now that I'm home, and I'm gaining weight. But I thought maybe I should see a psychiatrist, just in case I find that I need some help. What do you think?"

I was very grateful for the calm way in which he listened to me, for exhibiting no outward sign of shock as my story unfolded. He accepted me and was not judgmental in any way, and I relaxed perceptibly as I recognized that I had a friend here.

"I think you're right, Joan. Do you have any preference in a psychiatrist?" he asked thoughtfully. "No? ... Then I would suggest Ernie Runions. I think he's the ideal person for you. He's an excellent psychiatrist, and he's a Christian. In fact, he's also a Baptist minister and manages to find time to serve as pastor at West Park Baptist Church in addition to everything else ... A most remarkable man."

I sat in Dr. Runions' office a week later, indescribably nervous as I waited for him, wishing I had never come. *A shrink! Why on earth did I ever think I needed a shrink? What is he going to do to me? What will I say? I don't want my head changed. I don't want to get fat again! I can't change the way I'm eating. I won't!*

The sound of the office door opening interrupted these thoughts, and there entered a man of exceedingly small stature and light build. He walked briskly over to his desk, shook hands firmly, then sat down. We surveyed one another for a few moments as my discomfort intensified. He had a pleasant enough face and radiated a quiet warmth, but what riveted my attention were the most piercing blue eyes I had ever seen. They were intensely alive, luminescent, and almost hypnotic in their effect. I could not tear my gaze from his, and I felt naked before him. I thought he could see straight into my soul. I was terrified. I wanted to bolt from the room. I had no desire to open up to this man, and I would not do so.

He opened the interview with some casual nonthreatening remarks, then invited me to elaborate on what Dr. Hardy had told him already on the phone. I could see no immediate route of escape, so I steeled myself, forced my eyes from his face to the trees outside the window behind his left shoulder, and plunged into the same recital I had given Dr. Hardy. It flowed more easily this time, and I inwardly congratulated myself at its conclusion for getting through the story without showing any ridiculous emotion. I could handle my problem, if indeed it was one. I didn't need any help. I had been repeating these things to myself during the past few weeks as I allowed my old compulsions to dominate my behavior, and I was well on the way to believing them once again.

Dr. Runions allowed a lengthy silence to develop after I finished my tale. He simply met my eyes once more, and I flushed and broke the visual connection quickly before it could solidify and transmit that terrifying current of power again. *Damn it, what is he trying to do?*

Finally he spoke, gently probing, attempting to elicit some sign of emotion from me. The next twenty minutes were occupied with a game of cat and mouse as I evaded his efforts, determined not to break down and cry like a sissy. I felt that if he succeeded in making me weep, I would lose the battle.

I won. This time.

After another long silence he admitted defeat. "All right, Joan, I take it that you feel you don't need any help right now, is that correct? I have to accept that," he said calmly. "But I would like you to know that if you should change your mind at any time, I will be here for you. You will always be welcome to come back."

I thanked him in a perfunctory fashion, still refusing to meet those eyes again, then rose and all but ran from his office. I paused in the hall outside, my heart pounding and my mouth dry. After regaining control of myself, I made my way home, firmly putting the entire episode out of my mind. *I am not sick!*

Chapter 12

I succeeded in deceiving myself for the remainder of the summer as I lazed about in the sun and took my first vacation in three years. My eating habits deteriorated again, but I ignored these signs and continued to correspond with the Sisters of Service, fueling my fantasy that I was well and would soon enter the convent and live happily ever after. Mom left me alone, although I saw her covertly watching me. She was probably afraid to upset my uneasy balance, reasoning that at least I would not die if I continued to eat as I was now doing. She ensured there was a steady supply of meat and vegetables acceptable to me, and she knew that I was now consuming ice cream in addition to gingersnaps.

In early September I began to feel guilty about not working and decided that my laziness could go on no longer. I made a few phone calls, discovered a vacancy in the family practice residency program at the General Hospital, and within a week had been accepted into the second year of the program and started work.

During the next few months, my life began to resemble what it had been like in the Maritimes. My eating habits gradually worsened, to the extent that I would hide gingersnaps in the residents' on-call room at the hospital and sneak away to eat them for lunch. On nights when I was on call, I would eat them for dinner also, but fortunately three nights out of four I had to go home for dinner. Thus my weight did not drop below eighty pounds again, despite the fact that I was using every trick I knew to dispose of food and avoid having to eat. My mental state also deteriorated, as that familiar pervasive gloom and lassitude slowly enveloped me once again. I refused to admit that I was unhappy within the narrow confines of my prison.

Meanwhile Mom had formulated a plan that she hoped might somehow release me from my terrible cage. It was early December when she approached me with it.

"How would you like to go to Hawaii with me after Christmas, Joan? I've always wanted to go, but I'd rather not do it alone. I can finally afford it this year, and I've discovered a very good package deal including airfare and hotel for three weeks. I can even help you out with your expenses if you can't afford it. What do you say?" Her lovely hazel eyes searched my face, waiting, hoping.

"Wow!" I responded with enthusiasm. "I'd love to go, Mom. You know how much I hate winter. I'll see if I can take three weeks of my vacation in January." I leapt once again at the prospect of any new means of escape from the bleakness of my life.

We left Edmonton in a blizzard on New Year's Eve, 1973, and some five hours later arrived in paradise, certain that we were dreaming as the warm moist air embraced us when we stepped from the plane. The mingled potpourri of unidentifiable exotic flowers hung in the air, the tropical sun warmed our faces, and everywhere was the magic of laughter and music. I fell in love with Hawaii and savored every moment there, feeling as though I had been released from my prison, although objectively very little changed in my eating behavior.

I stopped eating gingersnaps, but every day at noon methodically consumed exactly one pint of ice cream and read a medical journal, regardless of what else we had planned for the day. My mother said nothing, but with perfect detachment tolerated my compulsive behavior. With that ritual completed, I then felt free to relax on the beach, shop at the Ala Moana Center, go sightseeing with Mom, or simply roam the streets of Waikiki. Reveling in the air and the sunshine, I was oblivious to the attention I attracted by displaying my cachectic body in the brief clothing all tourists wore. Mom on the other hand was acutely conscious of the way shocked passersby turned on the street after I passed, to stare at the pokerlike limbs protruding grotesquely from my shorts and T-shirt. I was still convinced that my thinness was beautiful and continued to deplore my potbelly, faithfully doing thirty minutes of strenuous calisthenics every morning in an effort to rid myself of it.

As our time in Hawaii drew to a close, I dreaded returning home. I was certain that this was where I belonged, since it was the only place I had found a semblance of tranquillity for years.

"You know what, Mom?" I said one afternoon as we lay on the beach. "I sure wish I could stay here longer. I wonder if I could get a job somewhere, rent an apartment, and just live here for a while? Do you think I could get a work permit?" The tropical sun was hot on my back, the salty sea breeze cool on my face, the deadly earnest in my eyes masked by dark glasses.

She erupted into laughter, to my intense annoyance, then mildly encouraged this latest fantasy but pointed out that I would have to return to Canada first and apply for entry by official channels. "And what about your job at home? You can't just walk out on that," she said reasonably.

I would have loved to do precisely that. Later that day I went so far as to inquire about a job waiting on tables at a nearby restaurant. Obtaining a license to practice medicine in the United States would not be possible until I passed the National Board examinations.

However, reason won out, as Mom insisted that I abandon this lunatic scheme for the present. On the eve of our departure I fell silent and sulked throughout the journey home. My mother laughed and joked with other returning vacationers while I sat by the window and sullenly stared at an earth thirty thousand feet below. I refused to smile, despite her cajoling and then her reproaches. Why should I smile? I wanted to weep. I wanted to die. I was a prisoner who had experienced one tantalizing taste of sun-drenched alpine meadows and laughing rivers flowing into an open sea before being chained up once more in a moldering dungeon to beg her captors for the mercy of execution. My heart sank further when I saw the snowdrifts and felt an arctic blast of wind as we left the plane. Never had I known such despair.

I had three free days at home before I was slated to return to work on Monday, and during this time my irrational behavior continued. I did not want to face the grim reality that I was back in Edmonton, so I closed myself up in my tiny bedroom with a vaporizer blasting continuously to simulate the balmy air of Waikiki. I ate only gingersnaps and tropical fruits during those days, and refused to leave my room.

Throughout the day on Sunday I became progressively uneasy. I knew it was mainly because I dreaded returning to work the next day, but there was also something more, some nebulous fear that I did not want to face. I attempted to ignore this inner distress, driving myself through my customary rituals. Before I went to bed I approached Mom, as I had been feeling increasingly guilty about my petulant behavior over the past four days.

"Goodnight, Mom. I'm going to bed now, since I have to get up early for work in the morning." I hesitated, then continued somewhat sheepishly, "Oh, and I also wanted to say I'm sorry for being so silly these past few days. I really enjoyed the trip, and I hope I didn't ruin it for you by being so childish. Thanks again for taking me along."

She embraced me warmly. "There's no need to apologize, honey … I understand." Her love was tangible, unconditional, and I felt even more guilty. I knew I did not deserve such love.

I lay in bed that night for hours, tossing and turning, but sleep would not come. I heard Mom say goodnight to Tim, then come upstairs and enter her bedroom, closing the door behind her. Some time later I heard the television set being switched off and listened to Tim's footsteps on the stairs. His usual bedtime noises seemed so loud tonight, so distinct, so intrusive. Water running in the bathroom, his footfall in the hall, the click of a switch as the line of light under my door disappeared, the closing of his bedroom door and the creak of his bedsprings as he settled for the night.

Then silence. Silence and darkness. It was the night of the new moon, and my bedroom faced away from the street, so there was not a single glimmer of light in it. I lay there and tried once again to pray, as I had not been able to feel God's presence for several days past.

But my mind wandered, and still sleep would not come. My thoughts flitted from one thing to another and then abruptly halted.

I was suddenly fully aware of the emptiness of my life. I saw myself chained down by my own obsessions and compulsions, powerless to escape. I wondered if I would still be eating gingersnaps and counting calories when I was forty, when I was sixty. It seemed ludicrous. Yet I knew also that I could never change my behavior. It had gone on this way too long, and I was growing old and weary. I had missed too many opportunities for growth, opportunities that could never be recovered. But I could bear the pain of my existence no longer. The logical conclusion was inescapable. I would have to end my life, since I could not change it.

I was stunned as this final thought filled my mind. I grew acutely aware of my surroundings, my eyes having now adjusted to the dark. I could distinguish the walls of my bedroom—how close they seemed to the bed! The nearby desk where I ate my gingersnaps day after day looked enormous. It almost filled the room, as I sensed myself growing smaller and smaller, like Alice in the world beneath the world. The hiss of the bedside vaporizer seemed very loud, but even that was gradually replaced by a distant roar that slowly came closer and closer, louder and louder, deafening in my ears, expanding in my head until I felt it must explode. What was it? I was petrified with fear, unable to move. I thought I was suffocating, the walls closing in on me. And then in my mind's eye I had a sudden horrifying vision of hell: myself, alone for all eternity, separated forever from God, condemned by my own choice to eat ice cream and cookies forever, without surcease, although my stomach felt as though it would burst. Alone for all eternity—by my own choice.

I struggled with every ounce of might against my paralysis and managed to sit up in bed. I was overwhelmed with terror, my heart pounding, my body shaking violently, my tongue glued to the roof of my mouth. I sensed the forces of evil all around me, closing in, crushing me. I had to escape! The door ... if I could only make it to the door! From somewhere I derived the strength to get out of bed, stumble across the room, and wrench open the door. Now what?

Outside in the hall I gradually calmed down. I stood there in my thin nightgown, shivering in the cold, for an unknown time. I knew beyond a doubt that a point of decision had come, that I had a free choice to make. I could return to bed and to work and to my gingersnaps, and go on and on until I died. Or I could stop deceiving myself, admit that I was sick, and reach out for assistance to change the pattern of my life. I could cling to the security of my familiar obsessions, painful as they were, or I could change. But to what? And how? For a moment my fear of an unknown future gripped me, and I almost turned to go back to my bed.

But I could not. I knew in the deepest place of my knowing, with absolute and undeniable clarity, that this was a moment given me by my God, and I knew also that he was already providing me with the courage to make the right choice. If I said no to him now and turned away, would he ever give me another chance? I saw that my decision was already made. Yet still I huddled there in that frigid darkened hallway, standing on the threshold of the rest of my life, loathe to step across it. I stared at my mother's door. I knew what I had to do.

Finally, after what seemed like an eternity, I did it. I accepted grace. I reached out and knocked.

The response was so immediate I jumped. It was as though she had been awake and waiting for something or someone. "Who's there?" she cried, her voice tinged with fear.

My own voice was unrecognizable to me, a hoarse strangled croak. "It's me, Mom. I need help."

Suddenly the door was open and I was in her arms, weeping as I had never wept before. I cannot recall what I said, but we communicated more clearly than we had in years. She took me into her own bed and held me, as she murmured soothingly, "It's going to be OK, Joan. There are so many of us who can help you, who have just been waiting to help you. All that was needed was for you to open up and want help ... You don't know how long I've prayed for this moment ... Hush now and sleep. We'll take the next step together, tomorrow."

And I did sleep, drifting away on a vast and uncharted but beckoning sea, that final promise echoing in the distance. *Everything's going to be OK.*

Part Three

Reprieve

For see, the winter is past,

    the rains are over and gone.

The flowers appear on the earth,

    the time of pruning the vines has come,

and the song of the dove is heard in our land.

        SONG OF SONGS   2:11–12

Chapter 13

The next few months brought dramatic changes in my life. A stay of execution. A commution of the death sentence I had envisioned on the night of my turning point. I opened up to feelings for the first time since childhood. I admitted to myself and to an outside world the reality of my disease and my helplessness to deal with it alone. I worked hard to surrender, to change my stubborn ways, to accept the loving help of others. However, none of us can accurately forecast the future, and it is only in retrospect that I see that failing to pursue tirelessly and at any cost the unremitting practice of ruthless honesty, and failing to accept from my God the courage to face my very deepest fears, put me in a holding pattern that looked superficially like partial recovery for nearly a decade. But I am getting ahead of the story.

Friday, February first, 1974, was a bitterly cold day, one of the worst in a winter that would go on record as the harshest in more than twenty years. As I tolerated the routine procedures in the admitting department of the University Hospital and was led through the long corridor to the psychiatric unit, I relived my interview with Dr. Runions ten days previously.

Entering his office I felt again the dynamic aura of power surrounding this diminutive man. He was a man who would never be overlooked when he walked into a room. His force field was magnetic, his eyes compelled, and this time I was too broken to offer any resistance.

"Have a seat, Joan." His voice was warm, embracing. "Your mother told me this morning on the phone that you're having a rather rough time just now." He paused expectantly.

"Yes, Dr. Runions, I guess you could say things have come to a head," I began haltingly, uncertain as to how to describe my anguish of the previous night. "We've been in Hawaii for the past three weeks, and I was scheduled to return to work this morning. I suppose it was the contrast between how wonderful I felt in Hawaii and how miserable I am here that has brought me to this crisis. At any rate, as I was lying in bed last night I just knew I had reached a turning point. I simply couldn't bear the thought of returning to my old routine ... I mean my anorexia, of course. So I felt the only alternative was to get help to change my behavior, to change my obsession with food and calories and everything."

He was listening attentively, his body perfectly still, his eyes riveting mine. He communicated total understanding, absolute acceptance, and immense strength without saying a word. He waited for me to go on.

"To tell you the truth, Dr. Runions," I faltered, "I don't know what to do anymore. I feel like my life is out of my control, like I'm completely powerless to change my behavior. I've made the occasional attempt to change, like last summer, but none of my efforts have been successful for more than two or three days at best. I ... I feel like I'm being controlled by some evil force that is pulling me down ... down to death. I feel like I'm in a dark steel box, and the walls are closing in on me inch by inch, and ..." I was weeping openly now, "and there is only one way out, and that is death."

He rose silently and came around the desk to touch my shoulder as powerful sobs wrenched my body. From his hand flowed a current of calm, of consolation, almost as though he were absorbing some of my pain into himself, and my agony was thereby diminished. After a time I dried my eyes, and he resumed his seat.

"How far are you willing to go, Joan, to cure your disease?" He must have seen my look of uncertainty, for he went on. "Would you, for instance, be willing to come into hospital for treatment?"

"Yes," I said slowly. "Yes, I would if you think it's necessary. I ... trust you, Dr. Runions."

"In that case," he said briskly, straightening up in his chair, "there are certain ground rules that must be clearly understood at the outset. First and foremost my immediate therapeutic goal will be to ensure that your physical health is safeguarded, and to do that, you must gain weight. We shall agree on a goal weight and an appropriate rate of gain after you are admitted, in consultation with the dietitian. You will agree to cooperate in your therapy, to eat the diet you are given, without any manipulative behavior. I in turn will commit myself to you indefinitely, for as long as it takes to complete your treatment. Until you are well, I shall never abandon you. In addition, in my judgment you need antidepressant medication, which should be started tonight. Are you agreeable to these conditions, Joan?"

There it was. No turning back now. He had spoken the words that for five years I had most dreaded to hear. "You must gain weight." Did I really trust this man? That was what he was asking.

After a long considering pause I replied, "Yes, I agree ... I'll do whatever you say."

A short time later I left his office with a prescription for amitriptyline clutched in my hand. This I filled at a pharmacy across the street. I was to begin taking the medication at bedtime. I was a physician with some experience, thoroughly familiar with the pharmacology of this drug, and I had seen it used in patients many times before. What I did next perhaps speaks more eloquently about my precarious state of mind at the time than any other description I could give. I looked at the small vial of tiny yellow pills in my hand and thought, *If I am to be cured, then let's get on with it.* I opened the vial and took one of the tablets. It seemed very small, innocuous enough.

Driving home thirty minutes later, something I would have instructed a patient never to do, I ran broadside into a car backing out of a driveway in front of me. I don't think I even tried to stop, and I don't recall feeling at all disturbed by what had happened. By the time the police arrived, I was in such a daze that I could scarcely respond to their questions. I remember being driven home in the squad car, but to this day I cannot recollect any details of how the incident was resolved.

I remained in this fog for most of the next ten days. I slept most of the time, a heavy dreamless sleep, then briefly awakened to stumble groggily around the house, oblivious of my surroundings. By the time a hospital bed became available on February first, I had adjusted to the sedating effects of the drug, although I still had a dry mouth, difficulty focusing at times, and felt lightheaded if I stood up quickly. All this from a dose of seventy-five milligrams, half the usual adult dosage, but perhaps understandable considering that I weighed eighty pounds, was suffering from severe malnutrition, and had almost never taken anything stronger than an aspirin before in my life.

I arrived on the ward in the early afternoon and submitted to the admission routine without demur: the interminable questions, first from the nurse, then from the intern; the indignity of a physical examination, the intern gazing at my naked body, palpating my breasts, prodding my abdomen, inspecting my genitalia. How many times I had done it myself … to patients.

Patients. There was the crux of the whole thing. I could not avoid looking at it squarely. I hated the thought that I was a patient, and a psychiatric one at that. *Oh, how the mighty have fallen*. For I suddenly realized how I had in the past always looked condescendingly upon the human beings who had come under my care. I had unconsciously regarded myself as superior to them, as smarter, wiser, healthier. And now my illusions were shattered, my eyes opened. I was one of them. Just another loony in the loony bin.

At this time I felt entirely responsible for this character defect of arrogance and was overwhelmed with shame. This was in fact a necessary step in my journey, for it was essential that I painfully acknowledge the reality of my self-declared superiority, that I claim it as my own problem, before I could heal from it. What I did not see until almost twenty years later was the fact that I was not entirely to blame for this fault, that a major power source engendering it was the subtly pathological environment in which I had been trained as a physician. All medical students in the Western world are insidiously led into the hierarchical system that pervades and dominates not only Western medicine, but every facet of our society—business, educaion, economics, politics, religion. Any physician who is being honest with himself or herself must admit this reality. We are *all* trained to treat patients as objects, to do things *to* them, to see ourselves as superior to them. Most of our patients have been reared in the same system and accept it unquestioningly as well. I attach no blame to my teachers in this regard. They cut their teeth in the same paradigm as I did, and few have succeeded in escaping from it. Those who have escaped no longer fit into the system and usually end up living and dying as mavericks or outcasts. Fortunately, more and more of us are waking up to these facts and crying out against the blatant immorality of such a system. When we reach a critical mass, we will succeed in effecting change in it. This I must believe.

I was led like a sheep to the dining room and a meal was set before me: fried chicken, mashed potatoes and gravy, mixed vegetables, a glass of milk. I looked at the food and my heart sank. I was still powerless. I had no more control over what happened to me now than I had over the evil disease controlling me. With a despairing sense of bowing to the inevitable, I picked up my fork and ate.

And ate and ate and ate, loving and loathing every bite. The weekend trickled to an end. It was Monday morning. Dr. Runions appeared and entered my room, where I was sitting on the bed. He was accompanied by his intern and probably by a nurse as well, but I saw only him, felt only his energy, and rose automatically to my feet to greet him.

He looked at me, his perceptive gaze seeing it all: the slump of my shoulders, my weak attempt to smile, my sadness, my defeat, my despair. And I saw that he saw. Suddenly I was on my knees at my bedside, my face buried in the blankets, and I heard anguished phrases escaping from my lips.

"It's no use, Dr. Runions," I moaned. "It's never going to be any different … I can eat until I explode but it's never going to change how I feel about food. It's never going to change the calorie counter inside my head. It's never going to change the fear … How can you change a person's thoughts?"

I could speak no more, but surrendered myself to my tears. Dr. Runions again placed his hand on my shoulder. He had observed the Bible on my bedside table. All he said to me was, "Read the Book of Job, Joan." And he left.

I huddled there for some time, vaguely aware of the murmuring in the hall outside my door. A few disjointed phrases filtered through the blackness enveloping me: "… profoundly depressed …" "… beyond the reach of psychotherapy …" "… increase her medication …"

By the next day the tears had run dry. I continued to drag my body through the empty hours, still immersed in hopelessness and a profound exhaustion of body and mind. *Death must be like this, except it must be better; it couldn't be so painful.*

In the afternoon I sat in the patients' common room. Emotional agony can continue for just so long. Eventually the human mind can bear no more. When it reaches saturation point it simply shuts down. The room was warm and sunny and very still. My mind was numb. And I heard from somewhere nearby the sweet strains of James Taylor's evocative melody:

I've seen fire and I've seen rain.
I've seen sunny days that I thought would never end.
I've seen lonely times when I could not find a friend
But I always thought that I'd see you again.

Won't you look down upon me, Jesus?
Gotta help me make a stand.
You just got to see me through another day.
My body's aching and my time is at hand.
I won't make it any other way.

Oh, I've seen fire and I've seen rain.
I've seen sunny days that I thought would never end.
I've seen lonely times when I could not find a friend.
But I always thought that I'd see you again…[1]

As I listened something melted within me, and I began to feel again. The haunting words echoed inside my head. I felt somehow close to something. To what? Could it be I felt close to the singer? Close to him in his pain? Could it be that I felt we had something in common, that our spirits were united in our private agonies? Perhaps suffering was never completely private, perhaps it drew you near to all those suffering around you ... if you let it. Perhaps everyone alive was suffering in some way ... Perhaps I wasn't so special after all. These thoughts formed wordlessly within me. I looked around at the other patients in the room, seeing them for the first time: sitting in various attitudes of pain and pleasure, staring straight ahead of themselves with parkinsonian masks, or chatting happily with their neighbors. And suddenly a great insight came upon me, like an enormous neon sign bursting into life: WE ARE ALL ONE.

I was ecstatic. How could I not have seen this obvious truth before? Being one with other human beings was not degrading. It was marvelous. It was to be celebrated. A flood of emotion washed over me. I started crying, no longer out of pain and despair, but out of joy and relief. I could never be alone again in the way I had been before. The burden of my solitude was lifted.

The following weeks were spent on an emotional roller coaster. They taught me the real meaning of the phrase "the agony and the ecstasy" as I swung like a pendulum between the elation induced by achieving a new insight and the resurfacing depression experienced when I realized that this fresh insight was not *the* key to my illness.

I had moved from an emotional vacuum to a state of exaggerated emotion. All feelings were excessive, both the highs and the lows. I came to understand that in isolating myself from other people through the course of my illness, I had also isolated myself from my own emotions. Ever since my devastating experience with Paul in England, I had succeeded in repressing all feeling. My emotional life had been reduced to a sequence of façades: *Hmm ... this is a happy situation. I should be feeling happy, so I shall act as if I'm happy ... This is a tragedy; other people are obviously suffering; I should be sad, so now I shall act as if I'm sad.* The process had occurred so slowly and insidiously that I was not even aware of the emotional wasteland in which I existed until the lid was removed from Pandora's box in the hospital.

It is interesting that what I did not know at the time of my hospital therapy was the fact that one of the principal functions of *all* addictions is to keep us out of contact with our deepest feelings, our deepest awareness, our deepest knowing, our deepest living process.[2] This knowledge would come much later in my life, as will be revealed. At this time I simply experienced the reality of my resurrected emotions.

But despite the budding self-knowledge engendered by this emotional orgy, the essential fear of becoming fat, of eating anything fattening, remained firmly entrenched, like a stone fortress at the center of my mind. And whenever I would become aware of its apparent impregnability, my heart would plunge into despair once again. Consequently the ensuing weeks brought not only stuttering progress toward wellness as I achieved one breakthrough after another, but also a series of battles between Dr. Runions and my sick self. During the vast majority of the time I cooperated wholeheartedly with my therapists, as I had committed myself to do, but at other times I struggled against everything ... and hated myself for struggling. I argued against Dr. Runions' caloric prescription and against its specific translation by the dietitian. I balked at the rate of weight gain that he expected me to achieve and at not being allowed to see what my weight was each day when recorded by the nurse. I cried out in dismay when I was not allowed to exercise. I resisted the behavior therapy program that the staff experimented with for a time. I fumed, I fretted, I worried, and I experienced the urge to punish them all by completely ceasing to eat.

And then I would suddenly find myself thinking rationally: *How would that punish them? Surely the only one who would ultimately suffer if I stopped eating would be me. Have I been doing this all along during the past five years? Punishing other people by not eating? But why? Why would I want to punish anyone? And whom? Whom was I trying to punish?*

Chapter 14

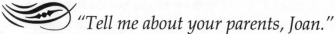 *"Tell me about your parents, Joan."*

We were seated in an interview room on the psychiatric ward, a windowless room approximately the size of a walk-in closet, scarcely large enough to contain the bare wooden desk, at which Dr. Runions was seated, and my straight-backed hard chair placed alongside it. No pictures adorned its nondescript gray walls; there was nothing to distract me from Dr. Runions' luminous blue eyes. His incandescent presence filled the room, compelling a response as always.

"I think I told you about them already," I began. "My mother is a marvelous woman. She is so strong; I don't think I've ever met anyone as strong as she is. After my father left ... I mean after they separated ... she was determined not to be dependent financially on anyone. My father was supposed to send child support payments every month, but within a short time he stopped doing so. He was in trouble financially himself most of the time, you see."

I paused, listened to the silence, and caught an expression on Dr. Runions' face. "He did love us," I went on hastily, "and he sent money when he had it; it's just that Mom could never count on it. So she went to work at the bank for a year while she applied for a bursary from the Edson school division to attend the University of Alberta for a one-year teacher training program. That was 1957, at the height of the teacher shortage—because of the Baby Boom, you know—so you could teach with only one year of training. Anyway, she took me and Timmy, who was just one year old, to live in Edmonton with her during the university term. I was eight, so I was a big help to her in looking after Timmy."

"What happened to the other children during that year?"

"Well, Mom left Adele, who was five, with my grandparents in Edson. They didn't feel they could cope with Betty, too ... she was a very active three-year-old, a real handful ... so she stayed with some neighbors across the road from Grandma's house. That way Adele and Betty could play together a lot. However, I think Betty suffered the most that year. She must have felt rejected by Mom or something, because after we were all back together in May of 1958 she threw some terrible tantrums. And I remember she would refuse to go to the bathroom for days or weeks on end, to the point that the doctor told Mom to give her enemas sometimes. I still remember hearing Betty's screams coming from the bathroom. Anyway, Betty remained a 'difficult' child for the rest of her years at home. She ran away a couple times in her early teens, and eventually she left home permanently when she was about sixteen."

Dr. Runions was listening closely to this cool recitation of facts. Now he began to gently probe. "How did you feel about Betty's reaction, about her rebellion?"

"Hmm." I hesitated, studying my fingernails. "I think I mostly felt sorry for Mom. She loved us so much, and everything she did was aimed at making our life better. So I tried to be as helpful as I could, to spare her any trouble I could, because she was having such a difficult time with Betty ... and later on with Adele as well, once she got into her teens. I used to feel so proud of myself when I would hear Mom talking about me to other people, about how mature I was for my age, about how much she depended on me to do the house-work and so forth ... I guess you could say I got my kicks from being a Good Little Girl."

"But didn't you have an adolescent rebellion like your sisters?" he persisted.

"No," I replied slowly, biting at a fingernail, "I really don't remember ever rebelling against Mom ... at least not until the summer of 1970, when I was twenty-one and flew to England against her wishes. I loved her so much, and still do, of course, that I never wanted to cause her any grief. And besides, I never *felt* like rebelling."

"You mean you never wanted to do anything that your mother disapproved of?"

"That's right," I agreed. "I guess I needed her approval, or something."

Dr. Runions leaned forward intently. "What did you think would happen if you did something she disapproved of?"

I squirmed in my chair. "I never thought about it ... I just told you: I never wanted to do anything she disapproved of."

"Well, think about it now," he insisted. "What do you think would have happened if you'd done something 'bad'?"

I let a moment pass as I counted the tiles on the floor. "Well, for one thing I would have been scolded terribly. My mother had such a sharp tongue, and such a way with words. I dreaded her scolding me far more than any spanking she ever gave me. I mean I was bad sometimes of course, just like any child is, so I knew what getting punished was like, and I couldn't stand it—the scoldings, I mean. "

"Is that all you were afraid of?" he said gently.

I was silent for a long time, feeling the pressure build behind my eyes.

"It's okay, Joan. It's okay to say what you're thinking, even if it makes you cry." His voice was an embrace.

"I guess maybe I also had a silly fear," I said at last, blinking back tears, "that Mom might leave me. I mean I know it's stupid, but I can remember being terrified at times about being abandoned. In the city in a department store I would get so panicky if I lost sight of Mom for a minute or two ... And when we were living in the basement suite in Edmonton that year when I was eight, I can remember lying in bed at night when Mom would be studying in the next room—there was only a curtain separating the bedroom from the living room/kitchen area—listening intently for tiny sounds to reassure me that she was still there. If I couldn't hear anything for a while I would get out of bed and crawl across the cold concrete floor, shivering in my pyjamas, not making a sound, and peek through the tiny space between the curtain and the door frame, to make sure her legs were still there, underneath the table that stood next to the door."

"So you had a real fear that your mother would leave you if you did something very bad."

"I guess I must have, although I didn't think that out consciously in those words at the time. I mean ..." I broke off abruptly.

"Go on," he prompted.

"Well, I was just thinking about how my father had left, even though he said he loved us ... But that's ridiculous," I said dismissively, then added with more uncertainty, "There's no connection between the two, is there?"

"Might you at seven years of age have *felt* as though your father left because you were a bad girl?"

"Honestly, Dr. Runions, I don't remember feeling that, ever ... but maybe I did. Maybe that's why I had to be so good all the time, because I was afraid my mother would leave too, if I did something really bad, if she got mad enough at me." I paused briefly and reflected on that, then shook my head and went on decisively. "But no, I knew my dad hadn't left for that reason."

"Why did you think he left, then?"

"Everyone knew why he left. He found another woman," I replied abruptly.

Another empty silence, broken again by Dr. Runions. "That sounds very simple."

"Well, it was simple," I said earnestly. I had to make him understand. I had to make him agree with me. "These things happen, you know. My parents just discovered they were incompatible, they didn't have much in common, and my father just found somebody else."

"You mean that as a child of seven you had all that figured out?" His tone was incredulous, his eyebrows raised.

"Yes! ... I mean I think so ... What else could I have thought?"

"How did you *feel* about your father leaving?" he persisted.

"I felt very, very sad," I said finally, after a long bleak pause. "For years I kept dreaming and daydreaming that he would come back. I wrote him letters all the time. I don't remember his replies, except that he never said he would come back. But I still kept on hoping that he would come and stay home and be my Daddy and I would be his little girl again ... He was never around much for years before he finally left, you know. He had his own lumber camp out of town and he would stay out there supervising the men for days and weeks on end. We were always so excited when he came home."

I hesitated, then went on with enthusiasm, the memory warm in my eyes. "I remember one night he came home after we were in bed, but we heard him and got up and were so excited that we started jumping up and down on the living room sofa in our pyjamas, and I bounced up so high that I fell right over the back of the sofa and hit my collarbone on the base of a lamp and broke it—my collarbone, I mean. And then even though it was late, my mother took me to town to the hospital and the doctor strapped me up and bandaged me and told me I looked like a football player! I remember being very proud of my bandages ... I was probably about four or five at the time ... But that's off the topic, of course. I just wanted to illustrate how excited we got when we saw Daddy ... Our times with him were pretty few and far between. It was Mom who raised us and took care of us, both before and after they separated."

Dr. Runions looked pensive. "You said you felt sad when your father left, even though or perhaps *because* you had never had much of a relationship with him. Do you think you felt anything else?"

"Nooo," I drew the word out doubtfully, "I don't think so. Should I have?"

"It seems to me," he replied gently, "that a child in your situation might also have felt angry."

"Angry!" I was shocked. "How could I be angry? I've just told you how it happened, how my parents were incompatible, how much they loved us, how it wasn't his fau—"

My voice trailed off in bewilderment and silence hung between us, broken finally by the sound of my weeping.

"But it wasn't your father you were angry at, was it, Joan?" he said softly.

"No, no, it wasn't." My voice was ragged as I saw something monstrous for the first time. "But it should have been ... I didn't think

I was angry at anyone, but now I realize I blamed my *mother* ... She should have kept my Daddy at home for me. She should have made it work ... Oh God, how can I be saying these things? I love her, I swear that I love her ... Oh my God."

I felt Dr. Runions' hand on my trembling shoulder, steady, warm, reassuring.

"Joan, it's okay to become angry with the people you love. It's normal. The problems arise when you don't recognize and admit your rage. But you have now. You're going to be okay, Joan. You're not seven years old anymore."

My sobs died away, and I replied weakly, "I guess I'm not so sure about that."

Chapter 15

By the end of my first week in hospital I knew that much had changed within me. From my reborn emotions were produced the fruits of deep joy, peace, and genuine interest in my fellow patients. I was beginning to talk with others again with enthusiasm, and I truly cared about them and their problems. Through a fellow patient there occurred one of the most significant events of my entire life.

Rachel was a beautiful middle-aged woman who could not speak. She was strikingly built, tall and slender, and she had expressive mobile features: a high forehead, patrician nose, decisive chin, her elegant face framed by thick auburn hair cascading to her shoulders. Her full mouth seemed always to have a smile playing at the edges, her brown eyes were knowing and attentive. Her warm, open manner attracted me, and I spent long hours conversing with her. I would speak and she would respond by writing on a pad of paper.

She revealed that she had been admitted for psychiatric assessment of a rather bizarre problem: a sudden total loss of all speech that had occurred during therapy with a well-known anticonvulsant drug. The medical side of my brain told me that her doctors must suspect a hysterical conversion reaction as the cause of her aphasia, or else why would she be on the psychiatric unit? But the newly regenerated human side of me saw only a beautiful lady who was suffering greatly, and I wanted desperately to somehow console her, to ease her burden. I encouraged her to "talk" about many things: her feelings, her life experiences, her values, her dreams. We soon discovered that we had a similar Christian background and that we both very strongly felt God working in our lives during this critical period of mental illness.

On Friday morning, just before lunch, we were seated side by side on the bed in Rachel's room, which was at the opposite end of the hall from my own. We were "talking" about Christ, and Rachel had just written down a comment on her paper. I raised my eyes from the written words to her face, and suddenly her countenance began to glow with the most loving expression I have ever beheld in my life. Her eyes were alight with an inner fire that burned into the deepest part of me, and her facial features were transfigured before my astonished eyes into the face of Christ.

I was utterly transfixed. The room around us disappeared from my perception; the background noises of the ward faded as I was totally overwhelmed by the certain knowledge that I was face to face with my God. My reaction was completely beyond any voluntary control. I could do nothing but fall to my knees at his feet and adore him, at the same time hiding my face from the unbearable Beauty before me. I was overwhelmed by the knowledge of my own unworthiness. I knew that I had done nothing and could do nothing in ten lifetimes to merit this experience. Nor had I ever suffered anything that could earn such a reward.

The words *My Lord and my God* were wrenched from my lips, and then I glimpsed his arms opening out to me and drawing me to him. I buried my face in his garments and clung fiercely, worshiping and thanking him and praying for the end of time, hoping that I might die at this moment, so that I need never be separated from him again. I heard a loud voice crying out and slowly realized that it was my own.

Moments later I felt rough hands pulling me off my Lord, and I held on tighter even as he gently indicated that I must let go, for now. I obeyed and looked up at him one last time as I was dragged forcibly from his presence. I can still see the indescribable look of compassion burning in his eyes. He knew me. I was his, no matter what would happen in the future, his look said, and he would help me to bear whatever suffering lay ahead. For had he not already borne it all?

It took four or five strong nurses to drag me, fighting and screaming, down the hall, and as they did so I had another strange experience. Looking up at them, I saw not nurses but Roman soldiers. I was filled with the horrifying certainty that I would be subdued by force, taken in a straitjacket to the provincial mental hospital, and left there for the remainder of my life. Everyone would say that I was insane (perhaps I was, by the world's definition) because I had seen Christ. I would live out my days isolated in a barren cell. That would be the price I would pay for this gift of direct experience of my God.

Although I judged it a fair tradeoff, I balked at meekly submitting to such a fate, so I continued to struggle and shriek in terror, even as we reached my room and I was forced down on the bed. I still could hear nothing but my own incoherent cries. I looked up into the faces of the female nursing staff I had known for more than a week and saw only strange male faces glowering at me with hatred in their eyes. I felt my buttock pierced by what felt like a spike, and an intense fiery pain spread out from it. Still I fought against the restraining hands, until all strength ebbed from my limbs and I slid into oblivion.

I regained consciousness in the late afternoon, very groggy, but calm and lucid and able to gradually comprehend what had occurred. I remember talking to a few people that evening, but I cannot recall the conversations. I think now that the massive injection of chlorpromazine probably prevented my memory from functioning normally. I do remember realizing that I had experienced what is technically known as an acute psychosis—the ultimate in "craziness"—and feeling at peace with this knowledge. I, who seven short days before had been too proud to accept without humiliation the simple designation of "patient."

The next morning Dr. Runions came in, enveloped as always in his aura of understanding and strength. He listened closely as I tremblingly recounted my experience of the previous day. He pondered for a long time before replying.

"Joan, you have had a powerful spiritual experience, the reality of which I acknowledge ... Nevertheless I must also view this incident from a psychiatric perspective, and from that vantage point I believe that you suffered an acute psychotic break, probably triggered by a dosage of amitriptyline that is too high for your body, coupled with the rapid emotional decompression you have sustained over the past week. I cannot allow you to lose control of yourself like that again, so I plan to lower the dosage and add a small amount of an antipsychotic drug to your regimen—probably trifluoperazine. Can you understand and accept the necessity for this?"

I nodded slowly. I did understand. Had I been the attending physician I would have done the same thing.

Thus was the incident rationalized, neatly labeled, and filed away to the satisfaction of everyone except myself. For I knew with undeniable clarity what had occurred: Christ had in fact miraculously revealed himself to me in the person of Rachel. Yes, he had used this "acute psychotic break" as the vehicle for his gift, just as he has always used natural phenomena to work his miracles. My heart remained filled with awe and with gratitude, but I could only speculate about his purpose in showing himself to me so vividly. I thought perhaps he did so to remind me that he is truly present in *everyone* around us, all the time. I also realized that normally he keeps himself hidden from our human eyes—with good reason. I understood for the first time the meaning of the common biblical phrase, "the fear of the Lord." For who can look into the face of God and still function? If we saw him physically present in our neighbor all the time, we would all be paralyzed with awe and unable to behave in any kind of normal fashion. So he generally remains hidden from all but the eyes of faith.

I went to see Rachel later in the day and explained my vision, apologizing for having frightened her by my actions. She remained kind and understanding, and "discussed" the incident with me. The following week she was discharged, and our paths have never crossed again. But I know, and she knows, that God used her, as he uses all his willing children, to touch me in this most profound and enduring way.

Chapter 16

"*Joan, today let's carry on* talking about a subject you broached last Wednesday. You told me how your mother took you, at eight years of age, to Edmonton to help her with your baby brother. Could you tell me a little more about that, please?"

We were closeted once again in the interview room, which was beginning to acquire a familiar air.

"Well," I shrugged, "it's just like I said. Mom had classes to attend, a very full schedule, and an enormous amount of studying to do at night. I was very mature for my age so I could help her. For instance, Mom dropped Timmy off at Mrs. Atkinson's house in the morning—she was a woman who lived about six blocks from the house where we lived in a basement suite. I was in third grade at St. Peter's School. After school I generally walked to Mrs. Atkinson's, picked up Timmy, and brought him home in the stroller, or on the sleigh during the winter."

I paused, vividly recalling that far-off time. "I remember how hard it was to make him sit still sometimes," I said with a rueful smile. "He was really 'hyper' right from birth. In fact we nicknamed him 'Terrible Tim' and he lived up to that name until he became a teenager ... Where was I? Oh yes, well Mom was always home by suppertime. I washed and dried the dishes while Mom got Timmy into bed. Then I did my homework and went to bed too, or sometimes, as a special treat, I was allowed to go upstairs to watch TV with the Fillmores ...

It was their house we lived in. I had never seen television before that year, so it was really a treat to watch "Leave It to Beaver" and "The Ed Sullivan Show" and programs like that. I enjoyed that year ... actually it was more like eight months, I guess. I felt very grown up."

"You certainly must have," Dr. Runions agreed. "What about after you returned to Edson?"

"Oh, essentially the pattern just carried on. We lived in Edson for two more years while Mom taught for the Edson School Division. Even as a younger child I had always assumed a lot of responsibility in the family because I was the eldest girl, so now I just did more: cooking and cleaning and stuff like that. In 1960 Mom moved us all to Edmonton. She realized there would be more opportunity in the city for us kids to broaden our horizons as we got older ... you know, go to university and so on. After that she relied on me even more because she was teaching full time to support us and also immediately began working on her degree. She took one or two evening courses every winter and two courses every summer. She went on like that until 1966, when she got her B.Ed.—'with distinction' yet! So two or three nights during the week she went straight to the university after school, leaving me in charge of the younger kids. I was eleven in 1960, and seventeen by 1966, so I prepared dinner, fed everyone, then made the kids do their homework, tried to keep the peace until bedtime, and got them into bed before Mom got home around ten o'clock at night."

"Sounds like a very busy program," Dr. Runions said thoughtfully. "How did you feel about all this responsibility, Joan?"

I studied the bare desktop on which my right arm rested, marshaling my thoughts before I replied. "Well, I felt proud to be so grown up and to have Mom depend on me. But I hated it when she didn't come home in the evenings, because Betty and Timmy were such brats. They wouldn't listen to me most of the time. So it was pretty noisy and chaotic."

"It doesn't sound like you had much time for yourself or for any social life," Dr. Runions observed neutrally.

"Oh, it wasn't that bad," I protested. "I always had time to do my homework, and I remained at the top of my class throughout those years. Also, in 1960 I begged Mom to let me take piano lessons, and she always managed to scrape together the money for that, till I finished high school in 1966. She even bought a second-hand piano, a lovely old upright grand. I loved practicing my music and played during every spare minute I had. I always played by sight, though, with the music in front of me, unlike Timmy who had a marvelous ear. He could just sit down and play anything by ear. He always was the creative one in the family ... Let's see, where was I? ... I'm sorry to ramble so much."

"That's all right, Joan," he said easily. "Sometimes apparent rambling leads one to unexpectedly useful places. You were talking about your leisure activities during those busy years."

"Oh yeah ... Well, Mom had no spare cash for allowances during that period, so on weekends I would often babysit for the neighbors to make pocket money for myself ... Gosh but I hated kids by that time! I remember promising myself that I would never have kids when I grew up. But the kids seemed to like having me as a sitter, I suppose because I played with them and told them bedtime stories and so on, so I guess I must have hidden my true feelings pretty well. I guess I've always been good at that," I added slowly, "but at least back then, before I got sick, I didn't hide most of them from myself."

Dr. Runions studied me with an enigmatic expression during the pause that followed. Finally he went on. "And what about your social life? Did you have friends your own age?"

"A few. My best friend was a girl from Edson named Madeleine, so after we moved to the city I didn't see her on a regular basis. However to this day she is still the only one with whom I have ever been really close. I had two or three more casual girlfriends at school, but we really didn't do much together outside of school hours. I was mostly a loner—I think that started very early. I never felt part of my peer group, probably because I was rejected as a result of my high academic achievement. I just took it as a matter of course that I wasn't one of the crowd, and honestly I didn't think about it much. And of course I was so busy at home that there wasn't much time for other activities ... Oh, I did join the St. John's Ambulance Society when I was about thirteen or so. I loved dressing up in my uniform and going to the meetings once a week. I took courses like First Aid and Home Nursing, and on Sundays I worked as a volunteer at St. Joseph's Hospital about once or twice a month. I had decided as a child to become a nurse when I grew up, so that fed right into my dreams ... And I had my music, too. I even accompanied the glee club and school orchestra in twelfth grade, which made me feel very special."

Dr. Runions paused significantly before he asked, "And what about boys?"

For the first time I noticed the initials that some lost soul had long ago carved into the ancient desktop beside my elbow. J.E. *How strange*, I thought, *they're my initials, too*. I shook my head slightly and looked at Dr. Runions once more. "Oh, I was never interested in boys, except for sometimes having a crush from afar on someone or other. I virtually never dated in high school. I always took it for granted that dating was for other girls. I guess I felt set apart from kids my own age, somehow ... Different ... Special, maybe ..." I pondered this for a moment. "And I was terribly shy with them, especially with boys ... I remember Mom arranged for a boy to take me to my senior prom. Although that embarrassed me horribly, I did go. The boy was Harvey Chadwick, and he was just as shy as I was, so the date was not terribly memorable. I do remember the struggle to make conversation ... To tell the truth, I always felt more comfortable around adults than around kids my own age."

"Did your mother discourage you from making friends?"

I thought about that. "No, I don't think so. It's just that I grew up knowing I had more important things to do, more responsibilities than most kids my age ... Don't look at me like that, Dr. Runions! I *liked* it. I got so much pleasure from hearing my mother's praise, from knowing that I was very grown up."

His eyes were upon me. "So you grew up without ever passing through adolescence?" he said softly.

"Yes, I ..." My voice trailed away and a poignant silence developed. Once again I felt tears stinging my eyes.

"Can you tell me what you're feeling right now, Joan?"

"I'm ... not ... sure," I said brokenly through my tears. "I thought I was happy in those years. I don't know why I'm crying."

"Could you be feeling that you have lost something?"

"Maybe ... Maybe I've lost something I never had ... Good grief," I said, brushing impatiently at my eyes, "I'm almost twenty-five years old. I *am* grown up, I am."

"Perhaps you're feeling the loss of your childhood?" he persisted.

"No, I had a happy childhood—in Edson, before Daddy left. Then I grew up ... fast. Maybe too fast. Maybe I just didn't have *enough* childhood. So what's the big deal? Why do I feel so sad?"

He forged ahead relentlessly, leaning forward close to me and speaking softly. "Who do you blame for not having had enough childhood, Joan?"

"NO ONE!" I exploded, to my own surprise. "I don't blame anyone. It's no one's fault ... it's not, it's not. Why does it always have to be about blaming, for God's sake? Why do you always try to make me mad? Damn it, anyway, sometimes I ..."

He waited with perfect calm as I raged at him, neither drawing back nor taking his eyes from mine.

"Oh hell! Why am I so mad? I'm not mad at you, Dr. Runions. I'm not mad at anyone ... I'm not ... Oh God, now I'm crying again ... I hate crying ..."

He waited for my sobs to subside. Then he spoke gently, his voice supporting me. "It's OK, Joan. We're here again, but it's OK ... Who do you blame? Tell me. Tell the truth to me and to yourself."

Slowly I raised my head and stared at him through my tears. "You know who I blame. I didn't even know until now, but you've known all along. I blame my mother ... Dear God, I blame her for that, too ... How come I never knew before this?"

"Remember the child, Joan. It wasn't safe for the child to blame her, was it? The child thought she would be abandoned."

I exhaled a slow deep breath as I allowed myself to absorb this. Suddenly the blood drained from my face.

"Oh my God," I gasped, "I've been getting even with her, haven't I? I didn't even know I was mad at her, but all along through my anorexia I've been getting back at her, punishing her. I would see her suffer when I refused to eat, when the pounds were dropping from my body, and I felt so guilty about that. I didn't want her to suffer ... I used to cry when I'd see her pain, but I couldn't seem to change my behavior. Now I can see that all along I really *wanted* her to suffer. Oh my God, what have I done? What kind of a monster am I? ... Oh God, forgive me." Again I dropped my head and wept bitter tears.

In the vast sea of my pain Dr. Runions' voice was a lifeline. "You're no monster, Joan. You're human. Hidden anger is like a poisoned subterranean stream. Eventually it must come to the surface, one way or another. And the longer it remains underground, the more damage it does to the living things above. You'll be OK now, Joan ... Trust me, you'll be OK."

Chapter 17

"*I talked to Mom last night,* Dr. Runions," I said as I dropped into my usual chair. "I told her what I've learned about myself and about my anger at her."

"And how did she respond?"

"Well, just fine really. She listened and didn't seem upset. She let me talk about everything, and she didn't even look surprised." I pondered for a moment, tracing the old initials in the desk with my forefinger. "Do you suppose she could have known how I felt all along?" I paused before continuing haltingly, "Something else came up last night, too."

Dr. Runions looked at me expectantly. "What was that?"

"As Mom and I were talking, I suddenly realized how deeply I've felt all my life that I had to live up to the expectations of other people. Especially my mother's. I've had this sense that she wanted me to live for her, that I had no right to live my own life. And I just accepted that and never knew how very angry I've been about it all along. I've certainly never verbalized these feelings before, but last night I did. I even accused her of projecting her dreams onto me."

Dr. Runions was listening intently. "And what did she say?"

"Again she just listened, and in the end she said, very quietly and a little sadly, 'I was just doing the best I could, Joan. I'm only human, too, you know. I've made plenty of mistakes.' And it was OK between us. It was almost as though we forgave one another for all the past hurt. I do love her, you know, and I do admire her, too. In fact, I think that all my life I've been trying to live up to her, to be as great as she is. But I see now she isn't perfect, and that's OK too ... I still love her, maybe even more now than I did before I understood my true feelings."

"That's good, Joan," he said warmly. "You've come a long way in the past couple of weeks." He paused briefly. "I'd like to focus today on your anorexia itself. What do you think about when you consider the concept of food, and eating?"

"That's easy," I said immediately. "I think about fat. I hate fat. I was fat before I started dieting in 1968, and I never, never want to be fat again. It was repulsive."

"But why is fat so abhorrent to you?" he persisted.

"It just is. It's ugly, it's unattractive. People look down on you when you're fat. They stare at you on the street. They laugh at you behind your back."

Dr. Runions thought about that for a moment. He looked puzzled. "So you would feel unaccepted by other people if you were fat. But I thought the acceptance of others, at least of your peers, was unimportant to you."

"Yes," I replied slowly, "I did say that I was a loner, but this is different. It's not the kind of acceptance I was referring to before. I mean I can tolerate not being one of the crowd as long as I'm not being laughed at ... No, that can't be right either, because other kids used to laugh at me because of my lack of athletic ability and because of my dedication to my studies. They used to call me names like 'Square' and 'Brain,' and that never bothered me, at least not very much. Not enough to make me want to change. In fact, it made me a little proud of my differentness ... Gosh, this is confusing, Dr. Runions. I just don't know why being fat is so much more horrible to me than my other differences from other people."

He was paying close attention. "Perhaps it would be helpful to think about people you know who are fat. Maybe that would give you a clue."

"Hmm, well a cousin of my mother's in Winnipeg is massively obese: three or four hundred pounds or so. But I don't know her well, so I don't have any particular feelings about her ... Actually a lot of people in my mother's family are pretty fat: three of my aunts, lots of cousins, and ..." I hesitated.

"Go on," said Dr. Runions with interest.

"Well ... I was just thinking about Mom. I mean, she's pretty fat, at least she used to be even worse than she is now ... Not before she had kids. She was beautiful then. I've seen pictures of her taken before she was married, and on her honeymoon, and she was absolutely gorgeous. Tall, you know, not like me, about five foot ten, and with a fabulous figure. She had a large frame but wasn't the least bit fat. She looks like a model in those pictures, great legs and so on. Then she started having babies, and she retained about ten pounds that she didn't lose after each of us was born, so by the time she had all of us she was really big, around two hundred pounds or a little more. She's less than that now, of course ... She and my sister Adele joined Weight Watchers when I was in my first year of medical school, and she lost quite a bit. She gained it back, but she returned to Weight Watchers last year and lost it again."

"Wasn't your first year of medical school the same year your anorexia started?" Dr. Runions interjected.

"Yes, it was. In fact, her attending Weight Watchers helped me start losing weight in the first place. I discovered how fat I was at the end of September that year. I'd gained fifteen or twenty pounds during the summer and during my first month in residence, so when I went home one weekend and weighed myself, I decided to go on a diet. Mom and Adele were already doing it, so it was easy to get started."

"So your mother was fat," he said thoughtfully. "What difference did that make in her life?"

"Hmm, I'm not sure," I replied. "Let's see, I guess for one thing when she lost weight that year she became more interested in men, or maybe they became more interested in her. She never dated anyone from the time Daddy left in 1956 until that year she went to Weight Watchers. Then when she did lose weight, she started to look more attractive, and she went out with one man a couple of times ... It never came to anything, but I remember her looking excited before her dates, almost like a schoolgirl, you know."

"So losing weight meant she could attract a man once again?"

There was a charged silence while I considered that, absolutely motionless in my chair.

"You look very startled, Joan. What is it?"

"Good heavens, you don't suppose that could be the key, do you? I mean, I was just thinking about my father. When he left, Mom was fat ... so he went off with another woman—a very thin one, in fact." I was growing excited now. "So being fat is connected with losing your husband to another woman, a thin one, and losing weight means you attract men ... And not just *any* husband, but *my father*, my father was driven away by my mother's fat ... I mean, I know that wasn't the cause, but maybe as a child unconsciously I made a connection between the two ... Good Lord, could it possibly be that simple, Dr. Runions?"

"I think you've hit on part of the answer, Joan, although there may be other factors involved." He pondered for a moment. "Let's focus now on how your fatness and thinness tie into your own attractiveness to the opposite sex. Can you think about that for a while?"

"Okay," I said easily. "Let's see now, I first felt seriously attracted to someone, enough that I actually dated him, in my first year of pre-med, 1966. In fact I was a bit coquettish that year. I wore miniskirts and bright colors and inexpensive but fashionable clothes. I wasn't really fat then, you know, just around a hundred and eighteen pounds, which I guess is about average for five foot three. Anyway there were two guys in my Latin class whom I liked: Warren Adams and Steve Something-or-Other. I used to go out for coffee sometimes with one or both of them. I really liked that. You know, feeling that they liked me and liked the way I looked and obviously liked being seen with me. I never got serious with either of them, though."

"What do you mean by 'serious'?" he interrupted.

"Well, you know ... serious," I said, returning my attention to the initials in the desk. When I realized that Dr. Runions was not going to break this silence I finally spoke, reluctantly meeting his eyes again. "I never got physical with them. I might have held hands, but I never kissed either of them, at least I don't think so. Or if I did, it never went any further than that. I certainly never got into necking or petting or sleeping together." I squirmed. "I mean, I knew that was morally wrong, to have sex before marriage, and I certainly wasn't ready to get married. I had my career to get started first."

"I'd like to return later to those issues: your morality, your ambitions," he said calmly. "For now would you carry on recalling your experiences with dating?"

"That's about it for 1966 and 1967. I don't remember much from my second year of university. The next major events, if you can call them that, occurred during my first year of medicine, 1968 and 1969, the year I developed anorexia. After I lost a significant amount of weight during the autumn months, I started hanging around with four guys: Ian Gorman from Prince Edward Island, Kumar from India, Soun Lee who was Chinese, and a Filipino man named Frank. They were all graduate students in mathematics, and they lived on campus in Athabasca Hall, next door to Pembina Hall where I lived. I met them over dinner in the cafeteria in about January of that year, and we used to talk together a lot, joke around, and sometimes goof off a little ... Not that I had much time for relaxation. But it was fun." I smiled, the memory warm in my eyes. "We called ourselves 'The Fearsome Five.'"

"Were you sexually attracted to any of them?" he said equably.

I hesitated, but maintained the visual connection this time. "I'm not sure how to answer that, Dr. Runions. I met Ian first and liked him a lot, but our friendship was strictly platonic. I knew he was engaged to a girl back in P.E.I. They were planning to be married in May. So we never did anything physical, not even holding hands. The one time I went to his room was to see her picture. He missed her and talked about her a lot, which was fine with me ... Maybe that's why I felt safe with him: He was no threat to my career. Kumar had a wife and kids back in India, so he was safe, too. Soun Lee might have had a crush on me—Ian says he did—but I never accepted an invitation to go out with him alone. And Frank certainly wanted to go out with me, too. In fact I did date him once or twice alone, but it never got past the first kiss. In fact, I ended the relationship when I saw how serious he was about me ... Really I mostly liked going out with the four of them together: being the center of attention, you know, going to a few graduate student socials with them, imagining that they were all competing for me—which they weren't. But it was all just good clean fun, just friendship."

"But you did enjoy feeling that you were physically attractive?" he persisted.

"Oh yes," I grinned, "very much so. I'd dress to show off the better parts of my figure: my legs and my bottom. And I think I really was quite pretty then ... I weighed around a hundred and ten pounds, so I wasn't emaciated yet."

"Have you had any other relationships since then? That was four years ago."

I looked at the desk and swallowed hard. "Yes," I said, "in the summer of 1969 I met Paul Tavistock when I was in Scotland. I've told you about him before, how I corresponded with him for a year and then impulsively flew to England in the summer of 1970 to visit him. That was like a fairy-tale romance, but I've told you how it all came crashing down around me. In fact, I labeled the whole affair as *The Disaster*, and pushed it away to the back of my mind. I just wasn't ready for intimacy yet. I was in way over my head."

I paused then and reverted to counting the tiles on the floor. *Eight across ... let's see, at ten inches each that would be eighty inches, or six feet, eight inches. Or maybe they're twelve inches each—ninety-six inches or eight feet in total* ... Finally I looked up and took a deep breath. Dr. Runions was still watching me, eloquent in his silence. "I feel guilty about Paul," I said at last, haltingly, "because I think I used him in trying to prove something to myself, and that was terribly wrong. I hurt him, and now it's too late to do anything about it."

Dr. Runions considered that for a moment before he spoke. "Can you accept that life is like that, Joan? That sometimes people hurt one another—sometimes deliberately, but more often without intending it? That it is possible for both of them to learn something from the experience? To grow?"

I looked at him doubtfully. "I'm not sure I do understand," I said. "I mean, it sounds great. It sounds possible. But I'm not sure what lesson I could learn that could justify all that pain."

He gazed at me unblinkingly, and I saw him measuring something. Gauging something. What? Strength? Reserves? Readiness? I shivered involuntarily for no reason that I could see. Finally he spoke, having apparently arrived at some decision. "Would you be willing to think about what happened that summer in England, Joan? Can you identify what was so very frightening to you about intimacy at that time?"

I cast my mind back to those pivotal days in England with Paul. Days that changed my life so critically, that drove me deeper into the clutches of my disease, deeper into lonely isolation, deeper into bleeding silent suffering. I began to tremble and pressed my sweaty palms firmly against my thighs to steady myself.

"It's still frightening," I said at last, "but even now I'm not sure exactly what terrifies me so much about it. Maybe it's the idea of losing control of myself, of allowing my body to take over my mind."

"What would happen if you lost control?" he said softly.

"I don't know," I said, trembling violently now. "I don't know what I might do. That's what scares me. Maybe when I got out of control I'd turn into somebody different, I'd lose myself, disappear, and I might never be able to find myself again, to come back. I might disintegrate, … dissolve, … die." My voice rose in pitch as I continued. "I can't take the chance of losing me. I want to stay me. I want to know who I am and what's going to happen, forever and always."

I stopped abruptly and that final phrase hung between us. Dr. Runions looked at me tenderly. "But you can't know that, can you, Joan?"

I felt the pressure building behind my eyes and shielded my face with a hand. "No," I said brokenly, "I can't. I especially can't know what men might do to me. Even my own father abandoned me. Even he let me down. Even he went away." I brushed aside the tears with an irritable swipe of my hand and snapped my gaze up to connect with Dr. Runions once more. "So it's a lot better not to need anything from anybody else. People are too damned undependable. If I admit that I need something, then they might let me down again. They might not have what I need or be willing to give it to me. Then where does that leave me?"

"Where does it leave you?" he said gently, his voice and his eyes flowing toward me like an abundant river of compassion.

I drank from the river in great thirst-quenching gulps. "It leaves me needy," I cried, "and with my need acknowledged to myself. It leaves me with an empty hole in me. It's better to deny the hole in the first place. It's better to feel intact." I dropped my head into both hands and wept with abandon. I felt his hand on my shoulder, steadying me as before, and felt sustained and supported and embraced. Loved.

When my tears stopped he handed me tissues but did not break the silence. I wiped my cheeks and blew my nose. "But it really isn't," I said finally, my voice very calm. "I know that now. Because it's a lie. I guess I have to admit that I do need something from somebody else. I have to be willing to stick my neck out, to take the risk that I won't get what I need. Because if I don't then there's no chance at all that I ever will get it."

His eyes burned into mine. They smiled and wept and danced and mourned all at the same time. "No," he said, "there's not."

I melted into the profound, healing, almost sacred connection between us. I breathed it and tasted it and rejoiced in it. Another lengthy pause ensued before another idea occurred to me, and I frowned slightly.

"What are you thinking about, Joan?"

"I'm trying to tie all this intimacy business into my anorexia," I said eventually. "I'm remembering how Paul referred to my body when he was angry at me for betraying him the night before I left England. I see now he was just trying to hurt me, which was fair enough, but it really *did* hurt. I forget the exact words he used, but it was something like 'You don't think I'd be interested in you for your body, do you?' As much as to say, I was so skinny that I was ugly, and it was really my genuine friendship he wanted."

His expression altered. "I can imagine how much that hurt," he said.

"I thought my thin body was so beautiful," I continued, "so desirable to men. Paul shattered my illusions."

Dr. Runions nodded. He understood. He cared. "So that relationship ended in deep hurt. Did you ever try again?"

"Only once," I said reluctantly. "That was about a year ago, while I was interning in St. John. My anorexia was at its worst at that time, and I was terribly lonely and homesick. I met another intern, an American fellow named Eliot Chapman, and we got to know each other a little. But as soon as he tried to date me I backed away. I was just too scared …"

"What were you afraid of, Joan?" he said gently, leaning forward.

"I guess I was afraid of physical involvement mainly. I had slept with Paul, as I told you, but we never had intercourse because of my hymenal stenosis, which I had known about for a year already at that time. I told you about that before, didn't I?" Seeing his nod I went on. "Yes, well I used that physical impediment like a chastity belt, I suppose, during my affair with Paul, and I guess I just couldn't stand a repeat performance with Eliot."

"You mean you didn't want to hurt him as you had hurt Paul?"

"To be honest," I said slowly, "I think it was more that I didn't want to be hurt again. I just couldn't risk it. I think my emotions were terribly weak then, just as my body was. I weighed close to my lowest weight ever by that time, and I felt very, very tired at times, though I didn't want to admit it."

"Let's return to Paul," he said, leaning back in his chair and swiveling slightly as he summed up what he had learned. "You said he thought your body was so skinny it was ugly … Prior to developing anorexia you were fat for a brief period, and you said that you saw yourself as 'repulsive,' which was the way you have always viewed fat. Then you began to lose weight and for a while you felt attractive, and in fact you did attract men's attention. But after you became too thin you were unattractive again. So why do you think you wanted to continue being thin?" He stopped swiveling and looked at me intently.

"Hmm," I pondered, meeting his eyes, searching them for the answer that I somehow felt he already knew, "that's a good question. Logically, when I learned that Paul was repelled by my skinny body in 1970 I should have tried to put on some weight to make myself attractive again as I was when I first met him. But I didn't. In fact, I deliberately lost even more weight … Why?" I stopped again, then went on haltingly, tentatively, fitting another piece into the puzzle. "It had to do with getting hurt and feeling safe ... Maybe I began to feel about my emaciated body as I did about my stenotic hymen ... Maybe by remaining skinny I felt protected from deep emotional involvement with a man. Because in truth I never, never wanted to feel as hurt as I did that summer with Paul ... so by remaining skinny nobody would want to have sex with me, and I'd never get hurt again ... maybe."

Still he held my eyes as I released a long slow breath, and he gave an almost imperceptible nod. I closed my eyes. I felt as though I had climbed a mountain.

Chapter 18

"The nurses mentioned that you had a bad night and ended up pacing the halls for several hours, Joan." He looked at me with concern. "Do you want to talk about that?"

I studied Dr. Runions' startling lemon yellow tie. Embossed upon it was a vague pattern in a slightly darker shade of yellow. Ochre perhaps. I squinted at it in my effort to interpret the design. *It's a strange tie for him. He's usually so conservative. I wonder if one of his kids gave it to him for Christmas?* Belatedly I heard his question.

"Yes, I guess so," I said, raising my eyes to his face with an effort. My eyelids weighed a ton. I blinked rapidly, trying to clear from my sight the veil that blurred and haloed his edges. "As a matter of fact, a nightmare woke me up, and I couldn't get back to sleep afterward. It's a really strange dream, the only recurring nightmare I've ever had, and it occurs quite rarely. I don't know what triggered it."

"What's it about?" he said with interest.

"Well, I first had it when I was about five or six years old, when I was delirious with a high fever one night. Actually, it was Hallowe'en night. I came down with this fever—the flu or something—so I couldn't go out Hallowe'ening with the other kids. Mom tucked me into her bed in the early evening and brought me ginger ale and stuff, and I suppose I fell asleep. Then my mother said I suddenly started screaming in terror, and when she came rushing in I was sitting bolt upright, eyes open, apparently awake, but incoherent and crying hysterically. She kept trying to soothe me, but she said I was inconsolable. I just kept saying, 'My tears are crossing the ocean, my tears are crossing the ocean.'"

He was listening intently, a small crease of concentration between his eyes.

"Anyway," I continued, "the next day I was able to remember the dream, in which I saw a vast gray body of water, an ocean without limit, blending into a gray sky at the horizon. In the dream I was represented by a few tiny drops of water—my own tears—suspended above the ocean and flying across it. I knew that it was my task to move across the sea without falling into it, because if I did I would simply disappear, as I became part of this ocean. Yet at the same time I knew with absolute clarity that I could not possibly fly on forever, that I would eventually run out of strength and inevitably drop into the water because this ocean was infinite, but I was not."

My hands were clammy and trembling slightly as I recounted this tale, so vivid and recent it was in my mind. "It's an utterly terrifying dream. I've had it periodically throughout my life ever since that first time, and I invariably wake up before the tears drop into the ocean, before I die, and it's always the same ... my heart is pounding, my mouth is dry, I'm trembling all over. I know, you see, that I have visualized my own death."

I stopped speaking and looked at Dr. Runions again. His eyes were filled with compassion. "I see," he said finally. "I see."

"What do you see?" I said curiously.

He did not at first reply. "There are many psychiatrists," he said finally, "who spend a great deal of time interpreting their patients' dreams, as you know. I expect you are somewhat familiar with the psychoanalytic concepts that support this approach. However, I have never much engaged in this pursuit, because I find other means of exploring the unconscious to be more profitable. Nevertheless, in the case of a single recurring dream such as yours, it may in fact be worthwhile to examine it more closely." He stopped talking for a moment and drummed his fingers on the desk. I continued to watch him, fascinated.

"You stated, Joan, that this dream is about your death, that the fearfulness it induces in you is fear of dying. I would like to suggest an alternative explanation. Are you aware that Freud interpreted water in dreams to frequently represent birth? Life before birth, the amniotic sac, and so on? ... No? ... Well, he did. Now I will grant you that any given dream may be interpreted in a number of ways, that a particular element in it may symbolize any one of several different things. But in your case I find it most significant that this dream should have occurred just as your therapy reached the point at which we finished on Monday. I believe," he concluded, "that your terror surrounding this dream is not fear of your death, but of your birth."

I raised my eyebrows, then slowly shook my head. "I don't understand."

"Joan," he said, leaning closer to me, "what you are doing here these past few weeks is being reborn. You are leaving the shelter—the womb—of your illness and emerging to face life on a new plane. You are accepting the challenge of confronting a harsh world without the walls of your obsessions to protect you. That," he said, "is what is terrifying ... not dying, but living."

I was stunned by this. We looked at one another. Finally I opened my mouth to speak, but what emerged was little more than a squeak. I cleared my throat and tried again. "I never thought of it like that before," I admitted, "but it really does make sense. I mean, even thinking about this terrific need I have to be in control—of what I eat, how much I weigh, how fast I gain weight, and so on—all the issues you and I still struggle over every day. All those things stem from the basic fear that I will get fat, that if I don't maintain control of my caloric intake I will just turn into a blimp, that once I start gaining I won't be able to stop. I guess all of that comes down to a fear of change, of the future. Once I go on, I can't go back ... I suppose it is like being born. Once the fetus has left the womb and taken her first breath of air, she can never return to life in an amniotic sac. Yes," I repeated with a smile this time, "that makes sense."

Dr. Runions nodded again. "It certainly is true that the future is scary, Joan, for everyone. We talked about that a little on Monday when we talked about risk." He looked at me intently. "To go on to tomorrow you must let go of today, you must take a chance that what you are losing will be made up for by what you gain by moving on … That's another risk … And life is just one long series of risks."

"But how can a person possibly take all those risks?" I said. "How do you get rid of the fear?"

"Life," he replied quietly, "has always required courage of those who would live it. And courage is not the absence of fear, but the determination to act in spite of it."

We sat in silence for a long time. I glanced down at my usual distractions—the initials near my right elbow, the gray tiles lined up so conveniently on the floor, begging to be counted—but neither of those worked today. I pondered what he had said. Suddenly something clicked in my mind.

"Growing up is a risk, isn't it?" I said thoughtfully.

"Of course it is," he agreed. "It requires giving up the security of childhood where others take care of you, for an unknown future where you must make your own decisions and take care of yourself."

"Maybe that's another part of what my disease is about. Maybe I'm afraid of growing up. Maybe that's why I want to live on cookies and ice cream—kids' treats. I want to remain a child … But it seems almost paradoxical, in that I do want to make my own decisions about what I eat and how much I am to weigh, yet at the same time …"

"Go on," he prompted.

"I was going to say that at the same time maybe I want someone to make the decisions for me. But that's not true. I don't want any *person* to control me, but I guess I must need to be controlled … so I've set up this rigid set of rules inside my head and I let them control me. That way I'm safe …"

"Safe from what?" he said softly.

I could not immediately reply. Then I raised my eyes to meet his and responded with growing passion. "Safe from change, safe from getting fat … safe from uncertainty, safe from having to make decisions and take chances … safe from having the sky fall in on me again … safe from being abandoned … by my father. I couldn't control anything when I was a child. I couldn't trust even my own father to be there for me. So I'm bloody well going to control my own body ... Oh damn, now I'm crying again."

The days passed as my tears flowed. And flowed and flowed and flowed. I hadn't known that one body could contain as many tears as I shed. But mine evidently did, and they just kept coming, like a subterranean river of pain that, having reached the earth's surface at last, must empty itself. For every insight I achieved during those weeks was at the cost of profound suffering. I learned that healing is never cheaply bought, that painful emotions repressed for a long time can only be released by actually *feeling* them in the process of therapy. And they must be experienced with all of the intensity they contained when the individual first buried them in the psyche. In no other way can deep healing occur.

By the end of the sixth week of my admission I had made sufficient progress that we began to make plans for my discharge. My weight had increased to ninety-three pounds. Dr. Runions had set my goal weight at 110 pounds, but I expressed confidence that I could continue gaining after I was discharged. My old familiar calorie counter still clicked merrily away inside my head, but we had agreed, Dr. Runions and I, that I must not allow it to control my actions. At least my obsession with it no longer demanded the enormous portion of my mental energy that it had before.

We decided that it would be inadvisable for me to return to my mother's home, as there was too much danger of backsliding into the old grooves of my rigid behaviors of the past. But I also felt panicky about living completely alone. I wondered if I would be capable of forcing myself to eat properly if no one else was around to police me. I did not openly share this fear with Dr. Runions in so many words, for I was ashamed of it. I simply said that I thought I would manage better if I were living with someone else. I was still a novice in the arena of honesty and had as yet no conception of how critically important absolute honesty in even the smallest matter was to my spiritual health. I didn't know then what I have since learned, that any deception of myself or others, whether by outright lying or simple withholding of the truth, tips me over an edge onto the slippery downhill slope of my disease.

By coincidence, my old friend Madeleine came to visit me at about that time and said she was planning to move in May because her two roommates were leaving Edmonton, and she could not afford to stay in the house that the three of them were currently renting. So we decided to share an apartment. I obtained a day pass, and we set off in high spirits to search for a suitable place. Almost immediately we found a spacious two-bedroom apartment in a high-rise building in the river valley. It was available immediately, so I made a commitment to move in on April first, the date set for my hospital discharge. Madeleine would join me a month later.

Life was marvelous. I could scarcely believe how everything was falling into place so quickly. I wondered at my good fortune and praised my God unceasingly for his loving care. I had even arranged to pick up the thread of my family practice residency program in April: a one-month stint in rehabilitation medicine, two months in community psychiatry, followed by a final two months in a family practice clinic working with a group of six family doctors.

My future was laid out. Everything seemed secure—challenging enough but not frightening. The only real anxiety I felt was a nagging doubt that lived and breathed in the darkest place in my mind, a fear that I pushed firmly away and refused to acknowledge at the time, a fear that I did not share with anyone, including Dr. Runions. It was a secret whisper, a chill voice speaking to me at unguarded moments: *You don't really think you can keep this up, do you, Joan? You don't want to keep this up, do you, Joan?* And it would laugh hollowly. Had I the courage to look this fear in the face at that time, to drag it out into the light of day and talk about it, explore it, demolish it piece by piece, I'm certain that the events of the following nine years would have been quite different.

But such is the nature of free will. The grace to assist us along the right path is available at every turn, but one can choose to accept it or not. And, almost invariably, accepting it means choosing the harder path; rejecting it means taking what appears to be the easy way out. Unfortunately, human beings have a natural proclivity, which some might label original sin, to choose the latter, the path of least resistance, which frequently leads to hell.

Chapter 19

The air was filled with the unmistakable sweetness of early spring. The sun at last radiated warmth in addition to light, the mountains of snow yielding to its power and collapsing upon themselves into dense soggy masses, the gutters filled with trickles and torrents of dirty water as the city awoke from the bitter dream of winter. It was Friday, March twenty-ninth, 1974, and I was leaving the University Hospital—healed, recovered, ready to resume my place in the world. I inhaled deeply of the soft spring air before climbing into the front seat of my mother's car. Mom leaned over and kissed me before starting the engine, and I saw her welcome, her warmth, her love in the dear hazel eyes I knew so well.

"Well, honey, how does it feel to be leaving here for the last time?"

I hesitated before replying. "I have mixed feelings, Mom. I'm happy and excited but I also feel a little scared, like I'm leaving a safe shelter and venturing out into wild territory. Rather like the first time I left here on a pass, except I was even more frightened then." I opened the window and took another deep breath of that miraculous air, crying out involuntarily at the sudden, unexpected explosion of unbearable joy that filled my breast. "Dear God, what a beautiful day! I am so glad it's spring."

"Yes," she said, "it's been a long winter ... in so many ways." She paused significantly and glanced over at me again. "You were saying you feel scared about coming home?"

I settled back deeply into the seat cushion and studied her strong profile as she concentrated now on negotiating the midday traffic of the university quarter. "Yes, I do ... In the hospital there are so many people eagerly waiting to help me analyze every feeling I experience. Out here in the real world people don't think that way. They just act without stopping to think about things like feelings and motivations and emotional needs ... I can hardly believe it was only eight weeks ago that I was admitted. I feel as though it was a lifetime ago, like I've been reborn, like I'm seeing things and other people with new eyes. Everything has changed."

"Yes," she agreed, "you've gone through a lot of changes in a very short time. I think you should go easy, honey, and give the changes a chance to consolidate. Just take things slowly, OK? A lot of changes all at once are very hard to cope with."

"It's funny you should say that, Mom. Dr. Runions said something like that yesterday in our final session, something about letting the changes integrate gradually into my personality. It sounds good, but I'm not quite sure how to do it ... Anyway, he'll be seeing me in follow-up every week or two at first, so it's not as though I'm completely on my own ..." My voice broke on the lump in my throat, and unexpected tears stung my eyes.

"And I'm here, too, Joan," she said with a warm touch.

"I know you are, Mom, and I really appreciate it. Did I ever tell you how much it meant to me when I was first admitted and you came to see me every single day? I know it wasn't easy for you to find the time to drive all the way over here, but I want you to know how grateful I am for your support. That was a rough time for me, especially the first two or three weeks in there."

"No thanks are necessary, Joan," she said simply. "I love you. I would have done anything on earth to help you get well. Coming to visit was certainly no sacrifice. It was something I could not have *not* done. You'll understand what I mean if you have children of your own someday."

"I guess anything is possible now. Before two months ago I would have said there was no chance that I could ever marry and have children, but now? ... Well, only time will tell ... Oh, by the way," I said brightly, "did I tell you who came to see me last week? Warren Adams! You could have knocked me over with a feather when he walked in. You remember: He's the boy I liked in my Latin class in first-year pre-med. I think maybe he was coming to see someone else and he saw my name on a list on the desk or something. Anyway, he just walked in and asked if he could talk with me for a while. Gosh, it was nice. And not only that, but he came back again twice more, and he asked if we could get together once I was discharged! I said 'Yes,' so I guess I'll be seeing more of him."

"That sounds good, Joan," she said, clearly pleased. She looked at me directly as she had stopped for a red light.

"Yes, I think it's good. I always liked Warren. He's very quiet but also somehow very solid and authentic. There's nothing phony or put-on about him. He was studying to be a teacher when I met him in 1966, but he went into the seminary for a while, thinking he would become a priest. In the end he decided it wasn't for him and he left there last year. Now he's back at university to finish his degree. I'm looking forward to seeing him again."

"Good for you ... but remember to just go slowly, OK?" Her eyes returned to the road as the light changed to green, and we began to move forward once more. "Incidentally, I've got some news of my own. I've decided to sell the house and buy a high-rise condo downtown, so you can have as much furniture as you want to put in your new apartment. I thought I could help you move in this weekend ... if you'd like some help."

"Gee, thanks, Mom! That would be terrific," I said with real enthusiasm. "I start my new job with Dr. Bedford on Monday, so I'd appreciate the help." There was a lengthy pause before either of us spoke again. At last I said with a carefully casual tone, "By the way, Mom, I've decided to see Dr. Dunsten again about getting that vaginal surgery done. I want to feel like a complete woman. Now that I'm gaining weight maybe my periods will even start again. I weigh ninety-six pounds now, you know!"

Chapter   20

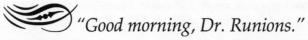 *"Good morning, Dr. Runions."*

"Hello Joan, come in and sit down," he invited. "How are things going?"

I took a seat in the comfortable upholstered armchair in his office in which I had first sat less than a year before. It seemed more like a decade or a century. Brilliant April sunshine, filtered by the budding birch trees just outside, poured through the bank of windows to my right, dappling the quiet blue carpet with bright dancing crystals of light. I met his steady gaze and smiled from my heart.

"Pretty well, I'd say. Work is going fine. Dr. Bedford is great to work for, and I'm learning a lot. Working with paraplegic and quadriplegic patients can be pretty heartbreaking at times, but all in all I'm glad I decided to do this as part of my rotation … I like my apartment, and living alone is really fun. Madeleine moves in next week, and I'm looking forward to that, but I'm not feeling as desperate for companionship as I was a month ago."

I shifted my gaze to the windows, which overlooked a narrow expanse of lawn and trees and, beyond that, a sidewalk crowded with students strolling by, chatting together—obviously about final examinations freshly completed, judging from the release in their faces, the buoyancy in their stride. "Let's see, what else? Oh yes, I'm developing a social life. Being able to eat again sure helps in that area. My friend Warren and I have been seeing quite a bit of one another and enjoying each other's company more and more." I looked directly, earnestly, at the perceptive face across the desk. "He's a very fine person, Dr. Runions, and we have a lot in common, including our religious background, so we see eye to eye on a lot of things."

"Such as?" he prompted.

"Oh, life goals and values and views on sex and stuff like that," I said with a vague gesture, looking out the window once again. *Those students look so happy ... I can understand that now.* He waited patiently while I decided whether to continue. Finally I made up my mind and looked back at him. "Actually we feel very strongly attracted physically to one another. I feel a little embarrassed to be talking to you about this, Dr. Runions, but ... well, we spent the night together on Friday. I felt glorious at the time and afterward. In fact, I'm delighted to say that I felt no guilt at all. It just feels *right*, you know, and Warren seemed to respond the same way."

I paused again, but still he said nothing. His eyes, however, compelled me to go on. "It's not like when I slept with Paul in England," I said, hearing the insistent note in my voice, knowing that I was struggling to convince myself as well as him. "I don't feel like I'm using Warren in any way. Of course we didn't have intercourse, because of my problem ... Oh, by the way," I said, changing the subject with relief, "I'm going in soon to have that surgery done, Dr. Runions. Dr. Dunsten said it's very simple. I'll be admitted the afternoon before and be able to go home the morning after my surgery and back to work immediately. So once I'm physically capable ... who knows what will happen?" I concluded with excitement.

"Your relationship seems to be moving very quickly, Joan," he observed neutrally. "But how do you reconcile your actions with the strong moral beliefs you've always held in the past, that you've told me about before?" There was no judgment in his tone, merely a genuine seeking after knowledge.

I dropped my eyes to the carpet, organizing my thoughts. "I don't know, Dr. Runions," I admitted finally. "I feel like I'm blundering through some vast uncharted territory here, and the only map I've been given is useless. It's as though I have to find my way blindfolded, feeling for new signposts, inching forward one step at a time ... Oh, I'm explaining this badly."

We studied one another for a time. "Do you suppose," he said, "that you could be experiencing now the adolescence that you never had before?"

I considered that, then nodded with tentative concurrence. "Yes ... I never thought about it in those terms before, but I think you may be right ... All those moral values and standards I had before—they were never really *me*. I always felt as though I were putting on an act when I proclaimed them so loudly. They were imposed upon me from the outside. I had never really incorporated them into my being. And now ... now my whole life has been changed, my whole *self* has been changed. The old me has been broken, shattered in fact, and I have to rebuild myself from the fragments. And in order to do that, I'm compelled to explore and experiment, to try out new things until I find what really *is* me, what fits, what is comfortable, what feels right—not physically but emotionally and spiritually ... Does that make any sense?"

He nodded slowly, his eyes burning into mine. "Yes, it makes a good deal of sense, Joan ... But remember that the old map you referred to may not be completely useless. Probably the most difficult thing about adolescence is the tendency to go overboard in one's experimentation, to do everything by extremes, to reject *everything* one has been taught in the past. You, Joan, are not truly an adolescent. Some levels of your mind are in fact adult, and you might be able to use those parts to help guide the adolescent part to maturity."

I smiled finally, recognizing the validity in this. "Yes, Dr. Runions, I think I know what you mean. I haven't lost my faith in God and in Christ, or anything like that. I'm continuing to pray a lot, and I've started to read the Bible more seriously than ever before. I started when you directed me to the Book of Job during my first week in hospital. I never knew the Bible was so rich, and it's not as difficult to read as people generally think. Sometimes I do have trouble understanding it though. I'm thinking about taking a course or something like that to learn more about it ... but I don't quite know where to look."

"That's an area where I can help you, Joan," he said thoughtfully. "In our church, West Park Baptist, we have a number of Bible study groups. They are generally fairly small groups of between five and eight individuals, who meet in one another's homes once a week to study the Scriptures. Each group decides amongst itself which book in the Old Testament, or which section in the New, it wants to focus on, and then the members go through it piece by piece. The group usually prays together as well, quite naturally and spontaneously … Does that idea interest you?"

"Very much so. It sounds like just what I had in mind."

"In that case, I think I know the group for you. The leader is Dr. Eric Thomson, who is a physicist about your own age. I think he and his group would be very receptive to taking on a new member, and I believe that you would fit in well. How would you like me to speak to him and let you know when and where they are next meeting?"

"That would be great! Thanks, Dr. Runions."

Unexpectedly, a sudden uncomfortable silence developed in the room. Dr. Runions studied me, and his tone grew serious. "Joan, we seem to have talked about almost every subject except your weight. Did you bring your graph in today?"

I swallowed. "Yes, I did … Actually it doesn't show much of a gain in the last month, as you can see, but I think that's probably due to my increased activity. I am eating three meals a day of 'normal' food, and I'm feeling great, so I'm not worried about my weight sort of … er … plateauing a little, just for a while. I'm sure I'll start gaining once more as soon as my body gets adjusted to my new pattern of activity."

Dr. Runions' unwavering electric eyes seemed to penetrate straight through me into the core of my soul. There was a long assessing silence before he spoke. "The reality, Joan, is that you have gained only one pound in the three weeks since your discharge, compared to sixteen pounds during your two months in hospital. I will not play games here, Joan. We have an agreement that you will continue to gain weight. You have demonstrated to yourself and to me that you are capable of doing that, and I expect to see you adhere to our contract. I am very pleased to see the progress you are making in other areas of your life, but I cannot allow either of us to overlook the condition that brought you to this office."

I flushed and dropped my eyes to the floor as he spoke, compressing my lips.

"Look at me, Joan," he said quietly.

Slowly I looked up to meet his gaze once more.

"Your next appointment is in one month. I shall expect to see your weight over the one hundred pound mark by then. Agreed?"

"Okay, Dr. Runions ... Agreed." My voice was like a tightrope.

I left his office that day fully intending to adhere to the bargain we had struck. I still saw myself as cured, and although I was aware of an increasing preoccupation with calories and with the types of food I ate, I was rationalizing it, explaining it away as something I probably had to expect in the natural course of events. After all, I told myself, who really knew what went on in the minds of former anorexics? Who knew what thoughts and obsessions continued to haunt them? How could a psychiatrist who had never himself been afflicted with this dreadful condition possibly tell me what I should be experiencing at this point?

Thus did my self-deception begin once again. I could not bear to look at the possibility that I was not yet completely cured, that I might have to embrace the agony of further healing. So I forced my consciousness away from such thoughts and continued to point out the evidence of my wellness.

Look at me! I'm living alone, dating someone, making plans for the future, eating normal food like a normal person. So what if I have a little ice cream now and again or an occasional gingersnap ... or two or three? Is that so bad? Just because they were the staple of my diet during my illness, does that mean I can never eat them again? Normal people eat them sometimes. Why not me? Forget about that analogy with alcoholism that keeps springing to mind! It's not the same thing, it's not. I don't suffer physical withdrawal symptoms if I don't get my gingersnaps. And stop referring to them as "my" gingersnaps, for God's sake! I mean "a" or "the" or "some." I am not addicted to them, I'm not!

Madeleine moved in the following week as planned. I was almost unbearably happy at times during the following two months. We often sat up late talking together like little girls at a pyjama party. We shared our innermost thoughts and secret desires. (Except, of course, those dangerous thoughts about my illness, which I judged did not rightly belong in my mind and which I felt I could control and dispel if I worked at it harder.) We did things together. We dated as a foursome with our boyfriends at times, Madeleine having been deeply committed to a young man for the past four years. Occasionally we ate our meals together, but I found myself wanting to eat alone as much as possible, so I would make excuses to justify coming home for dinner, or getting up for breakfast, at a different time than Madeleine. I would lie. That way I could eat the foods I wanted to eat, prepared in the way I wanted them prepared.

Madeleine had always been a free spirit. This was revealed even in her physical appearance: her tall willowy figure filled with fluid grace, poetry in every movement. Her face was long and angular, with delicate bones, a slightly jutting chin, clear laughing green eyes, straight nose, and full lips that twitched with vitality. Her perfect skin was very fair, her long hair fine, perfectly straight, and jet black from birth.

She did everything spontaneously, acting on wild impulses and letting her creative instincts flow. She loved trying out new recipes and experimenting with different foods and ways of preparing them. She wore old clothes in new ways, changing accessories and color combinations every time she dressed. She created different hairstyles to match her mood of the moment. She engaged in different activities at different times whenever she could possibly change her routine. She loved music and listened to many different types of it, singing and harmonizing along with the artists. She sketched and painted with enormous energy, pouring out her spirit on paper and canvas to share her perceptions with the observer. She loved people, listened to them, felt with them, laughed and wept with them. She loved life and lived it with joy and passion.

She was everything I was not. I was everything she was not. Such is the attraction of opposites. We had known each other for fifteen years at that point, and our mysterious friendship had survived all the changes those years had brought. She had come to know me intimately before my neurosis manifested itself. She had watched from a distance throughout my illness and, although bewildered, had tried desperately to understand me and not be hurt by my attempts to push her, and everyone else, away. Now that I was "cured" we renewed our intimacy, experiencing again the things that had first attracted us to one another as children.

I so wanted everything to be as it was before my illness that I succeeded in ignoring the early warning signs in our life together, which should have told me that everything was not right with the world. But Madeleine had no such capacity for self-deception. She saw clearly what I was doing. She knew I was not free of my disease, and although she still attempted to understand me, she was frightened for the integrity of her own spirit. She had no inclination to live as I lived, constrained by rigid barriers of my own making: eating the same foods at the same time whenever possible, holding to the same schedule, regimenting my days, and regimenting my thoughts to avoid the threat of the new.

And so it was that about the middle of June she told me that she would be moving out at the end of the month, that she could not afford her half of the rent any longer and would have to find a cheaper apartment. In her well-intentioned but misguided desire to avoid hurting my feelings, she did not confront me with the truth.

Chapter 21

"*Good morning, Joan.* Come in and have a seat. You appear very cheerful today."

I bounced into Dr. Runions' office and dropped into my chair, smoothing out the crisp folds of my flowered cotton skirt as I did so.

"I'm *feeling* cheerful," I said brightly. "This beautiful June weather! I'm seeing the world again for the first time. It's many years since I've reveled over the coming of spring and summer as I have this year. I love the warm seasons of the year and detest winter. And this year the colors of the flowers seem brighter, the sun shines more radiantly, the sky is bluer ... I'm still feeling as though I've been reborn."

He smiled in response to this eloquent declaration. "And how is everything in your life? Are you cheerful about that too?"

"Well, as a matter of fact I am, although events are not really unfolding the way I expected they would. Madeleine will be moving out this weekend. She had to find a cheaper place to live. So I'll be living on my own again, but I'm really enjoying my freedom. I come and go as I please, I'm not accountable to anyone for my hours or my activities, and that feels great. I've been working with Dr. Philson at Community Mental Health Services, which is really fascinating, and you know Dr. Philson! He's such a character, but such a warm and caring person, too. I'm having fun there and learning a lot about public health, which is not an area that we really paid much attention to in medical school." I looked at him with a fresh sparkle. "I've even been offered a permanent job with the city as a public health physician, to start as soon as I complete my residency at the end of August. I haven't decided whether to take it or not. It's not what I really want to do professionally, but it might be a good interim step, until an opportunity in family practice presents itself."

Dr. Runions listened intently throughout this progress report, absorbing, interpreting, reading between the lines to arrive at, no doubt, some unexpected conclusion. I saw him watching me and deliberately slowed down to choose my next words more carefully.

"As far as my social life goes, everything is very exciting, although it's not progressing as I might have predicted either. Warren and I are not sleeping together anymore." I looked at him with undisguised triumph, assessing the effect of this announcement. "As a matter of fact, Dr. Runions, you'll be interested to know that the main factor leading me to that decision was something I read in the Bible just after my appointment here in April—a passage in the Song of Songs that reads, 'Do not arouse, do not stir up love before its own time.' I was just reading one day and that verse leapt out at me and spoke to my heart. I knew that God had led me to it, and I saw its meaning for me instantly. Warren and I have not committed ourselves to one another yet, so it's premature to be sleeping together. So I talked it over with him, and it turns out that's what he really believes, too. He was also feeling uncomfortable about what we had done."

I caught the flicker of approval in Dr. Runions' eyes, and smiled ruefully to myself, knowing how important his blessing upon my actions had become to me. *You see him as God, don't you, Joan?* This flash of insight caught me off balance, even as I recognized its truth, and I hesitated, losing the thread of what I had been saying.

"You're making rapid progress in this area, Joan," he interjected. "Keep it up—this slow, thoughtful approach to your relationship with Warren, the honest seeking for the right choice at each point of decision. You are evidently learning that that is the only possible way to cultivate a genuine connection with another human being."

"Yes," I agreed, "I am. I'm even learning to deal with setbacks. Warren has decided to work for the summer on an Indian reservation somewhere in B.C., teaching. He says he feels the need to get away and think about his life, and he's always been attracted to missionary work. He's done it before. I guess I should be sad that he's going away, but strangely I'm not." I dropped my eyes to the floor and hesitated again. "He asked me if I would live with him if and when he comes back in September, and I ... I thought it over and said that I would. I know it's a big step but ..." I faltered and stopped.

"Why does he want to live with you, rather than marry you?" Dr. Runions' tone was suddenly cool.

I shrugged. "I never thought about that ... I mean marriage is a very big step. I don't know if we're ready for that yet ... I mean ..."

"What do you mean, Joan?"

I had no reply, and a highly charged silence developed. Finally, Dr. Runions spoke, his tone flatter and more matter-of-fact than I had ever heard it. "I am always suspicious, Joan, when young couples tell me that they want to live together rather than get married. Usually what they mean is they wish to reserve a way out of the relationship in the event that it does not go smoothly. Unfortunately, their union is almost always doomed to failure if begun under those conditions. Because no human relationship ever goes smoothly. And unless one has the assurance that one's partner will not run away when the going gets tough, then one does not have the freedom to be oneself, making mistakes and growing through them."

He paused, lending greater impact to the words that followed. "The union between a man and a woman is a mystical one: As the union deepens, so in direct proportion does each partner become more fully himself or herself and thereby also come closer to God. It is not a frivolous joyride to be abandoned when it's not fun anymore. Invariably, the joyride ends in deep hurt, usually for both parties."

There seemed to be no reply to this, so I said nothing.

"Will you think and pray about this some more, Joan, before you make any further promises to Warren?" He seemed to be saying that he expected a more adult response to this issue than I had yet shown, now that I was healthy.

I swallowed and forced myself to meet his eyes. "Yes, I will."

He visibly relaxed. His demeanor warmed. "Now tell me about what else is happening."

"That's about all, I think … Oh, except that I've started attending weekly Bible study sessions with Eric Thomson's group. I do seem to fit in well with them. They are all very kind, especially Eric himself. He is a very remarkable person, isn't he? He's not like anyone I've ever known before. We've talked on occasion after some of the evening sessions have concluded. He seems interested in me. But he knows that I'm involved with someone else, from the occasions when I've prayed aloud about Warren during our prayer time. However, I do like him, very much."

"That's good," he said, his voice still tinged with careful neutrality. "Now what about your weight, Joan?"

I looked out the window at the June morning and fervently wished that I were somewhere else. "Oh," I began, then stopped to clear my throat of the lump that had suddenly filled it. "I forgot my chart today, but I can tell you it's pretty much the same as it was at my last visit. I'm just over one hundred pounds."

"How much over?"

"Well," I admitted with reluctance, "just half a pound. I haven't gained lately, but I think it's due to all the emotional turmoil: you know, with Warren and everything. But I'm feeling great, and … and I'm eating well, and … I'm still taking my antidepressant as you instructed."

My voice trailed off lamely. I could not look at him, for I knew he could see into my heart. He knew me too well.

"Joan, I'm concerned about this," he said gravely. "We both know that there is some hidden game going on here. Surely you have learned by now that there is nothing to be gained by deception. You are not deceiving me and …"

I broke in with a rush. "Of course I'm not deceiving you, Dr. Runions! There is no game. I admit that sometimes I think about calories a bit too much, but I already told you I've been struggling with that all along, all the time in the hospital and all the time since. I've been unable to turn off the calorie cash register inside my head. I told you that! I never deceived you."

"Then what is going on here, Joan?" he asked quietly.

"There's nothing going on, nothing," I said too emphatically. "It's just as I've said. I'm eating the calories I'm supposed to every day: twenty-five hundred, as we agreed on in the hospital, but I'm just not gaining weight."

"Joan," he said firmly, "I don't care about calories. I care about you, and I think that you are deceiving yourself in some way. My job is to confront you with that, and that is what I shall do, even if it causes pain for both of us. You agreed to gain weight. So far, in the three months since you left hospital you have gained … what? About four pounds? To me that is essentially an insignificant change. Will you promise to increase your weight by four pounds by your next appointment in one month?"

"I can't promise, Dr. Runions," I confessed, suddenly feeling weighed down by a familiar deadly force. "I'm still too scared to get much heavier … I really want to keep a buffer zone between my current weight and the goal weight you set for me … but I'll try … I'll do what I can."

"Don't say you'll 'try', Joan," he said pointedly, "for we both know what that means. I'll see you in July. God bless you."

The interview was over.

"God bless you," he had said. Indeed, God help me, please … I can't stand to go back where I was. Please keep me moving ahead, please, please, please.

Such were my thoughts as I left Dr. Runions' office that day, and over the next few weeks. But not for long, for I was moving away, in the slow measured pace of a death march, from God, from God within me. Every time I indulged my penchant for self-deception, I took another step away from him, from the God who had revealed himself to me so powerfully and so vividly only four short months before. But I did not see my actions in that light. I continued to pray, read the Bible, and attend my weekly study sessions, while at the same time I permitted my behavior to become more and more regimented and impoverished during the times I was alone, when no one could watch what I was doing.

I had not deliberately lied to Dr. Runions, only bent the truth a little. I was eating twenty-five hundred calories daily … almost. My diet was a feast compared to what I had been eating prior to my hospitalization, but I continued to experience so much anxiety about eating anything new that I varied my intake very little. Every morning I ate a slice of dry toast, two poached eggs, and black coffee. Lunch was a cheese sandwich and fruit. For dinner I prepared four ounces of lean meat or fish, a small serving of green vegetable, and a large tossed salad. Then, having fulfilled my obligation to the principles of good nutrition, I would make up my caloric "deficit" for the day by eating carefully measured quantities of ice cream or gingersnaps, relegating the ensuing vague disquiet I felt to the back of my mind. As I consumed my comfort foods, I would slowly relax and feel satisfied for another twenty-four hours, much as junkies must feel as they mainline their fixes.

I continually reassured myself that I was fine, that giving in to these cravings for my ritual foods was not a dangerous activity. I focused on the positive aspects of my life. But I could not completely hide from myself. Problems arose, for instance, when others would offer me food or invite me to share a meal or a snack with them. At the time I left the hospital, the acceptance of such invitations provided my deepest joy, simply because for the past five years I had been unable to accept them without panic that my routine was being disturbed, that my calorie intake for that day might be ten or twenty calories too high. Now, by late June, I was experiencing this panic again, and with it a chill sense of horror, of dreadful recognition. *Oh God, no, it can't be true. I am OK, I am cured, I'm not feeling panicky, I'm not. I can accept this invitation. It's OK if I miss my usual meal or my ice cream and cookies … Oh God, no!*

Denial maintained its rule, an absolute monarch in my psychic kingdom, probably assisted by the several distractions that relieved my mind from these troublesome preoccupations. Principal among them was my love life. Late in July I received a letter from Warren Adams. He had been gone for nearly a month and he had reached a decision. He would not be returning to Edmonton or to me. He hoped I would understand. He really cared about me, he didn't want to hurt me, but he felt his calling was elsewhere, probably in the mission field as a lay missionary. He wished me well. He asked God to bless me. Sincerely, Warren.

It was the only "Dear John" letter I ever received in my life. I did cry. I did feel despondent ... for about six hours. But later in the evening of the same day on which the letter arrived, I suddenly thought of Eric Thomson. In my mind's eye, I saw his tall lean frame, narrow hips, powerful shoulders developed through years of competitive swimming. I recalled the well-shaped blonde head, the blue eyes dancing with laughter as at some perpetual secret joke, the firm decisive chin, the aquiline nose and cheekbones that would look just as good in twenty years as they looked now. I heard his deep articulate voice, at one moment tossing off a witticism to put someone at ease, at the next earnestly discussing an issue with intelligence and passion. He was a man of compelling charm, utterly without subterfuge ... so immensely attractive to me, a master of the art of deception who yearned for honesty. Suddenly I longed to be with him. He had said to call if ever I needed anything, so ...

I picked up the phone.

"Hi, Eric! This is Joan Eisener calling."

"Hi, Joan," he replied, his voice filled with the deep kindness that was his hallmark. "What a pleasant surprise. How are you?"

We chatted for a few minutes about nothing in particular. He must have heard what I did not say, because ...

"Are you busy tonight? Would you like to come over? Actually, I have a friend coming whom you might like to meet."

"Oh, I don't want to intrude, Eric," I objected.

"You wouldn't be intruding at all. My friend is Zak Pendleton. He's ..."

"Zak Pendleton!" I exclaimed. "But I know him. We worked together as student interns. He was a year behind me in medical school. We did pediatrics at the same time. He's a super guy."

"Yes, I agree. We've known each other since we were kids. He's a resident in orthopedic surgery now, and he's got a free evening, so he's coming over for a visit. He'll be here in a few minutes. Come on over and join us."

Predictably, I went on over and joined them. It was a memorable evening. We talked for hours, drank tea—Eric rarely indulged in alcoholic beverages—and ate chocolate chip cookies donated by Eric's mother. I even ate one, quite happily, mentally congratulating myself for my spontaneity in doing so. Zak left about eleven. As Eric showed him out, I looked around at the small apartment. Although the decor was similar to that of my own, Early Student Poverty, it possessed a quiet harmony that soothed me. I felt at home here. I looked up as Eric entered the room.

"I should be going, too, Eric," I said diffidently. "You have to get up for work in the morning, and so do I."

"Relax for a few more minutes," he replied with quiet direction that permitted no objection. "Have another cup of tea ... So how come you seem to be at loose ends tonight? Not that I'm complaining, of course. I've enjoyed the evening enormously."

I traced my forefinger along the swirls in the sofa upholstery under my hand. "Well, to be honest I was feeling the need of a friend tonight." I paused, then summoned my courage and continued with as much nonchalance as I could muster. "I just got a letter from the fellow I've been dating. He left town last month and now he says he's not returning to Edmonton, ever."

"I see ..." He regarded me thoughtfully. "So you must be feeling pretty upset, eh?"

"Yes," I sighed, "but life goes on, I suppose. I hope you don't mind my calling you tonight. You said I should call if ever I needed anything, and ... I did need something, someone to talk to, someone I could trust. We've gotten to know each other a little over the past two or three months, Eric, and ... you've been so good to me, and ... well, I've liked you right from that first time I came here, and ... well ..." My voice trailed off into uncertainty.

"And I've liked you too, Joan," he declared with perfect simplicity. My heart somersaulted at his words. "In fact, when you feel ready to start dating again perhaps we could take in a movie or something like that. I'd like to get to know you better, but I don't want to push you."

I swallowed. "That sounds good, Eric. I'd like that a lot."

He held my eyes, a universe of meaning in his gaze. "How about if I give you a call in a few days?"

"I'd like that," I said again. "Please do." My voice sparkled, my heart danced.

Thinking back on that evening, I realize that most North American males would have tossed a woman out on her ear if she had come to them in such a fashion, with such a tale. Most men's pride would have reared up when they were told, in essence, that they were being picked up on the rebound. But Eric was not like most men. He did what he said he would do: He called me four days later. We went to a movie.

Four weeks later we went hiking in the mountains with another couple.

Four months later we were married in West Park Baptist Church. Dr. Runions witnessed our vows.

All my problems had come to an end. Cinderella was rescued by the prince and lived happily ever after.

Didn't she?

Part Four

The Second Fall

*Cain then left the Lord's presence
and settled in the land of Nod,
east of Eden.*

GENESIS 4:16

Chapter 22

The bubble burst during our honeymoon.

Eric knew that I had suffered from an emotional disorder for which I had been hospitalized, but he did not know the precise diagnosis. I saw no need to lay bare all the humiliating details about my former neurosis. After all, I was well now, totally cured, and I was absolutely convinced that once married I would, magically, have no further problems centering around food, calories, or weight. My fantasy might seem ludicrous to the reader, but I maintain that my belief in magic was no greater than that of many otherwise rational, intelligent human beings.

In any event I did manage to eat normally, only vaguely aware of calories ... for nearly twenty-four hours after the wedding. We were honeymooning in Victoria, a small city on Vancouver Island, just off the Pacific Coast of Canada. In late December it had a much more pleasant climate than Edmonton's, and thus had earned its reputation as a haven for "the newly wed and the nearly dead."

On my first morning as a married woman, I was dismayed to find myself awakening to thoughts of caloric plans for the day. *It isn't possible. I am not really thinking about this ... How could I be? What would Eric think if he knew what is in my mind?* So I put on a brave front as I tried to organize my thoughts.

"Good morning, love. How did you sleep?"

"Like a log! It's so good to wake up and see you in bed beside me, Eric, and think that this is the way it will be every morning for the rest of our lives. I love you ..."

Time passed.

"What would you like to do today?" Eric was bursting with enthusiasm. "How about starting out with breakfast in that little restaurant we saw across the street last night? I'm starved!"

"Well, I'm never very hungry first thing in the morning, sweetie, but I could sure use a cup of coffee. So I'll have coffee while you have a good breakfast. Then maybe we can go for a walk along the sea wall. That sunshine looks glorious!"

"Sounds good ... How about a shower together first?"

That was pretty easy. Now I just have to figure out what to do at lunchtime.

"This is fantastic. Just think: It's December twenty-ninth. Eat your heart out, Edmonton! ... Say, there's a restaurant down there overlooking the water. What would you say to having a nice quiet lunch, then wandering back toward our motel, Joan?"

"Okay, but let's check out their menu first ... Oh, they don't seem to have any decent salads here, Eric, and that's what I feel like having: a great big shrimp salad. Shall we try another place?"

"How about some soup instead? I'll bet their clam chowder is great."

Clam chowder! Good grief, it has about four hundred calories per cup.

"Oh, I detest the taste of clams."

"Okay, how about the lobster or shrimp bisque then?" he said patiently.

"Well, actually, I don't like thick soups at all. They always sit too heavy on my stomach. I prefer a lighter meal at noon."

"But you ate that chowder my mother served last week when we went over for Sunday lunch," he said, puzzled.

"I just ate it to be polite, sweetie. Now that we're married I'd prefer to eat the way I normally eat. I have to watch my waistline, you know."

"Good Lord, Joan," he said incredulously, "you're as thin as a rail. What do you weigh? A hundred pounds soaking wet?"

"Heavens, no! I'm at least a hundred and five, or maybe a hundred and four. On my final visit to Dr. Runions in September I was a hundred and four and a half, and I may have gained a bit since then. You may find it hard to believe, but I was fat once: one hundred and thirty-six pounds back in 1968. And I have to watch it like a hawk. I can gain weight just by looking at food. I have a very efficient metabolism—the opposite of yours. You wouldn't want me to get fat, would you?"

"No," he said doubtfully, "I like you slim, although you could probably stand a few more pounds on. However, that's up to you. At any rate, I can't believe that a bowl of soup is going to make you fat. After all, you had no breakfast."

"You have no idea how many calories there are in thick soups," I said stubbornly. "Honestly, I would really like a salad. Can we please try someplace else?"

"Of course, darling, anything you like … How about that place in the next block?"

Whew, that wasn't so bad. And I told him the truth too, about how I feel about food … Well, at least part of the truth. Now he knows, so everything will be OK. Now there's just dinner to get through, and the day will be over. Then I can relax.

"This looks like a good place to eat, darling."

"Oh no, this is a French restaurant, Eric. French cuisine is loaded with sauces, and everything is sautéed in butter. It's far too rich for my taste. I like very simple foods, plainly prepared, not swimming in grease. Let's walk on and try someplace else."

"How about a Chinese restaurant then? I love Chinese food."

"Oh, no," I said, aghast. "They fry everything. I never eat fried foods."

"But it's stir-fried, Joan." His patience was wearing thin. "The vegetables stay crisp, almost like a salad. I thought if you like salads you'd like that."

"But they put oil in the wok, Eric. I never add oil if I stir-fry something. I use a *Teflon* pan instead. Fat isn't good for people, you know," I pointed out with eminent reason. "North Americans eat far too much fat. That's part of the reason why atherosclerosis is so prevalent here."

"I've read that polyunsaturated fats are OK."

Why does he have to be so bloody logical?

"I don't want to argue with you, Eric. I just don't like fried foods, including Chinese food. Let's try another restaurant, please, sweetie," I pleaded. "I'm looking forward to a nice romantic dinner with you ... please."

"Whatever you want, Joan," he said with an edge in his voice.

And so it went. By the end of the week, Eric had heard every excuse in my repertoire, which was extensive. I had been working on it diligently for five years with all my creative energy and fertile imagination. During the time when I was not weaving my tangled web of half-truths and lies I was growing sick at heart about what was happening in my fairy-tale marriage. And still I partially deceived myself. *This is not happening. Everything is fine. So what if I have to watch my weight? Lots of women do. You can't tell me that those glamorous models in the fashion magazines don't struggle just as I do to maintain their slender figures. And for goodness sake, get rid of those thoughts that keep popping up about absolute honesty in marriage! I am being honest with Eric, I am, I am ... And why do I feel guilty? Get rid of that feeling!*

As for Eric, he grew increasingly quiet as the week of our honeymoon limped to an end. Sometimes I would look up unexpectedly and catch him regarding me thoughtfully, an inscrutable expression in his eyes. I could not bear to label it or to admit its cause, which I already knew: What was going on here? Something was dreadfully wrong. Where was the girl he married? The joyous, caring, and giving girl who was always ready to follow any suggestion he made about going out for dinner, or camping, or dropping in on friends? What had he got himself into?

He wasn't yet ready to give voice to these thoughts. Ever the scientist, he was prepared to allow adequate time for data collection, to return home, back into more normal surroundings, and to see how I would be then.

But he was already wondering.

Chapter 23

I *had crammed* most of my belongings into Eric's tiny one-bedroom apartment one week before our wedding. Life slipped into a nonholiday routine. Eric went off to work every morning: He was employed as an electrical engineer by a private power company. He had his doctorate in physics as well, and had done extensive research in laser physics in England during the course of his training. Now he was using his specialized knowledge, working in the field of fiber optics.

For my part, I had completed my family practice residency in September and had decided to accept the part-time salaried position offered me by the City Public Health Department. This occupied my attention for seven half-days per week. Following a daily routine and being in control of grocery shopping and meal preparation helped me immensely. My fears subsided, and most of the time I was able to forget about my problem. I relaxed and acted more like my old self with Eric, and he seemed reassured. He taught me to swim, and I took up this new pursuit with enthusiasm, quickly developing an addiction for daily swimming, which persisted for the next ten years.

Sexually our relationship was satisfactory. Although we were both technically virgins when we married, we managed to chart our course through the mechanics of coupling, propelled by our enormous physical desire. We fumbled at first, as I suppose most couples do, but improved with practice. I became fully orgasmic after about four months, and that made it all even better. We had fun.

The first real crisis occurred two months after the wedding. Eric's parents had gone to Hawaii for their annual winter vacation, and we had volunteered to stay at their home during the month of their absence, to oversee Eric's two teenaged brothers. I took charge of meal preparation, shopping, and housecleaning; the fellows did laundry and the outdoor chores. Their home was elegant. Eric had grown up with wealth and had rebelled against it as a symbol of what he labeled materialism during the three years prior to our meeting. Nonetheless, he truly loved his family and was always willing to help them whenever possible. I also liked his family and was happy to have assumed this house-sitting and brother-sitting assignment.

But I felt uneasy living in their home. Surrounded as I was by more luxury than I had ever known, I felt tense and out of place. I grew increasingly anxious and began to yearn for a quiet isolated corner, a good book, and some comfort food. But where could I go where I would be alone and unobserved? Then I thought of our apartment five blocks away. What was to stop me from going over there in the mornings after Eric left for work and the boys went to school? I would have an hour alone.

Accordingly I established a new secret ritual: As soon as the fellows were out of the way in the morning I would quickly finish up the chores, rush out to my car, drive to our apartment, let myself in, and lay out my book and my foods: yogurt, which I had substituted for ice cream since I met Eric, and graham crackers, which seemed more socially acceptable than gingersnaps. Then I would settle down and read while I savored my breakfast, chewing up every graham wafer morsel by morsel, sucking with delight on each small spoonful of yogurt, until I had consumed my allotted calories. Then with a sigh of relief and a nebulous sense of guilt, I would methodically destroy all evidence of my having been there and go to work.

Within a few days this routine had become so important to me that I became obsessed with it: thinking about it the night before, longing for morning to come so that I could get on with it. If the boys were a little slow in the mornings I found myself wishing they would go so that I could leave and begin the highlight of my day. If they lingered for a chat I would reply automatically while scheming how to end the conversation ... I was hooked once again.

One morning about two weeks after initiating this routine, I was deep into my book and about halfway through my food when suddenly I heard a key scrape in the lock of our apartment door. I leapt to my feet, heart pounding, knowing who was the only person who possessed that key besides myself. Where could I hide?

Too late. Eric entered the hallway, glanced through the living room automatically, and started when he saw me poised like a frozen thing beside the kitchen table.

"Joan! What are you doing here?"

"Oh," I said, recovering myself quickly, "I decided to come over this morning, to ... to check on everything and ... to get a couple of things I need."

I saw his gaze fall to the table, where all my guilty secrets lay exposed: a graham wafer crumbled in a saucer, a small stack of intact graham wafers lined up beside it, a large bowl of yogurt.

He looked into my eyes. I had the grace to blush. "I thought you never eat breakfast, Joan ... You've never eaten with me," he added, puzzled and hurt.

"Well, I ... I was hungry this morning." I saw the skepticism in his face and hurried on. "Actually I like to have a little snack by myself in the mornings, Eric. It's the only time I have all to myself all day long. I ... er ... need a bit of privacy," I concluded lamely.

"You mean you've been coming over here every morning?" he said, astonished.

"Well, not every morning, but ... well, most of the time."

"But why didn't you tell me?"

"I didn't think of it, Eric. It didn't seem important. I mean, I didn't think it mattered. I didn't think you'd care. I didn't think ..."

"Good Lord, Joan, I *don't* care, not if this is something you want to do. I just don't know why you never mentioned it to me. It almost seems like you wanted to keep it a secret," he said slowly. "The way you were just standing here looking so flustered when I came in."

Now I took the offensive. "I was just startled, that's all. Anyway, what are *you* doing here?"

He gave me a long searching look before replying, "I came home to get some papers that I need for a research project we're starting today. Joan, I don't understand this. What is going on?"

"There's nothing going on," I said firmly. "I told you why I'm here. There's no mystery. Why don't you believe me?"

I could not meet the pain and bewilderment in his eyes. A moment of eloquent silence passed. Then without another word he turned on his heel and walked out.

Trembling now, I dropped into my chair and wept bitter tears. *Why is this happening to me? What have I ever done to deserve it? And why oh why am I hearing a cock crow in my mind?*

That evening I went to Eric after he returned from work and apologized for my secrecy. I told him that I didn't know why I had kept my activities hidden, that sometimes I failed to understand myself, that I loved him and wanted everything to be open between us, always, and I promised to try never to hide anything from him again. I sounded convincing ... I even convinced myself. Eric, generous and forgiving as he always was, took me into his arms, assured me that he loved me too, and never even mentioned how hurt he had felt. We made passionate love that night, and I fell asleep in his arms, content that everything was wonderful, now and forever.

I did not return to our apartment again until we moved back home a week later. The pleasure I had derived from my secret ritual was ruined now that my privacy had been violated. I beat down my cravings, determined to force them from my mind by sheer force of will. I prayed to God to deliver me from my disease, from this terrible affliction that had again come upon me, the innocent victim, and that I was no longer able to ignore.

My resolve to do better lasted about two weeks. By that time my craving for secret food had steadily increased until it dominated my thoughts by day and haunted my dreams by night. One night I lay awake listening to Eric's steady breathing beside me, and I had a brilliant idea. *Why not go into the living room and eat an apple? There's nothing wrong with that, is there? It isn't like eating yogurt and graham wafers. It doesn't count as satisfying an addiction because I've never been addicted to apples in my life. Besides, fruit is good for me, and I can afford a few more calories.* I hadn't told Eric, but my weight was down to 101 pounds, to my great delight, so I didn't need to worry about seventy calories for an apple. *Maybe I'll even have two. That would take more time to eat, and give me more time to enjoy myself. Besides, if Eric wakes up and catches me ... Now why did I use that phrase? ... I mean if Eric wakes up and ... observes me in the living room I can just say that I couldn't sleep, so I got up to read so the light wouldn't disturb him. And isn't that the truth? Of course it is. I really can't sleep, can I? Perfect!*

So now I had a new ritual. Each night I would wait until Eric was asleep, and then creep softly into the living room, stopping in the kitchen to open the refrigerator door with great stealth, extracting two or three apples—however many I could "afford," based on my calorie consumption that day. After my craving was satisfied I would sneak back to bed and immediately drop off to sleep. I was free for another twenty-four hours. Occasionally, if Eric was restless and unable to sleep, I would make love to him, because I knew that always acted like an instant sedative for him. Then I would extricate myself carefully from his arms and carry on with my secret business.

My downfall occurred when summer came. I was a little tired of all those apples, so I started buying summer fruits: strawberries, peaches, plums, nectarines, and cherries. It was the last of these that was to prove my undoing. For I loved crunching things with my teeth: gingersnaps, graham wafers, chicken bones, apple cores, and ... cherry stones. After I ate each cherry I would crush the stone with my molars, then chew it up and swallow it. I didn't realize how much noise it made. One night in June, shortly after midnight, I was busy with my usual activity when suddenly I heard the bedroom door open, Eric's footsteps in the kitchen, and ...

"Joan, what on earth is going on out here?" he demanded.

"Nothing, sweetie," I said innocently, my heart thumping. "I couldn't sleep so I got up to read. I didn't want the light to disturb you, so I came out here."

"But I heard a cracking sound. I've been listening to it for the last ten minutes trying to figure out what it is."

"Well, I ..." *What can I say? What lie can I get away with? Something outside the open windows? What? What? Think, Joan, think.*

"What's that on the arm of the sofa?" he said, peering, coming closer to where I was seated. "Oh, it's a pile of cherry stems ..." Suddenly the light dawned. "Joan, have you been sitting out here eating cherries and chewing up the stones?"

"Well, to tell you the truth ..." I began.

"Yes, why don't you try the truth for once, if you can remember what the word means," he said bitingly. "Damn it, Joan, why do you keep doing this? Sneaking around behind my back like some sort of ridiculous three-year-old afraid of getting caught with her hand in the cookie jar? What on earth is going on?"

I was cowed by his fury. I didn't know how to respond. I needed time to think ... think ... think ...

"Joan, I want to know what's going on. I have a right to know and, one way or another, I'm bloody well going to find out." Vibrating visibly with overwhelming rage he stormed from the room, slamming the door, leaving me shaken and weeping with the abandon of one who has lost everything. I fell to my knees.

Why, oh why is this happening to me? Good grief, I thought I had this all sorted out more than a year ago. It's come back ... Maybe it was never really gone ... Maybe I've been kidding myself all along. What on earth am I going to do now? Oh God, help me. Oh God, tell me what to do. Oh God, oh God, why have you forsaken me?

Finally, my tears spent, I dried my eyes and tried to think what to do. It seemed there was only one possible course of action: I would have to tell Eric about the anorexia, which meant having to admit I was not cured of the disease, which meant I'd have to see a psychiatrist again, which meant ... *Oh God, no, I can't stand going through it all again. It's too bloody painful. All that garbage about my parents, and my feelings and ... I can't stand it. It did no good in the end, anyway, so why go through it all again? There must be some other way out of this mess, some easier way than facing it.*

I fell asleep there on my knees in the living room and awoke as dawn bloodied the eastern sky. I was stiff and cold and emotionally spent. But I knew clearly what I had to do. What I didn't know was where I would find the courage to do it.

I prayed for courage. Somewhat later I heard Eric moving about in the bedroom. *Well, there's no time like the present.*

"Hi, sweetie, how did you sleep?"

He was already dressed for work and standing in front of the mirror brushing his hair when I entered the room. Slowly and deliberately placing the brush on the wooden surface, he turned to regard me with a black unfathomable look. I noticed he was wearing a pink tie I particularly disliked.

"Don't call me 'sweetie,' Joan," he said coldly. "Don't pretend nothing has happened. I'm not forgetting about last night, and ..."

"I don't want you to forget," I broke in. "I'm just trying to initiate the conversation. Eric, don't look at me like that, please don't be angry with me. This is hard enough as it is." I paused and took a deep breath. "Eric, there's something I have to tell you. When I was in the hospital last year, just before we met, I was being treated for a condition called anorexia nervosa ... Wait, don't interrupt, please. Let me finish. I developed the disease during my first year of med school. It worsened gradually until I weighed seventy-eight pounds at the end of my internship year. Part of the disease is a total inner denial of what is happening, and I didn't see a psychiatrist until I was almost dead from starvation."

Eric was evidently stunned by this revelation, as he backed up automatically and sat down on the edge of the bed. I forced myself to continue. "I reached such a low point that Dr. Runions admitted me to hospital for two months. I thought I was cured by that admission, but now I see I wasn't, or if I was then I've developed a relapse ... That's why I've been hiding to eat in secret. That's the crux of the disease: the secrecy, the feeling that what I'm doing is so shameful that I can't let anyone else see me."

The room grew very still as Eric took the time to grasp all that I had said. Through the open window the song of a bird drifted in on the cool morning breeze. It seemed like an eternity before he finally looked up at me, and I realized I had been holding my breath.

"Joan, why did you never tell me about this before? Can't you understand that that's what has been driving me crazy? The not knowing what on earth was going on?" His voice was filled with bewildered shock.

"I didn't deliberately conceal it from you, Eric. I was not trying to deceive you. I really thought I was cured when I met you, and when I married you. This may sound ridiculous, but I didn't think the name of my disease was important. I didn't think it would ever come back. And I was ashamed and ..."

"And maybe you thought I wouldn't marry you if I'd known," he said slowly.

"No! ... At least, I don't think that was in my mind, unless it was in my unconscious mind ... I don't know," I added, now confused. I shook my head impatiently and sat down on the bed beside him, reaching out a quivering hand to touch his knee. "Look, Eric, I fell in love with you so deeply that it blocked out everything else. All I knew was that I wanted to spend the rest of my life with you."

"Then why didn't you tell me about it sometime in the last six months? Like on our honeymoon, or back in February when I found you in here eating? Why did you tell me all those lies?" He brushed my hand away as he stood up with a resurgence of rage. "And don't tell me that you didn't know what you were doing, because we both know that's not true. Good Lord, the guilt was written all over your face. You never could tell a lie!"

"You're right, Eric," I said earnestly, looking up at his face. "I knew that I was lying, but only part of me knew. The other part was still denying that the disease had come back. And then after I lied I would feel absolutely worthless, but the sick part of me would just try to smooth everything over and ..."

"And pretend that nothing had happened," he finished quietly, in a flash comprehending the whole, overwhelmed by its enormity, sensing the undescribed, horrific implications.

"Yes!" I agreed eagerly. "Now you see. That's exactly what I would do."

His face grew pensive again. "Where in God's name does this illness come from?" he said, shaking his head.

"Oh, Lord," I sighed, "it's awfully complicated. It goes back to my childhood, and losing my dad, and unconsciously blaming my mother for the loss, but not being able to tell her that I blamed her because then she might abandon me too. It has to do with concealed anger, and feeling like I have to live according to the expectations of others, and trying to gain control over something in my life, and rejecting my sexuality, and a whole bunch of other stuff. I'm not sure now that I even got it all worked out ... Well, I guess I didn't because otherwise I'd be well, wouldn't I?"

"I don't know. I don't know anything about it. It sounds fairly complex." He sounded like the scientist once more, his balance well on the way to full restoration. "The point is, what are we going to do about it?"

"We?" A sudden jolt of hope brought me to my feet. Ten inches shorter than he, I still had to look up.

"Well, I'm involved, too, you know. I love you, Joan," he said calmly. "I married you 'for better or for worse,' and I guess this constitutes part of 'the worse.' So what do we do?"

I still could not believe it. "You're not going to divorce me?"

"Why would I do that, for heaven's sake?" he said with a flare of exasperation. "Do you think I'm the kind of man who runs away when the first problem arises? Don't you know me any better than that after all this time?"

At last I stretched out my arms and stepped forward to embrace him. Without hesitation he responded and drew me close. A great shudder of joy ran through me as I felt the warm strength of his firm body. "Oh Eric," I said, not altogether in control of my voice. "I'm so happy! Yes, I know you don't run away from problems, but something like this, I mean ... something so critical and basic and important."

He held me away from him, both his hands on my arms, and looked into my eyes. "A problem is a problem, Joan. If it's an important problem, then it's all the more important to solve ... I don't run away."

I thought about that, suddenly seeing something for the first time, and then replied in wonder, "I guess you're not my father."

Chapter 24

We decided that I should see a psychiatrist again. Dr. Runions was making plans to move to Vancouver within a few weeks time, so I called and asked him which psychiatrist he would recommend for me to see. I had to tell him that I was having a few problems and felt that I might need some further professional help. He suggested that I call Dr. Roberta Carr. I did so, and was given an appointment to see her very quickly. She proved to be a businesslike middle-aged brunette with a trim figure, large intelligent brown eyes, and an indefinable air of competence. Although she lacked Dr. Runions' charisma, she listened just as intently as he had while I related my history.

"... So that's the whole story, Dr. Carr. I really don't know where to go from here."

After a brief reflective silence she said, "Tell me what your relationship with Eric is like since you told him about your disorder two weeks ago."

I looked at her with respect. "It's funny you should ask that, because actually things are better since Eric knows the truth. He seems happier and more relaxed, and strangely enough I feel better since the load of having to hide everything has been lifted from my shoulders. I still carry on with my rituals, and I still can't stop counting every lousy calorie I put into my mouth, but I feel happier about my life, more at peace somehow ... And Eric and I are talking more now. All of a sudden we seem to have more to say to each other. We've started planning a trip to Europe for the month of September. Eric took his Ph.D., or D.Phil. as they call it, at Oxford, so he lived in England for four years. He wants to show me the places where those important years of his life were spent. That's where he became a Christian, you see ... So we'll spend two weeks in England and then another two or three weeks kicking around the Continent, where neither of us has been before. We figure we should do that now ... you know, before we have a family or anything like that."

"Are you planning to have children, Joan?" she said with interest.

"Well," I shrugged, "to tell you the truth, it's not something we've really talked about much. Somehow I can't see myself as a mother. I want to get my career in family practice going first. And anyway my periods haven't resumed yet, so it's out of the question at the moment. Eric has made a few comments that make me think he'd like children someday, but not yet ... We have to get ourselves, or rather me, I guess, sorted out first."

She considered that before asking her next question. It was not the one I had expected. "Do you use some contraception?"

"Yes," I said, surprised, "I use a diaphragm. At the moment we don't want to take any chances, although I think it's only remotely possible that I would just start ovulating again without any warning. After all, it has been more than six years since my last period."

Again she picked up on what I had failed to say. "I thought you were Roman Catholic, Joan," she said mildly, all judgment suspended. "How do you reconcile your use of contraception with the Church's views on the subject?"

"Oh, I haven't gone to mass for almost a year now," I said easily, "not since Eric and I started getting serious about each other. I think it's very important that we share the same religious views. Eric came to Christ through the Baptist Church and he made it clear he didn't want to convert to Catholicism, so I decided to start going to church with him. It feels right to me ... It's the same God I worshiped before, even though the Baptist approach is quite a bit different from what I'm used to. You know, the informality of their services, the absence of sacraments and liturgy ... But pretty well all of the things they believe about God are what I've been taught, too. After all, it's the same Bible," I continued with mounting conviction. "What does it matter which Christian church you attend? It's belief in Christ that is important, isn't it? Isn't that what the Ecumenical movement within the Catholic Church is all about? Christian unity?" *Methinks the lady doth protest too much.*

My plethora of logic sounded eminently convincing to me, but Dr. Carr went incisively to the heart of the issue. "So you left the Catholic Church without a qualm?" she said, clearly registering doubt.

"Yes, I did," I said defensively. "Actually a priest who is a friend of my family's made a point of coming to speak to me before our wedding. He said I could apply for a dispensation to marry outside the Catholic Church, so that my marriage to Eric would be recognized as a true marriage ... Then I could still receive the sacraments and so forth. But I just didn't feel right about that. I felt that God brought Eric and me together, and that we already had his blessing upon our union, so what did I need a Catholic dispensation for? Somehow it seemed like a put-down to the Baptist Church and to Eric. So I didn't apply. I suppose I've excommunicated myself by marrying in the Baptist Church. As far as the Catholics are concerned, I'm living in sin right now. That seems very funny to me," I said without a glimmer of humor.

Dr. Carr gave me a long assessing look. My palms grew clammy and I squirmed in my chair, which suddenly felt inexplicably uncomfortable. "Let me get this straight now. You left the church in which you grew up, and to which you had always been deeply committed, in order to marry Eric ... And you left your apartment and moved into Eric's bachelor pad after your wedding ... Is that what you wanted to do?"

"Sure, it was fine with me," I said quickly. "Eric likes walk-up apartments and detests high-rises. Also, he really likes living near the university. Besides, his rent was lower than mine, so when he suggested living in his apartment after we were married, it seemed a reasonable thing to do."

"Are finances a problem for the two of you?"

"Oh no," I laughed. "Neither of us has any debts. We own our cars. Eric has a large salary from Nu-West Power, and I've made good money with the City this past nine months. I'm leaving that job, though. I've been invited to do a *locum tenens* for the family physicians at Coldwell Medical Clinic during July and August. Then when they open their new clinic in October, if they like my work during the summer, they may even invite me to join them full-time in my own practice. It's what I've always wanted to do, and I'm looking forward to it. I've got temporary admitting privileges for the summer at the Royal Alexandra Hospital, so in October if I join the clinic I can probably get on active staff without too much trouble. So my prospects are looking pretty good right now." I stopped abruptly, floundering. "What were we talking about?"

"Saving money by moving into Eric's apartment."

"Of course ... well we have no financial problems, but it's just that Eric has this thing about money. He hates wasting money; he hates the materialism in North America; he thinks we should be using our wealth more wisely as Christ's stewards on earth. He takes his commitment to Christ very seriously," I said earnestly, my voice reflecting my pride in my mate, "so he lives very frugally. He rides his bicycle everywhere, he dresses in inexpensive clothes, he eats simple foods. He likes granola and yogurt and stuff like that. I think he's rejecting his parents' wealth since he became a Christian. Anyway, that's how he feels."

"And do you feel that way too?" she asked, her level eyes upon me.

"Well, sure," I said promptly, stifling another unseemly urge to squirm, "I mean, what use are worldly goods? The trappings of wealth are almost obscene ... Eric didn't think I should have a diamond ring, and that was OK with me. I mean, it's the simple gold band that means the most, isn't it? So that's what I've got."

She said nothing to this, and I found myself sweating again. *How can I convince her that I really believe what I'm saying?* I felt compelled to offer further explanations. "Sure, I like pretty things, things I never had as a child. I love looking at nice furniture that matches, and beautiful china and crystal, but I don't need to *own* those things. I can go to a store or a museum to see them. Buying stuff like that would be a waste of money. Our apartment is furnished in a very utilitarian fashion: Both Eric and I had complete sets of hand-me-downs and castoffs from our parents, so we asked people not to give us any wedding presents. Instead we asked them to donate money to a charity if they wished. Eric suggested that idea, and I thought it was a great one," I added with enthusiasm. "He asked me to pick the specific charity, and I selected Birthright. We got a note from them in January thanking us for what we did ... I guess they got quite a bit of money, which is good."

I stopped talking then, and although she allowed another oppressive silence to develop I crossed my arms and looked beyond her out the window, resolved to say nothing more, not until she revealed what she was thinking. In the end she relented. "All right, Joan, let me recapitulate here. In order to marry Eric, you left your church and your apartment, you gave up having a diamond ring and any possibility of acquiring beautiful china and crystal—things you have always admired—you rejected wedding gifts and ..."

"We didn't *need* wedding gifts!" I exploded with totally unexpected force, shocked to find myself seething with fury. "You've missed the whole point, Dr. Carr. You've twisted it all around. You make it sound like I sacrificed everything I value when I married Eric. That's ridiculous! I fell in love with Eric ... He's such a fantastic person, and as I listened to him talk about his views, I just felt that they were my views, too, like we were kindred spirits or something."

"That may be partially true, Joan," she said equably, "but a red flag goes up in my mind when I see a marriage where one partner subjugates himself or herself to the other so completely. People are individuals. They invariably have different feelings and needs and values, and a good marriage involves reconciling those differences to the furtherance of both partners' spiritual growth. That is the meaning of love. It does not mean submerging one person's identity so that the other's may survive. Because if that happens, sooner or later the oppressed personality rises up and, in its rage, burns down the whole house."

A short eloquent moment passed.

"I'd like you to think about this before our next session, Joan. I know you may believe this is unrelated to your anorexia, but I think it is an issue that you and Eric will need to deal with if your marriage is to survive. I would like you to think about the possibility that the recurrence of your anorexic symptoms may be an unconscious, and therefore somewhat convoluted, attempt on your part to reassert your individuality in your relationship with Eric."

"But my anorexia is not *me*," I objected boldly. "It's something I'm trying to get rid of, so that doesn't make sense."

"Just think about it, Joan, please. And now, I think it would be wise to put you back on an antidepressant. Quite apart from my view that there is a large depressive component in anorexia nervosa in general, I see enough evidence of depression in your current symptomatology to justify the diagnosis: your sleep disturbance, poor appetite, weight loss, your preoccupations and lack of concentration, your feelings of helplessness and hopelessness. Rather than placing you on amitriptyline again, I'd like you to try clomipramine, a drug that I have found very useful in dealing with obsessive-compulsive disorders. I think we should increase the dose as quickly as possible to a level of at least one hundred milligrams nightly, and one hundred and fifty if you can tolerate it. Do you have any questions about that?"

"No," I said curtly, "no questions."

"Will you give it a trial then?"

I met her eyes. "Yes, I'll give it a try."

I left Dr. Carr's office that day even more confused. *What on earth is she trying to do? Why doesn't she just deal with the anorexia? ... That is my problem. Why is she trying to make it into something it is not—a marital problem? Good Lord, as if I don't have enough to deal with without having to examine the whole basis of my relationship with Eric, too. She doesn't know the first thing about us! What is she trying to do ... break up my marriage?* I was not impressed. I was not ready to hear her message.

And I would not be for many years to come.

Chapter 25

When I told Eric about my session with Dr. Carr, I chose not to share with him the disturbing part. I disclosed only what I thought were the essentials: that she would see me again, and that she had recommended I go on a new drug called clomipramine. I duly filled the prescription and began taking it that night.

I did sleep better. But within two weeks, as I slowly increased the dosage, I began experiencing some very unpleasant side effects. The worst one was violent muscle spasms and twitches that would strike without warning, disturbing my motor control and jerking me awake just as I was dropping off to sleep. In addition, I was completely unable to achieve an orgasm after I started taking the medication, a side effect that frustrated both of us.

"I can't stand this, Eric. Obviously this drug does not suit me. I'm stopping it as of today."

He looked at me with concern in his steady blue eyes. "OK, I can understand why you want to, Joan, but do you think maybe you should talk to Dr. Carr about it first? She might have some suggestions to modify your side effects, or perhaps put you on an alternative drug."

"Yes, I will talk to her about it, but I'm flushing this stuff down the toilet in the morning. I don't have another appointment scheduled with her yet. I'll have to call her office tomorrow ... Actually, come to think of it," I added as an afterthought, "I may not be able to get an appointment with her for a while, because she'll be away for the whole month of August, and then we'll be leaving on our trip right after that. So I guess I'll have to wait till after we get back before I see her again."

"That's a long time away, Joan," Eric said doubtfully, then added with budding suspicion, "Why didn't you make your next appointment on your way out of her office two weeks ago?"

I avoided his eyes. "Oh, I forget," I said in my best offhanded manner. "I think her secretary was away from her desk, or my parking meter was about to run out, or something like that. Anyway, don't worry ... I'll call tomorrow and set up an appointment for October. Besides," I added brightly, "things are going a lot better between us now that you know about my illness, don't you think, sweetie?"

"Yes," he said slowly, "but you haven't modified your eating behavior at all. The underlying problem is still there. Isn't that your goal: to solve the problem that is causing your symptoms?"

"Of course it is!" I cried, registering hurt that he could think otherwise. "But in the meantime your acceptance of me having this problem makes all the difference in the world to how I feel about it. Don't you feel that way too?"

"To some extent I do," he reluctantly agreed. "But ultimately I think we both want your disease to be cured ... don't we?"

"Of course we do! I've already said that. But meanwhile let's just enjoy this new closeness we have ..."

Lies, all lies, Joan. You're doing it again. Face it: You don't want to change at all. You want to have your cake and eat it too. Such was the still small voice that whispered from the center of my heart. But I was already turning a deaf ear to this disquieting message. I pushed it down, down, down, and once again took the path of least resistance.

We went on our trip to Europe. We even managed to enjoy it—at least some of it. By this time Eric had learned to work around my peculiar eating habits. He was accustomed to my rejection of restaurants on the basis of the menu posted outside, and he had even come to accept it with some degree of equanimity. His first question whenever we were seeking an eating place had become, "Can you find something to eat here, Joan?"

Problems arose, however, when we were arranging visits to his friends in Oxford. One marvelous woman who had been his landlady and surrogate mother for two years, invited us to come and visit her at teatime. When Eric, speaking with her on the telephone, relayed this message to me, I immediately had visions of little sandwiches and rich pastries and cakes. I knew English people rarely eat salads. What would I eat if we went for tea? Dinner would be so much easier for me. Or better still, a visit after dinner. My mind was turning cartwheels as I frantically sought for an answer to give Eric. But by then he knew me too well. I saw his mouth tighten and a coldness creep into his eyes.

"Look Joan, I'm going for tea. You can do as you like," he said with his hand over the mouthpiece, and then, into the phone, "I'd love to come, Mrs. Disdale, but Joan may not be able to come along. What time would you like me? ... No, she's not ill, she's just ... she just may not be able to make it ... No, tomorrow would not be better. I'd like to come today. I'm really looking forward to seeing you ... Yes, four o'clock would be fine. See you then."

Eric would never lie for me. He would never play the game. He turned to me in fury after hanging up the receiver. "Don't do this to me, Joan. This is my life, too. I will accommodate myself to your needs as best I can, but when your sickness gets in the way of my seeing my friends at *their* convenience, you're expecting too much of me. I can't accept that."

I was immediately contrite. "I'm sorry, sweetie. Of course I'll come with you this afternoon. It's just that I always have to get past that initial panic I always feel at the thought of a meal that is outside my control."

"Don't bother coming on my account, Joan. I'll have a good time without you, you know," he said coldly.

"No, I want to come, not for you, but for me." *Lies, all lies.*

But Eric still had enough trust in me that he took me at my word. We went to Mrs. Disdale's home that afternoon. I remember very little about our arrival. Until tea was laid out I could think of nothing except what she might be planning to serve us to eat. Once the feast was on the table, I quickly assessed which items had the least calories, and which ones would be the easiest to discard surreptitiously. I took the minimum amounts that politeness allowed, pleading a small appetite and a slightly upset stomach. Then I proceeded with my usual devious maneuvers to dispose of as much of the food as possible, eating only a bare minimum.

Mrs. Disdale had an affable, ingenuous nature and was solicitous over my well-being. Could she get me something else? I was so thin, she was sure I needed a little something to eat. Was I sure I was all right? She had some medication for upset stomachs. Would I like to lie down? Eric, on the other hand, studiously ignored me, tucked into the meal with gusto, ate an enormous amount of food, probably in an attempt to compensate for my rejection of it, and distracted Mrs. Disdale with a steady stream of conversation on other topics.

On the way back to our lodgings Eric was very quiet, while I wrapped myself in a cloak of self-righteousness. *What right has he got to be mad? Look at what I went through for him! He has no appreciation of how hard that was for me. See how much I love him!*

Perhaps Eric already knew that he was in a "no-win" situation. Perhaps he already had a vision of the future. But he said very little to me that night. He was not a man to beat his head against a brick wall. But he was also, as he had said, not a quitter. For he remained with me for another three years.

When we returned from Europe Eric said nothing about the appointment with Dr. Carr, which I later canceled. He waited for me to show some sign that I would follow through in my stated commitment to get professional help to change. But of course I had no intention of changing. Not as long as I could have my cake and eat it too.

For the next two years our lives settled into a more or less comfortable routine. I started working at Coldwell Clinic in my own private practice. I learned about the economic realities of "hanging out my shingle" with no patients to see at first. I went into debt for the first six months, or rather Eric covered my shortfall, quite cheerfully. During the next six months my income matched my expenses. After that I began showing a profit.

For I was a good physician. In my work I was always able to bracket my own neuroses, listen to my patients, extract the data needed to make accurate diagnoses, and prescribe appropriate therapy and follow-up. My patients liked me, and they consistently told me so. That was enormously satisfying for me because I had an insatiable need to be liked, to have the approval of others in order to contradict my own unconscious opinion of myself.

I also became fully aware and properly respectful of what a privileged position a family doctor is in: seeing into the lives of others, sharing their joy and their pain. I loved communicating with patients. I loved sharing my expert knowledge with them. I loved feeling that I had something to offer, that I could make a difference in their lives. I loved delivering their babies, easing their pain, even on occasion sitting at their deathbeds with them. I received so much from my patients, far more than I ever gave. But as I acquired experience and learned from my mistakes, I had more wisdom to offer them. So my work has always been a mutually beneficial arrangement for me and my patients. In the times of which I write, it was virtually the only area of my life in which I acted with honesty and integrity of purpose. The satisfaction I obtained from it enabled me to continue clinging to my disease. It kept my life looking viable in my own eyes.

I also got along well with the five other physicians in the clinic. I always maintained a friendly distance between myself and them, of course, but this seemed to be acceptable and we enjoyed a good working relationship.

But life at home was less satisfactory. Eric and I grew ever more distant from each other as the months dropped away. We had less to say to one another. We spent less time together. We stopped praying together. We made love less often. We seemed to have less in common than when we were married, because I was gradually forced to recognize that many of the activities we had shared during our brief courtship were really of little inherent interest to me. I had only thought I liked them because Eric liked them, and I was head over heels in love with Eric. In reality, of course, I had not the faintest idea of what love truly meant. I was incapable of extending myself for the true benefit of another person, outside of the safe confines of my professional life. I was too embroiled in my neurosis, too self-absorbed. And in my heart of hearts I loathed myself. How could I love another?

My response to our growing lack of intimacy was threefold. First, I escaped into my work. I worked late, made hospital rounds after office hours whenever possible, went to the office on weekends on one pretext or another, arranged to be on call for the other physicians when Eric had time off that we could have spent together.

Second, my eating habits became increasingly pathological as I tried to fill the massive void in my spirit by gorging my body with comfort foods. I returned to ice cream for about two-thirds of my caloric intake, consuming a full quart of it in the mornings before I departed for work, but after Eric had left for the office. On weekends, if necessary, I substituted cookies—arrowroot "baby" cookies—which I ate while Eric was out of the apartment. I resolutely ignored the infantile symbolism in these food choices. I reassured myself that everything was OK because I was not losing weight. I had dropped to ninety-eight pounds during our trip to Europe and I remained at that point, weighing myself daily at the swimming pool to make sure.

Third, to assuage my profound sense of guilt over my treatment of Eric, I prepared excellent evening meals that I would spread before him, while I consumed an enormous salad with a dollop of cottage cheese on it. In addition, about twice a month we hosted a dinner party to which we invited friends or family. On these occasions I cooked gourmet feasts that earned the high praise of our guests, and that I used to reassure myself that I was a model hostess, an excellent homemaker, a fitting wife for any man. Naturally I would rarely eat this meal but rather fill my plate with salad, sometimes pushing a small portion of the entrée around with my fork. I always had an excuse ready if people commented on my eating, but generally by clever use of dim lighting and flowers on the table I was able to keep my plate hidden. When absolutely obliged to accept return dinner invitations to the homes of others, I starved myself earlier in the day, fretted over what I would have to eat, and once there used any excuses possible for not eating much.

It is a tribute to Eric's fortitude and stamina that he was able to tolerate this existence for as long as he did. For it was not until New Year's Day of 1978 that the camel's back broke.

We had been married for three years and three days. I was in the kitchen finishing my yogurt, the food I still ate if Eric was in the apartment and I had no prospect of getting rid of him for a while. Eric came in and sat down opposite me.

"Joan, I've been doing a lot of hard thinking," he said calmly, "and I've reached a decision. I can't live this way for the rest of my life. I want something more."

I laid down my spoon with the utmost care. *Oh God, the ax is falling.* I stared at him, my mouth dry, my heart pounding, my body stunned with sickening disbelief. "What are you talking about, Eric?"

"You know what I'm talking about," he said with more heat. "Stop playing games. I can't live with your anorexia any longer. I thought I could. God knows I've tried, but I can't. I've decided that either we are going to see a professional and get some help for you and for us, or else I'm leaving. The choice is yours."

"But we're doing OK, sweetie," I pleaded desperately. "All married couples have problems. I'm not happy about having anorexia, but I live my life in spite of it, and since you know about it and accept it ..."

"I can't accept it," he broke in passionately, "not any more. Too much has to be sacrificed to it, it interferes with too many things. Joan, I want a *wife*. I want a family. I want a home that I look forward to coming to, not one where I dread opening the door because I don't know what I'll find on the other side."

"But we have a home: Look around you." I was begging now. "And someday maybe we can even have children, maybe I can take a drug that will make me ovulate and start my periods again, maybe ..."

He stared at me incredulously. "Do you really think I would want you to be the mother of my children? What kind of man do you think I am that I would bring children into a barren existence like this? For God's sake, Joan, grow up! Look at things the way they are for once, not the way you want them to be! Look at what we've got! We've got nothing ... nothing at all that is worth anything."

I wept as his words plunged like a dagger into my heart. I felt a crushing pain in my chest. I could not speak. I had no words to shield me from facing myself, and nowhere to hide from the hideous deathmask that leered back at me and laughed.

Minutes passed as Eric waited for my tears to subside. I sat with my face buried in my hands, unable to move. Eric stood up and walked from the room without another word.

Oh God, here I am again. When will this nightmare called my life end? Oh God, please let me die. Please set me free ... please ... please ... please.

Some time later I joined Eric in the living room, utterly defeated. "All right, Eric, I'll go with you to see somebody. I'll try to change my behavior. I don't know how to do it, but I'll try again. Because, whether you believe it or not, I love you ... and I don't want to lose you."

He looked at me with immense sadness in his eyes. "You can't lose me, Joan ... You can't lose what you have never had."

Chapter 26

We decided to see Dan Slater, the new pastor of West Park Baptist Church, who was also a professional family counselor. Our first appointment was a week later.

"… That's about all I can tell you, Dan. The bottom line is that I am still as deeply embroiled in my anorexia as ever, and Eric feels he can no longer live with me as I am. So we're here to get help for me to change."

There was a long pause. Dan shifted his gaze to Eric. "Have you anything to add, Eric?"

"No," he said dispassionately, "Joan's given a fairly accurate portrayal of the situation. And she's right: I can't live with it any longer."

"Could you tell me a little more about that?" he said gently.

Eric shrugged. "When we got married, I expected that I was going to have a wife, a companion to share my life with, someone to care for and who would care for me. As things stand that's not possible, or if it is possible, it's not happening."

"And why is that?'

"Because every time I turn around," he exclaimed, his voice rising, "the anorexia is there, like an impenetrable wall between us. Joan's first priority in life appears to be her eating, her bloody rigid commitment to eating certain foods at certain times in certain ways. It gets in the way of everything: seeing friends, going places, living a normal life. Everything else takes second place to her behavior patterns ... even me! Well, I just can't take it anymore ... I won't take it any more."

Dan absorbed this with a long considering stare, then probed further. "How do you *feel* about this perception of yours that Joan has placed top priority on her anorexic rituals?"

"Feel about it?" he choked. "How do you think I feel? Mad! Screaming, raging mad! I want to throttle her sometimes! I want to shake her till her teeth rattle! She betrayed me! She said she loved me, she promised to be my wife forever, for better or worse, and she hasn't even begun to be my wife in three bloody years! She doesn't care about me, she's never cared about me, she lied to me, she ..."

The rest was drowned in the tears pouring down his face, and I discovered that I was weeping, too. It was the first time I had ever seen him cry about this. It was the first time he had ever so fully articulated his rage. My heart swelled with pain, with the pain I had inflicted on him and on myself. I wanted to take him in my arms, as I had when our relationship was new.

"Eric," I said brokenly, "I do care for you. Maybe I'm not really capable of loving anyone very well, but with as much capacity as I have, I love you. I'm sorry for what I've done to you. I never intended to cause you all this suffering. I never intended to hurt anyone, especially you. I never deliberately deceived you. You see, I deceived myself so thoroughly that I really believed I was cured four years ago. I thought the anorexia was gone, but it wasn't ... I don't know how to get rid of it. I don't know how to make it go away, but I swear that with the help of God I'll try as best as I can."

Dan waited through a lengthy emotionally charged silence before he spoke again. "I think that you both can see that there is far more involved here than just getting rid of Joan's anorexia. What Eric has expressed is his anger, the cause of which is his sense of betrayal, his feelings of loss, his hurt. And that is something you both will learn, that behind every angry person is a hurt person, a person who feels disappointment that his or her love has been rejected. We are going to have to deal with that hurt, with that disappointment, and get back in touch with the things you two saw in each other and wanted from each other four years ago."

Eric gave me a sideways glance, wondering no doubt what he had ever seen in me. Dan interpreted this glance correctly and continued, "Because those things are still there, and they are the tools we have to begin with to rebuild your relationship. We are going to have to work on communication. For instance, we are going to have to discover why you, Eric, have waited such a long time before communicating your anger and your pain to Joan. And we are going to have to work on trust, because it is only through trust that you will learn to really love one another. We have a lot of work to do ... Are you both willing to do it? Do you both *want* to do it?"

A moment of decision passed. Eric looked up at me and then at Dan, courage returning in the lift of his head. "Yes," he said, his voice definite.

I swallowed. "I do, too." And I did.

We met with Dan once every week or two for the next four months. We made some progress. We both ventilated further our feelings of pain and disappointment. We worked on communicating more openly, and on compromising. We were given "homework" to do, which we both worked on diligently, separately and together.

But somehow with the primary focus on our relationship, the issue of my anorexia was overlooked. In all fairness to Dan, I think he perhaps believed that my anorexic symptoms would evaporate if I could learn to assert myself and my needs more openly and directly. Perhaps he had never dealt with an anorexic before. Perhaps he took me at face value and trusted what I said. But regardless of the reason, he underestimated the intensity of my neurosis, he overlooked my phenomenal capacity for self-deception. *Oh, that one can smile, and smile, and be a villain ...*

And in all fairness to myself, I was no Iago, maliciously deceiving all and sundry. I genuinely wanted to change, I wanted to learn to love Eric and save our marriage—but with only the healthy part of myself. The sick part was still there, lurking more or less in the shadows throughout our therapy, and it was delighted to see the focus remain on our marital relationship. It wanted no attention drawn to itself, it wanted to remain intact, waiting for its chance to reassert itself and lead me again to hell.

I of course knew that my anorexic thinking had not abated in the least. The familiar calorie counter clicked away inside my head, the craving for my rituals was as intense as ever, although I was able to modify my eating behavior slightly for a time.

But as the months passed and I saw no change in my underlying disease process, my hopes for cure faded. Dan and Eric still felt that progress was being made, but I knew better. In a peculiar way, I saw the situation more clearly than they, sick though I was. And my vision led only to despair. I saw no way out of the trap in which I was caught. And that meant only one thing: Under the terms Eric had spelled out, it meant the death of our marriage.

So I quietly made arrangements to move into an apartment of my own. For it was I who must do the moving. Our home had been Eric's apartment, and I was the guilty party, not Eric. I was the one who should suffer more in the separation and divorce.

Divorce. My spirit shrank from the thought. But there was no other way out. It had to be. I must suffer the consequences of my choices. The choice was clear: Eric or my anorexia. And since I could not free myself from the anorexia ...

"Eric, I have to talk to you."

It was a rainy Sunday afternoon in May, and Eric was reading by lamplight as a lowering sky outside the windows had cast a dusky gloom over the living room. He put down his book and looked up at me expectantly as I stood in the doorway.

"We both know that nothing has really changed as far as my anorexia goes," I began bravely. "And I have to admit I've lost my hope that I'll ever be cured of this disease. So I ... I've decided that I'd better leave ... in keeping with the ultimatum you gave me in January. I've arranged to move into a furnished suite downtown. They can be rented by the week or month. I can move on Saturday."

Eric stared at me as an irritable wind drove a fresh sheet of rain against the windows on my left. Was I imagining the relief I saw in his eyes? I didn't think so, and my heart sank. Suddenly I realized that I had still hoped for a magical solution, for Eric to drop to his knees, pleading his undying and unconditional love, like the love of the father I had never had, and beg me to stay with him. Then I could fall passionately into his arms, and we would live happily ever after…

"Okay, Joan," he said calmly, "maybe you're right. Maybe it's for the best." He had given it his best shot, but it wasn't good enough. He had failed. We had failed. It was over. He could live with that.

Could I?

The first Saturday in June, 1978, was a beautiful sunny day. But as I drove downtown, the sun could not drive the chill from my heart; I saw not the beauty of the world around me. I felt an inexpressible emptiness as I looked around at the impersonal apartment I had rented. It appeared to be precisely what it was: a hotel, a stopping-off place for the traveler, somewhere to stay till one could go home again to those one loved.

Oh, Eric! What have I done?

I got out my ice cream, sat down to eat, looked at it, and pushed it away. I wanted to throw it through the window, flush it down the toilet, stomp on it, crush it, utterly destroy it once and for all. How could I be doing this? How could I trade Eric for a carton of ice cream? It was ludicrous; it was hilariously, outrageously funny; it was obscene.

I subsisted in that hole for seven days. I cannot remember any of it. I must have slept. I must have risen in the morning, brushed my teeth, gone to work, talked to patients. I must have eaten, made coffee, read books, gone swimming, watched television. But I cannot remember it. All I can recall is the screaming agony in my soul. *No! I don't want my life to end like this! If I stay here I shall die!* It blocked out sight, sound, smell, taste. It prevented memory from functioning. I was living my own death.

On Friday evening I drove to our apartment. Eric's car was in our stall in the parking lot. My heart was pounding as I climbed the stairs, as I recalled climbing them four years before, a lifetime before, the first time we met. I knocked on the door, remembering another door on which I had knocked, in a distant time and place. I held my breath. The door opened. He looked at me … What was the expression in his eyes? To this day, I do not know.

"Eric, I can't do it. I can't leave. I'll die if I leave. Please can I come back?" I was trembling violently.

He stepped back. "Come in, Joan," he said gently.

We talked long into the night. Neither of us made any promises. I told him I couldn't promise that my anorexia would ever be gone and said I would never use the word "try" again when I talked about curing it. But somehow there had to be a way to salvage our marriage. He agreed that I should come back home. We went to bed.

The remainder of June and July passed on a monotone. No highs, no lows. No explosions of rage, no passionate cries of joy. We went to work, we ate our meals, we went on vacation together, we slept together, we loved each other as best we could.

One evening at the end of July, I was seated at the kitchen table. Eric had gone out to a meeting. I was looking out at the sunset, smelling the evening air wafting in at the window, thinking of nothing in particular, when suddenly I felt a great "click" inside my head. That is the only way I can describe it, as a kaleidoscopic image suddenly falling into place. It was just there, complete in itself, unified and whole. In my mind's eye I saw a woman with a broken leg encased from foot to groin in an enormous cast. But she was not unhappy or in pain. She was at peace, and she was working industriously on a beautiful and intricate piece of embroidery that was taking form before my eyes.

And I knew, instantly I knew with a tremendous surge of calm and acceptance, that the woman was me. My anorexia was the broken leg bound up in that cast. It was cumbersome, it restricted my mobility, it prevented me from doing many things I might like to do, but it was not fatal. It need not signal the end of my life. I still had two perfectly good hands and one good leg. I could still do many good things. I was not powerless. But I must do them alone. I must resign myself to living alone. I could never inflict this burden on another human being. I must carry it alone ...

Yet I was not alone. *Oh God, I'm not alone, am I? You'll always be there to support the weight of that cast, won't you? Oh God, thank you.* I had not prayed with such depth of feeling for a long time. My heart was filled with love for my God, for the God who created me and to whom I belonged, fight him as I may ... *My grace will always be sufficient for you ... Our hearts were made for you, oh God, and they cannot rest until they rest in you.*

I knew now that I could leave, with peace in my soul, and carry on with the next chapter of my life. When Eric came home I shared my revelation with him, and he shared my joy. We prayed together that night for the first time in many months.

Before another week had passed I found a spacious one-bedroom condo in a downtown high-rise overlooking the river valley, and I had made a down payment and arranged for a bank mortgage. Eric and I sat at the kitchen table together one evening and in one hour divided up our earthly assets between us, without any dispute whatsoever. No animosity was possible. We felt more at peace with each other than we had for many years.

Still one task remained: to tell our families about our impending separation. Throughout our difficulties, our problems had remained our own. Neither of us had ever run to our parents for advice or consolation. I had told Mom that we were getting some counseling to help us through a bad patch and had solicited her prayers, but she knew none of the details. And she and her new husband, Archie, had been away during our brief separation in June, so she knew nothing of that. Thus it was that our news came like a lightning bolt out of the blue. Eric and I went together to Mom and Archie's home one evening in mid-August to tell them of our plans.

"... So I'll be moving to my condo on Labor Day weekend, Mom. We wanted to tell you about this together."

I had been watching with growing alarm as the blood drained from her face during my prepared speech. Archie sat helplessly by her side through a brief horrified silence.

"What on earth do you mean by 'incompatible,' Joan?" she cried. "You two are completely compatible ... You made vows to each other. You have to work at marriage. No marriage was ever made in heaven ... Joan, this has to do with your illness, doesn't it?" I sat dumbfounded as she turned to Eric and continued the diatribe. "Eric, how dare you? How dare you desert Joan when she needs you most?

You promised to take care of her, in sickness and in health. Can't you see that she's sick?"

"Mom, Mom, stop!" I interrupted passionately. "Listen to me! You don't understand. Eric is not to blame here. If anyone is to blame it's me ... No, don't interrupt! Let me finish. I have to accept that this disease is not going to go away. Simply understanding why and how it developed has not made it go away. I'm going to have to live with it, and I can do that. I can continue to be a good doctor; I can continue to help people. But it's unfair to expect another human being to live with it too."

I had her full attention now, her streaming eyes fixed upon me. I gulped back my own tears and forced myself to continue. "In a way I married Eric under false pretenses, although I don't blame myself for that. I thought I was cured, and I led him to believe that I was cured. I was wrong, that's all. Perhaps this disease is incurable ... I don't know. But whether it is or it isn't, Eric and I have made a joint decision that we must let one another go."

I gave Eric a long regretful look, which he returned, before I turned back to Mom and went on with absolute calm. "Divorce is not a wonderful solution. In an ideal world it would not exist. But in our world, in our case, it is the lesser of two evils. We want you to know we have struggled with this thing for many, many months, and this is our decision. I hope that you will accept it and not bear any animosity to either of us, but especially not to Eric. I still love Eric, and I will not have you blame him for something that is not his fault."

Mom continued weeping through a long bleak silence before she finally looked up at us again.

"I can see that you've thought this decision through," she said brokenly, "and you appear to be reconciled to it. I still think you are both dreadfully wrong, but I will accept that it is your decision to make. I'm sorry, Eric, I should not have blamed you. Joan is right. Marriage takes two ... It's just that I liked having such a perfect son-in-law, and I'm going to miss you!" She made this last declaration with a weak grin, and we all broke into smiles with her, and some of us into tears.

Part Five

Resurrection

I have dealt with great things that I do not understand,

things too wonderful for me, which I cannot know. ...

I had heard of you by word of mouth,

but now my eye has seen you. ...

JOB 42:3, 5

Chapter 27

I moved into my condo as planned that September weekend. I never looked back ... well, almost never. I had no need to do so: I was fortified by God, I had him with me, and I felt all-powerful. I knew I could do what I had to do without difficulty.

I embraced my new life. I was truly happy as I set up my home in a way I had never lived before. I redecorated the suite in a luxurious off-white carpet, into which my bare feet sank deeply when I walked across it in the mornings. I bought an elegant suite of blue-gray living room furniture and white and silver lamps—all color-coordinated—and I assembled glass-and-chrome coffee tables myself from a do-it-yourself kit. I purchased a solid glass-topped dining room table and four top-quality teak and fabric chairs. A massive teak wall unit spanned the entire length of one wall in the living room. My chaste single bed, a donation from my mother, had a beautifully crafted wooden headboard.

I did not spend money recklessly, however; my mother had schooled me too well for that. Every one of my purchases was made at bargain prices, clearance sales, discounts. I bought inexpensive bookshelves to house my extensive library. The stereo in the living room was one that Mom had bought for me when I moved into my first apartment in 1974.

I adored shopping, and over the next four years I slowly added to my collection of material goods. I bought delicate china and expensive crystal, and cabinets to display it—gifts for my eyes. I loved to handle my possessions, to feel the weight of the crystal and catch the sparkle of it in sunlight, to feast my eyes on the perfect symmetry of china and silver laid on the table before one of my dinner parties. I felt like King Midas reveling in his gold, and I immersed myself unreservedly in my newfound hedonism, expressing fully this part of myself that I had always previously denied. I savored all that the world had to offer. Except, of course, food. But I was resigned to the fact that the delights of novel taste sensations were, for me, forbidden fruit, and I was content.

I loved to stand in my living room in the morning, gazing through the wall of floor-to-ceiling windows at the broad expanse of the river valley, flaming with autumn colors. I loved surveying my domain at night, sitting in a comfortable chair surrounded by the serene, beautiful order of my home, flanked by a clear star-filled sky outside. It was truly my haven, for body and spirit.

But I did not sit still very often. For the next four years my practice was busier than ever, and I plunged into it heart and soul, dedicating my time and energy to my patients with a new unconflicted fervor. In my spare time I swam, visited family, hosted dinner parties for friends and acquaintances, frequented the theater and the ballet. I traveled abroad to England annually, spending a week or two in London immersed in the sights, sounds, and smells, attending the theater in the evenings, walking mile upon mile around that most exciting of cities.

And I prayed. I found myself drawn back to my spiritual roots, to the Catholic Church, and discovered that my heart had never really left there. Yet it was a new spirit I brought back to it, one that had passed through the fire and survived, one that could praise God with a new and deeper love.

But I remained, by choice, alone. I had vowed never again to infect another human being with the cancer of my anorexia. Encapsulated though it was, I was nonetheless constantly aware of it. It was like a barely tamed monster that had to be fed once every twenty-four hours, and that would then lie down quietly and leave me alone for the rest of the day. The most efficient way to feed this demon was with ice cream, so each morning I would consume one quart of it, in the calm of my apartment, before venturing forth for the day. I was then free to live. Naturally there were many things unavailable to me: a casual lunch with a friend, a spur-of-the-moment acceptance of a dinner invitation. But this was the price I was willing to pay. I focused on the rewards. My social life was limited and superficial, but at least I had one. My friends and family accepted me as I was, anorexia and all. My colleagues and patients knew nothing of my disease, and they accepted me. What more could I ask?

For more than three years it was sufficient. Then, in the late autumn of 1981, I became aware of a haunting loneliness, of a deep-seated dissatisfaction creeping again into my soul. *Oh no! Not again. I'm not going to go through this again, am I? I've accepted my anorexia. I can live with it … I worked it all through three years ago, I can live with it. I don't have to change it. It can't be the anorexia that is causing this terrible lassitude, this growing sleeplessness, this deepening sense of futility in the life I lead. The cause of this depression must lie elsewhere; it must! What could it be? Of course, my work! Family practice after six years is just getting a little tedious. I'm burnt out. I should think about changing my work in some way. Then I'll be happy once again. Let's see now … of course! Obstetrics! Nowhere am I happier than in the case room, participating in the miracle of birth. Even after hundreds of deliveries I still feel the mystery of it, the nearness to God. Why don't I specialize in obstetrics? It's not too late. I'm only thirty-two years old. I'm still young!*

So, convinced that this must magically solve the problem of my depression, I applied to the University of Alberta for admission to a four-year residency program in obstetrics and gynecology and was immediately accepted. I told my colleagues at Coldwell Clinic of my plans, wound down my practice over a six-month period, and prepared to begin the final process of my salvation.

I started the program on July first, 1982. It was so exciting being back in training, like stepping backward, returning to a more comfortable time in my life. I blocked out the fact that the year of my internship had been a year of pain and horror as my anorexia had peaked. *Forget that.*

I plunged enthusiastically into my new job. I cheerfully worked twelve-hour days, spent nights on call when I would sleep for one or two hours, and worked half of every weekend for the entire summer. I took histories, examined patients, learned to do ultrasound examinations, responded to calls to the emergency department, delivered babies, sutured lacerations, learned to do cesarean sections, hysterectomies, vaginal repairs, laparoscopies. I loved dealing with pregnant women and quickly realized that the gynecological surgery did not interest me. But I must learn to do it in order to qualify. Then I could restrict my practice to obstetrics if I wished.

I told everyone that I loved my new work. I told myself too. And I believed it for about four months. Then I began to glimpse that I was still as lonely and depressed as ever, deep in the stillness of my soul. *This cannot be! I'm really happy, I am, I am. I can't possibly want to change what I'm doing. It's just the exhaustion, the overwork. Everyone has to endure this in first year. I can survive, I can, I can.*

I was losing my touch—I lied to myself successfully for only about a month this time. Then I admitted that I was on the wrong track; I could never survive four years of this. I had lost a few pounds already, as my heavy work schedule ate up more calories than I was able to consume through my secret eating rituals. My insomnia was worsening. I had to get out. So I handed in my resignation, concocting plausible explanations for my decision. I couldn't cope with the politics of the hospital. I couldn't stand the trauma of being a lowly resident, taking orders from everyone, after having managed my own practice for seven years. I missed my old patients too much. The reasons weren't bad, probably because each one had a grain of truth in it. In fact they sounded so convincing, I again half-convinced myself.

Until January first, 1983, the day after my resignation took effect. I sat in my apartment, reflecting that it was precisely five years since Eric had first delivered his ultimatum regarding our marriage, and five months since our uncontested divorce had been finalized. I felt utterly void but not weightless in my emptiness. Rather I felt crushed beneath a massive lethargy of spirit. There was nowhere to hide, no further delusions to run to. I had finally exhausted my store of excuses. I had come full circle and was again face to face with the leering deathmask at my center. The beautiful shiny trinkets surrounding me mocked at me: "Of what ultimate value are we?" they seemed to say. "We cannot go with you to your grave."

Store up not treasures on earth, where moths and rust destroy ... Look at yourself, Joan. Stop using euphemisms; stop making excuses. It's the anorexia that is the problem. You can't live with it after all. It's not a broken leg. Admit it: Broken bones heal. You are not healed. You cannot live much longer with this disease. It will eat you up in the end, it will swallow you whole, and you will surely die.

A flood tide of depression washed over me, and I wept bitterly. I did not know what to do. But I admitted my emptiness. I had run out of lies. *Oh God, how can I dare to turn to you again? I keep rejecting you. I have no right to even address you. Oh God, have mercy on my soul! So many chances you have given me. So many years I have wasted in fighting you. So many times you tried to lead me to the solution, so many times I turned back in fear at the last moment. Oh God, show me the answer, please. Where can I turn?*

Three days later I saw Dr. Hardy again, almost ten years after he had first referred me to Dr. Runions.

"... And I feel as though I'm back at square one, Dr. Hardy. My anorexia is alive and well, after fourteen years of struggle and half-solutions, and I don't know what to do anymore. I can't carry on with my life as it is."

He regarded me thoughtfully. "Joan, I don't know which psychiatrist to refer you to at this point. Dr. Carr has left Edmonton, Dr. Runions is in Vancouver, and at the moment I cannot think of an appropriate therapist for you. But I will. I will think about it and make a few inquiries, and we'll find someone who can begin therapy with you again. However, in the meantime, I am struck very forcibly by how deeply depressed you are. I really believe that we should place you back on amitriptyline, at the dosage that helped you in 1974. That will be a good start, I think. Until we elevate your mood to a more normal level, it is doubtful whether you would even be capable of entering psychotherapy."

I nodded mechanically, but with despair in my heart. I knew that no little yellow pills could cure me. I knew what I had to do. I had to surrender, and I didn't know how to do it. But I agreed to start the medication, and I did so that night.

I had made plans months earlier to go to Hawaii with Mom and Archie for two weeks at the beginning of February, and I saw no reason to cancel. I had nothing else to do, no job to occupy me, and no will or energy to seek one. I might as well be warm for a while. So we went, and had a pleasant enough vacation. I smiled and smiled and pretended to be enjoying myself. But in my heart, I was not deceived. I knew that my core was hollow, and I knew that no yellow pills would help. But I took them anyway, night after endless night.

On the airplane coming home I wrestled with the problem of my emptiness. What could I do? I couldn't just sit around waiting to die. Yet the thought of returning to a medical practice almost physically nauseated me. I could not do it, I the nullified woman. Suddenly I had an idea. Why not do some volunteer work, something completely removed from medicine? Something to at least fill the long days, something to take my mind off myself. I had to do something to try to help myself, and—who could say? Maybe I could help someone else, just a little, and that might even make me feel better.

For some reason I thought suddenly of the Marian Center: a small institution located in the slums of Edmonton, operated by a group of Catholic lay apostles who were dedicated to assisting the residents of the inner city in whatever way they could. I had not thought about this place for years, but I had done some volunteer work there when I was in high school, so I thought they could probably use me in one capacity or another.

I called the center the morning after our return to Edmonton. I spoke to a woman named Catherine, one of the apostolic staff. I told her that I was temporarily unemployed and wondered if they could use a pair of hands for a few weeks at the center until I got a full-time job elsewhere. She accepted my offer immediately, and I arranged to start the following week.

I had not the slightest premonition of what lay ahead.

Chapter 28

I started work at the Marian Center on Tuesday, February twenty-second, 1983, reporting to Catherine at the back door around 1:00 P.M. We chatted for a few minutes. I told her nothing specific about my background; she asked no questions. Then she gave me a few chores to do: sorting out some papers, cleaning a few cupboards, doing some mending, washing dishes in the soup kitchen. She remained working with me for most of the afternoon, and our conversation ranged comfortably over a wide variety of subjects.

I noticed an almost palpable spirit of peace as I entered their house, and this spirit seemed to embrace me throughout the afternoon. I felt very calm and relaxed, more so than I had been in a long time, and I was almost cheerful by the time we broke off for coffee at mid-afternoon. Catherine introduced me to the other lay apostles in their sitting room. I marveled at their spirit, at their open, loving, wholly dedicated unity of purpose. Christ was in their midst. They all knew it. I knew it. And I was humbly grateful just to be there.

At 5:00 P.M. we stopped working. Catherine told me that during Lent they had daily mass at 5:15 in their chapel. I didn't want the afternoon to end, and I asked if I could attend mass with them. A few minutes later I was ushered into the chapel. It was a privilege to be in their midst. They celebrated the mass *with* the priest, as it should be celebrated. Their unwavering attention, their total concentration created a dynamic force in the room that I could feel as well as see. I felt shaken as I left the chapel. Oh, to have such faith! Oh, to be tapped into that power as they were! One could do anything. One could move mountains …

As I left the center, we arranged that I should return on Thursday to work again. Catherine invited me to join them for lunch at noon before starting work. She stated that they ate very simply, the same meal prepared for the derelicts whom they served. But she told me they would be pleased if I would share their meal. With only a flicker of hesitation I accepted her invitation.

All day Wednesday and Thursday morning I wrestled with my familiar dilemma. Could I do it? Could I eat lunch in such an uncontrolled situation? Should I call Catherine and apologize, make up some excuse, arrange to come after lunch instead? I certainly could do that; she would think nothing of it; it was very tempting. That way I could have my ice cream on Thursday morning as usual.

NO! Something stirred within me. I knew I had enough power to change my routine, just for once. I could skip my ice cream on Thursday and have lunch at the center instead. I could and I would. Because I knew that I could never feel that wondrous peace of Christ while working on Thursday if I started out the afternoon with a lie. And I so wanted to experience it again, that warm encompassing love within their walls.

I went for lunch with only slight trepidation. I sat with four or five of their group and shared their meal: a bowl of vegetable soup, a crust of bread, a bit of fruit. Although my calorie counter was ticking away as usual, the food tasted wonderful. We cleared the table and set to work for the afternoon. Catherine gave me a large basket of ironing to do: altar cloths, priestly vestments, some personal clothing. I assured her that I liked ironing (which was true), that I enjoyed the peacefulness of it, that I did some of my best thinking while I was ironing. She went away and left me alone for about two hours.

Thoughts percolated gently through my mind as I worked. I was not *trying* to think, I was not forcing my thoughts into any particular groove. But certain ideas and images appeared in my mind, seemingly at random and with no apparent pattern to them.

I thought of the alcoholics and drug addicts who lived in the streets around the Marian Center. I thought about the nature of addiction. I thought of my anorexia in this context, which was not a particularly novel or profound concept. I had thought along these lines many times before. The idea occurred to me again that I had made an inadequate analogy five years earlier when I saw my anorexia as a broken leg in a cast. It was partially true, but it was incomplete. My illness was much more like a drug or alcohol addiction; it was much more an integral part of my being than was a broken leg. It was in me, it was mine, I was *responsible* for it. But not in the sense of blaming myself for it. I had done nothing to deserve it, I was not being punished for wrongdoing by having the disease inflicted on me, any more than Job had deserved all his suffering and afflictions. He had cried out to his would-be comforters that they were wrong when they said his tribulations were punishments. He had seen the folly in their thinking.

And now I cried out in the same way. *No one is to blame!* I had said these words before in another time and place, but I saw them now in a different light. I could not blame God for my illness, nor my parents, nor my society. I could not blame my heredity nor my environment. Nor could I blame myself. No one was to blame for the disease. It just was! And it was a part of me. God had permitted this condition to develop, to enter into me and become a part of my personality, not because he hated me and wanted to see how much I could suffer, but because he loves me and wants me with him always.

Examine the evidence, Joan. Use that scientific brain you've been given. Look at the outcome! Look at how much closer you are to him today than you were fifteen years ago. Look at how much better you know him. See how your faith in him has been tested by this disease, and has survived ... not intact but stronger, truer, and more powerful than it was before. It is a gift! The illness is a gift because it has given you the opportunity to grow. You may not have grown far, or quickly, or steadily, or without setbacks, but you have grown! Praise be to God!

I was completely stunned by this sudden insight, which I recognized instantly to be true. Never before had I seen my neurosis in this light. It was so exciting. Somehow it changed everything.

Catherine returned. I had finished my task. We had coffee, then she took me to a large open foyer and set me to work washing shelves, walls, and finally the floor. Once again she left me alone. It was pleasantly warm in the room, it was very quiet, and the mid-afternoon winter sunshine streamed across the floor in bright changing patterns.

My mind continued working along with my hands, the images again appearing unbidden. I thought once more of the paradox of my disease, of this thing that was part of me, yet was alien to me. It had allowed me to proceed some distance along my path of spiritual growth, but it had also blocked me at every turn, blinded me, and made me shrink in fear from embracing the fullness of life's opportunities. I reflected on how it split me into two pieces: a "good" Joan who wanted desperately to live in the truth as a whole person, open to others and to all the joys of life, including such things as a meal with a friend; and a "bad" Joan who did the opposite: a scheming manipulative childish liar who spent every waking moment preoccupied with thoughts of how to go on getting her own way. I thought of my previous attempts to get rid of it: of my hospitalization, of the antidepressants, of my psychotherapy, of the insights I had achieved that had been only a small part of the solution. I remembered the times I had cried out to God from my agony to take it away (but don't take it away), to make me well (but don't make me give up the twisted pleasures of the disease), to cure me (but don't expect me to *do* anything to attain or maintain my recovery).

I suddenly saw that all along I had been asking for the wrong things! Real prayer, the best prayer, cannot be a Christmas list of requests to God. It can only be a turning to him, an opening up to him, an admission of the emptiness of one's soul, which yearns so desperately for his filling, for the peace that only he can give. I had been asking for the wrong things all along, and God reads hearts: He knew I never truly wanted his help anyway. I had tied his hands.

How then could I pray? What could I legitimately say to him, to the One who knows me so completely, who even sees my thoughts before I do, who looks upon the whole of my existence—past, present, and future—as one unified ever-present "now" in the ocean of eternity? I thought again about alcoholics. They may be drunk or they may be sober; they may choose to give in to their addiction or to not give in. They are still alcoholics. And if they do not give in, they do so for only one day at a time.

So I could pray for courage. I could pray for the courage to accept my cravings without acting upon them. It was actions that counted, not words or feelings. One could feel murderous toward another person, but unless one acted on that feeling one was not a murderer ... But no, that was not completely true. An evil man could set out intending to commit an evil act, yet the outcome of his action might, through no merit of his own, be a desirable one. His action nonetheless deserved no reward, for he had evil in his heart. And if he dropped dead en route to the scene of his intended crime, he would end up in hell, where he had willed himself to be.

I was missing something here, some key concept. What was it? Of course: *the intent*. The intent is just as important as the action itself, if not more so: If a person acts with the intent of doing what he knows to be good, then he is deserving of reward, even if his action has an undesirable outcome that he could in no way have foreseen. Conversely, if a person acts with the intent of doing what he knows to be evil, then he is deserving of punishment, even if his action has a desirable outcome beyond his own control.

So I could legitimately pray for a change of intent, for the will to do what I knew to be right by living one day at a time, cognizant of my cravings but not acting upon them. If I really wanted this change of heart, God would give it to me. *My grace will always be sufficient for you* ... But did I truly want it? This was essentially the point at which I had arrived in 1974 when I left hospital: to not act on my continuing compulsions. I had thought at that time that I really wanted to follow this course of action, but I had done so for only a matter of weeks. Why? Because I had not, in fact, truly wanted it at all?

I dropped to my knees and began scrubbing the floor, becoming one with the sunbeams that danced about the room. It felt good to work with my hands, calming, soothing. I inhaled deeply of the solitude and the silence. I sank into it and allowed it to enfold me and penetrate me.

I thought next about the decision I had made five years earlier to live *with* the disease when I left Eric, to go on living in spite of it. I had thought that I accepted the disease as an integral part of myself at that time, and I had, in fact, done so—but only partially. What had been lacking? I saw the answer at once: In my heart of hearts I had still wanted to be rid of it, I had still felt too keenly the pain of bearing it, I had not totally accepted it and welcomed it. I yearned for something more from my life than could be found within the prison of my neurosis. It had taken more than four years for me to recognize that fact. And that was what caused the pain—the residual *wanting to change* was at the root of the pain. If I could give up that desire, then I would be rid of the pain, free of the struggle to change. But could I ask God to take away that desire? Could I ask him to integrate my deepest nature completely so that I would no longer *desire* to be free of the neurosis? I did not know. This seemed to me an extraordinary request, somewhat akin to Job crying out to God to take away his suffering.

I had no right to ask God for that, for freedom from suffering. But I could ask him for healing: for integrity, for the restoration of oneness within my being, for an end to the incongruity between my will and my actions. This was a little confusing … I could not quite grasp all the convolutions of the problem.

And then, thinking on to the ultimate cure I had wanted but not wanted, the most obvious way to achieve spiritual integration: to have the compulsions disappear from my mind so that I would be capable of living the honest and righteous life I longed for. Did I have the right to ask him to miraculously remove the obsessions from my mind? To cast out the "demon" of my disease? The Son of God did perform dramatic miracles when he walked on the earth. And most of them were worked in response to suffering individuals asking him for specific miracles of healing. He restored the sick, gave sight to the blind, made the lame walk. He even raised Lazarus from the dead ... and in that instance no one asked him to do it. Lazarus's friends and family simply lamented the fact that he was dead, that Christ had arrived too late to save him.

God had already worked miracles in my own life. I reflected back on the more obvious ones: Rachel's transfiguration, the insights achieved through Dr. Runions's work with me, the revelation of the woman with the broken leg that had allowed Eric and me to separate with equanimity. I knew these were miracles. And all of them were healing works, aimed at allowing me to follow a process of recovery from the clutches of my disease. Furthermore, although all of them followed some definite effortful action of my own in the direction of seeking healing, God had worked them when and where *he* willed, totally unsolicited, totally beyond my control.

Who was I to think that I could control God? Who was I to think that I *should* control God, that I knew what was best for me? Only he knows that, only the Weaver can see the design in the tapestry of our lives. Only he knows how to use the flaws in the pattern, so that they will work toward our ultimate perfection. What gave me the right to question him? Why not let him decide what to do with me, what great or small miracle to work or not to work at any given moment in my life? Who was better qualified to know what I needed to bring me closer to him?

I thought of Christ in the Garden of Gethsemane, on his knees, praying and sweating drops of blood. For he somehow knew the indescribable agony he was to suffer. Yet he could say to his Father, even knowing what was ahead: "If possible take this cup from me, but not as I will but as thou willest ... If it be thy will, I will drink the cup ... Thy will be done."

Could I not follow his example?

I was deeply moved as I reached this final thought. Catherine returned then, and we entered the chapel for mass. I was still wrapped in the peace I had been given. I knelt and concluded the essentially wordless prayer I had begun: *Lord, you know my thoughts. You read my heart. You know that I can no longer live with the pain of this disease. You see my longing for inner peace, for integration of my being, that*

I might go on with my life as a whole person, united with you in truth and in goodness. My God, I beg of you to heal the soul-destroying schism between my will and my actions, between my healthy desire to let go of my compulsions and the sick continuation of my neurotic behavior, day after day after day. I ask you, Lord, if it be your will, either to fully release me from the hold of these obsessions or to remove my desire to be free. You decide which route to take. I trust you absolutely. Lord, make me open to your will for me. I ask only for oneness with you, then do with me what you will.

We stood for the Gospel reading, which changes every day, 365 days of the year. I had no idea which Gospel was to be read. The priest opened the Scriptures and read from the seventh chapter of Matthew:

"Ask and you shall receive, seek and you shall find, knock and the door shall be opened to you. For everyone who asks will receive, and he who seeks will find, and the door will be opened to him who knocks ..."

I stood there wholly transfixed, in a state of shock identical to that I had experienced when Rachel was transfigured before my eyes, but this time I remained in control of myself. He had done it again! I could scarcely believe it. He had seen fit to give me that which I had dared to ask of him in faith. For I knew in that instant that I was healed. Absolutely, totally healed! The anorexia was gone from my mind, as so much smoke before the wind. After fourteen years of struggle and pain it was *gone*, as a raindrop evaporates in the face of the sun. I knew I could leave the chapel that evening and go home, or to Mom's, or to a restaurant, or to Timbuktu, and eat whatever was set before me without thinking about calories, fat, weight, control, or anything except how good the food tasted, or how bad, for that matter!

And simultaneously with my healing I experienced the deepest forgiveness I had ever known. I felt cleansed, expunged of every shred of guilt emerging from the past fourteen years: Nothing I had done mattered to God when contrasted with my present turning to him. All wrong that I had inflicted on myself, on others, and on him was now dismissed as unimportant, irrelevant, forgotten in his eyes. The slate was wiped clean.

I was filled with unspeakable joy. I wanted to laugh, to jump, to dance, to sing, to praise his inexpressible goodness. I did none of these things except the last, and that I did silently. I participated in the remainder of the service, astonished that no one else in the room knew what I knew, that no one else had experienced this miracle. And I wondered who in that room, and elsewhere in the world, had been praying for my welfare. The one thought that filled my heart was, "Thank you," and the phrase, "Oh Lord, I am not worthy ..." How could I ever be worthy to be granted such a miracle? It seemed impossible, ridiculously impossible that God should want *me* for his own, but I knew that he did, that my healing was part of his plan to draw me closer to himself. I wondered without anxiety what he planned to ask of me in the future, what the next step was to be in my journey into him.

Chapter 29

It was as I had known it would be. From that moment forward I was well. I ate anything and everything. The internal calorie cash register that had ruled my life for fourteen years had been smashed in the blink of an eye. I tasted foods I had not had for fifteen years and enjoyed them. I went everywhere, accepted all invitations that came my way, and spread the good news of my healing to one and all who knew me. What a delight that was, to give testimony to his power! And we all knew it for the miracle it was. The little yellow pills did work to improve my frame of mind: He used them for that purpose, as he uses all natural and manmade devices and all persons who will let themselves be so used, to work his will, but it was he who healed and forgave me, the God within me who is the same as the God without, the God who is One and who has created me to be one with him.

Over the next three months I gained fifteen pounds in weight. I watched in wonder as my flesh bloomed with the health God had intended for it, as my loins filled out, my abdomen rounded, my breasts swelled. I cherished my body for perhaps the first time in my life, for I knew now that I *was* my body, that body and spirit are one inseparable whole, created and beloved and cherished by God. In the face of that, how could *I* not cherish me? I loved and celebrated every moment of my life, I was overwhelmed with joy, I was filled with unceasing praise for my God.

I had wondered what God had in mind for me to do next. I soon found out, as I felt drawn toward the practice of medicine once again and yearned to be back in my profession, doing what I was trained to do. And how much better a physician would I be now that I was whole! How much more effective a healer now that I had been touched by the Healer himself. I made plans to return as a solo practitioner. I found a small office in a downtown professional building and was able to obtain equipment and furnishings easily. Everything fell into place. It was right, it was meant to be, it was what God wanted. I started looking for a receptionist to work with me.

At about this time, in early June, my old friends Ian and Betty Gorman came from the East to visit me. It was the first time they had seen me in three years, and we had a marvelous visit. I shared the story of my recovery with them.

"Yeah, I wondered when I saw you at the airport last night, Joan. You're looking better than you have in a long time. The extra weight suits you, you know!"

We were seated in the living room of my condo finishing our breakfast coffee. A cloudless azure sky gave promise of a hot day ahead, but as yet the morning breeze drifting in through the open patio door to my balcony was cool and sweet, carrying with it the evocative scents of early summer flowers and shrubs from the river bank opposite my building.

I smiled. "Thanks, Ian, I know it does. I'm back pretty well to my normal weight now, to what I weighed when I first met you. I already had the anorexia by that time, of course. It had just started, and I didn't know what it was at that point. It's strange when you think of how you knew me at the beginning of the story, and now you're here to see the end." I studied my friends as I made this observation: he still the same self-contained individualist he had always been, she a large motherly redhead with a perpetual smile in her calm brown eyes.

"You know, Joan," Betty interjected, "that's a pretty amazing story—almost incredible. If it were anyone else telling it I would be nodding and saying, 'Oh sure,' and not believing a word of it. But since I know you … well, I guess I have to believe it. It would make a good novel, wouldn't it, Ian? … Maybe you should write a book."

"Maybe I will someday, Betty," I said thoughtfully. "One never knows ... Listen, guys, what do you want to do this afternoon?"

"Actually," Betty said with diffidence, "we'd like to see one other friend while we're here: Peter Johnston. Ian's known him since 1969, the same year he met you. Anyway, we've always kept in touch over the years, and we'd like to visit him. Ian called him a while ago, just before we started talking, and it turns out he will be home this afternoon. He has to teach a class at the university later this evening, so it will be a fairly short visit, but ..."

"Oh yes," I broke in, "I remember you talking about him and his wife a few times when you were living here in Edmonton. He's that computer fellow, isn't he?"

"Yes," Ian replied in his Maritime drawl, "he's a senior analyst in computing systems at the university, and he teaches a lot of computer courses on the side. He's also starting up his own consulting firm right now. He's a very interesting guy ... He's actually an engineer by training."

"Oh yeah? I was married to a member of that species once," I said with a twinkle. "He sounds pretty talented." I thought for a moment. "Look, do they want you to stay for dinner or anything? Because I sure don't mind dropping you off so you can have a visit and then picking you up later."

There was a small blank pause in which they exchanged unreadable glances before Betty replied with sudden comprehension, "Oh, didn't you know he's divorced now, Joan? I'm sorry—I guess there's no way you could have known that. His marriage ended about a year or two ago ... So I wouldn't expect him to prepare a meal or anything. And besides, he has to teach tonight."

"Of course. I had forgotten you said that already. Well, I can still drop you off at his house. It's no trouble," I assured them.

"But he lives way out in Spruce Grove," Betty objected. "Look, why don't you join us? We'll only be there for a couple of hours, and I think you'll like him. He's a neat guy."

"OK, that sounds like it would work," I agreed.

Three hours later we were ringing Peter's doorbell in Spruce Grove. Betty was at the bell, Ian behind her on the front steps, and I hung back a little on the sidewalk. I planned to maintain a low profile and allow the three old friends to have a great reunion.

The front door opened. Peter's face lit up when he saw Ian and Betty. I knew how he felt, for I loved them, too. They embraced and greeted one another joyfully. Then Peter's gaze fell on me. I couldn't help grinning like an idiot. He had such an amused expression in his clear blue eyes, such self-assurance in his strong square face. He looked like a man who had seen much of life and had not let it defeat him. I felt him appraising me with those perceptive eyes. I felt warm all over, and it was not from the sun on my back.

"And who are you?" he said with a smile in his voice.

Betty was instantly apologetic. "Oh, I'm sorry, Peter. This is our good friend Joan Eisener ... I mean, Joan Thomson ... Joan, meet Peter Johnston."

I stepped forward and we shook hands. Peter opened his door wider and transferred his attention to Ian and Betty.

"Come on in ... I'll buy you a drink," he said affably.

Ian and Betty passed into the house. Peter looked back at me again. "You can come in, too. I even let skinny short-haired women in here ... but only if they have good legs," he added with a grin.

I blushed and choked on my reply. *What nerve this guy has, saying something like that to a woman he doesn't even know!* But I preceded him into the house.

We sat in the restful greenery of his backyard for two or three hours and had a stimulating talk over cool drinks. Too soon it was over, to allow Peter time to get to his class. He followed us out to my car, said his farewells to Ian and Betty, and then came around the car to where I was standing beside the driver's door. Ian and Betty were occupied with climbing into the vehicle. He looked at me directly and smiled into my eyes. My heart gave a precipitate lurch.

"I'd enjoy seeing you again, Joan. Would it be okay if I called you in a few days? Maybe I could take you out for dinner or some-thing."

I returned his smile. "Yes, Peter, that would be fine. I'd like to see you again, too ... very much."

Chapter 30

~~~~~~~~~I am concluding this story at a completely arbitrary point. In selecting this point I have perhaps succumbed to the influence of popular fiction, earnestly desiring to leave my reader with a happy ending. Life does in reality often contain happy endings, but unless the individual is at his death this ending can never be a permanent one. For the essence of life is change, and each ending carries within it the beginning of the next chapter.

Nonetheless I have elected to conclude here, for my purpose in telling this story is to give testimony regarding these very critical years in my life. I sincerely hope and pray that this book will speak to the hearts of even a few of its readers.

I acknowledge that my recovery from anorexia nervosa was truly miraculous, but I also maintain that miracles occur daily in every individual's life. What do I mean by this? Webster's dictionary defines miracle as: "1. An extraordinary event manifesting divine intervention in human affairs. 2. An extremely outstanding or unusual event, thing or accomplishment."[1]

Leaving "divine intervention" aside for the moment, I prefer to expand these definitions of miracle by including the effect of the miraculous event on the observer, as *a phenomenon that is experienced with awe or wonder as being outside the boundaries of what one might ordinarily or reasonably expect*.

Note the highly subjective nature of both Webster's definition and my own. Different people frequently consider different things "outstanding" or "extraordinary." What is extraordinary to one may not be so to another. For example, people consistently express awe of all that I managed to accomplish while in the clutches of my disease: topping my class academically, earning countless accolades including two gold medals, working eighteen-hour days—all while I was starving. Were those accomplishments miraculous? To the nonanorexic they might be. But for any anorexic reading this, they will seem quite ordinary. In fact, it is the disease itself that *allows* us to do such things, for it assures its victims that we are absolutely different in every way from mere mortals, superhuman, living on a different plane from the common herd. We do not even require food. Anorexics will clearly recognize the miracle as residing not in my accomplishments but in my abrupt recovery, in the expulsion of the obsession from my mind after fourteen years in its thrall.

It should be obvious that, by definition, one cannot witness a miracle unless one is capable of experiencing awe or wonder. And as a corollary, the more one is capable of wondering or marveling at things or events, the more frequently one will see miracles. Let us admit, then, the subjective nature of miracles.

Do you need a miracle in your life? Do you need something to occur that will fill you with awe, something extraordinary? Are you suffering from an eating disorder or an addiction of some other kind? Are you still bleeding from a deep wounding in your child- hood? Or is a loved one suffering in one of these ways? If so, read on, for part six of this book is designed to assist you in your journey out of this pain. You too can experience the miracle of recovery, although it will most certainly occur differently than mine did. It will be your recovery, not mine.

Dramatic miracles take place relatively rarely. To revert to my own spiritual language, I suspect God uses them when he has a "hard case" to crack, when he has exhausted lesser means. St. Paul was such a case. He could not be convinced to stop persecuting the Christians by any lesser means than being struck down from his horse, blinded, and hearing God's voice come out of the sky. I must somewhat sheepishly admit that I was another tough case. God had to heal me dramatically in order to convince me that I *was* healed and forgiven and that he really does love me. So if God has already worked a major miracle in your life, you have no reason to be proud of that fact. On the contrary, such a dramatic event broadcasts to the world that you too are a "hard case," one of the toughest fighters against God. Nothing to boast about there, I'm afraid.

So what about less dramatic miracles? Let me digress for a moment to lay the background for what I see as an obvious example. Our lives are experienced one day at a time, one hour at a time, one moment at a time. And, much as we might like to live in the comfortable state of feeling that we can predict and thereby, to some extent, *control* what tomorrow will bring, such a state is an illusion. A lie. For the reality is that at any given moment none of us knows, or can ever know, what will occur in the moment that lies ahead.

Scary? Definitely. In fact, it is potentially paralyzing. Small wonder that as humans faced with this reality of an essentially unknowable and uncontrollable future, we are tempted to live the moments of our life in a greater or lesser state of illusion that it is not so. We have all grown up in a society that not only encourages us to embrace this illusion of control from infancy onward, but virtually *requires* us to do so in order to function within it, as Anne Wilson Schaef has so eloquently pointed out.[2] Without the pseudosecurity of this illusion, or some alternative form of support, even the bravest in our world would be too terrified to get out of bed in the morning. We need some psychic security, all of us, in order to live our lives with vigor and celebration.

In my anorexia, this normal need for security was expressed in an extreme fashion. My terror of an unknowable, uncontrollable future was so overwhelming to my deepest self that, in order to keep my psyche from disintegrating, I had to defend myself against it by denial, by creating illusory certainties. It felt safe to know precisely what I would eat and what I would weigh, to know that by consuming a given number of calories and exercising for a given amount of time I could lose one pound in a day or a week or a month. It was predictable. It gave me a feeling of power, of control over the future. It was warm and cozy. In reality, of course, it was also very nearly fatal.

You might think that what I have said about the illusion of control leads logically to the conclusion that I believe in the pseudosecurity of addiction as the only possible way to live one's life in our Western world. Not so. In fact, I also happen to believe that living in an illusion is essentially sick and leads *invariably* not to the fullness of wholesome living we humans desire but to the inexorable suffocation of all life forces within us, to the annihilation of all joy and eventually of life itself, spiritual and physical. I have good reason to know this truth, since I lay mired in it for fourteen years.

What is all of this leading up to? What does it have to do with miracles? Simply this: that I see the greatest miracle in my life, and in that of others like me who are in the process of recovery from a life of illusion, to be the way God assists us in giving up pseudosecurity by flooding us with the *true* security of faith—which is just another word for trust. *Knowing* that God loves me, will always love me, and will always be available to guide me and strengthen me, is what allows me to get out of that bed in the morning. And not just to slide out cautiously but to leap out laughing, arms flung wide to embrace whatever the day will bring: laughter and tears, wounding and healing, work and play, celebration and grieving, birth and death and rebirth. What a miracle! And it occurs each day for any of us and all of us who will turn to our God and ask him for this gift of trust.

If you are an atheist you may be thinking right now that I am a candidate for a lunatic asylum. You may be right, but I challenge you also to keep on reading, for I have no hidden agenda. I wish only to serve as a catalyst along your own personal journey. Atheist or otherwise, who among you will deny the reality of the mind? Who will deny their own consciousness? Who among you will claim that your life is anything other than a journey, in space and time, from birth to death, with your mind accompanying your body inextricably along this path? Spirit is a synonym for mind. I use the terms interchangeably, for who can differentiate between them?[3] In this sense, therefore, even the most committed atheist must be willing to admit the reality of the individual spiritual journey. And I make bold to assert that you too are experiencing miracles all the time. Is not existence in itself a miracle? The fact of sentient being, of consciousness, of experiencing the individual self as differentiated from the rest of the universe yet paradoxically part of it. Awesome? Wondrous? I think so. You must make your own decision.

Where does all of this lead? If you are in need of a miracle then take hope, for I believe that any one of us can *ask* for a miracle—and receive it—provided that five conditions are met. If you are an atheist, then an additional and prior necessity is to assess what you do believe. Do you accept that there is a power that energizes the universe, a life force, an essence that is something other than yourself; something that is greater than yourself (greater in the sense of "more than")? If not, close this book and return it to the library. If so, then carry on reading and, wherever I have written "God," merely substitute your own label for that cosmic force.

What are the five conditions I see as prerequisite for a miracle? First, what is requested must be something that is directed at *true benefit* for a member of the universe, at fueling the personal or communal journey into God and furthering the reign of Life, or All-That-Is-Good (God), in the world. Most frequently the request will be for healing from a condition that is hindering the spiritual journey of a human person.

Second, one must *truly want* what is being requested, which means being wholly prepared to accept all of its consequences. Frequently this readiness is lacking from the deepest level of the seeker's mind, for one intuitively senses that the consequences of miraculous recoveries will usually be profoundly effortful and often painful. The security of a sick but familiar way of life may outweigh for a long, long time the fearsome risk of changing to an unknown healthy future.

Third, one must *believe*—absolutely and without any shadow of doubt—that God has the power to grant the request. Such deep faith is indeed rare among the sons of Adam and the daughters of Eve. In fact, it is a miracle in itself. Coming to this faith, like all miracles, is a *process* that may require many years of honest and humble and courageous searching. Yet if one undertakes the quest it will be successful.

Fourth, the request must be made *humbly*, that is, in the full acknowledgment of one's true position with respect to God. Real humility is another virtue rarely found in our world today, where an admission of weakness in the face of another's strength is equated with the pathological. Humility includes by its very essence a declaration of surrender to God's will, and a recognition that God's vision of what is truly best for each of us, and for his world as a whole, is broader and more accurate than ours. Humility accepts this truth as a reason why God may not grant the requested miracle in the precise form and time-frame that the seeker has deemed appropriate.

And finally, one must be prepared *to act in one's own behalf* when requesting a miracle, to take a concrete, visible, and often public step that serves to prove one's trust in God. "God helps those who help themselves," as our grandmothers taught us. Throughout history, God has always required human beings to act in some definite way prior to the granting of his miraculous help. Joshua had to march around the walls of Jericho blowing his trumpet before God caused the walls to crumble. Jesus Christ told the lepers to go and present themselves to the priest, and when they got there they discovered they had been healed. In taking visible actions, the individuals involved were making themselves vulnerable to the ridicule of others. I daresay Joshua looked like a fool as he carried out what appeared to be pointless and even crazy actions. The lepers must have felt ridiculous parading off to show their hideous stinking sores to a priest who would most certainly shun them.

And God required an action of me, too. I had to accept an invitation to share a meal with the staff at the Marian Center, foregoing my usual eating ritual for that day. Not an enormously difficult or especially brave action, I might add. Not even a public one, for only God and I knew what it cost me. The only reason I could do it at all was because it was *just for that one day*. I judged that I could sacrifice one morning of ice cream in order to experience God's peace once again. So I joined the staff for lunch. And what a banquet it was!

The difficult part about this step taken on one's own behalf is that at the time one must take it, one is completely in the dark about the true nature of what one is doing. Before the miracle occurs there is no vision of hindsight, no discernment of the test at the time it is being taken. God did not tell me that if I went for lunch on that February Thursday I would be released from my obsession. And I venture to say that Joshua and the lepers were not told beforehand that their faith was being tested either.

Nor does God's voice come booming out of the sky to give the directions. No, the instruction comes in hidden form. For me it was a simple invitation issued by a woman with whom I had just spent four hours engaged in menial service. I suspect Joshua "heard" his instructions from a still small place in his heart. I heard that faint whisper, too, as I wrestled with the temptation to wriggle out of the meal with a lie. The small voice in my heart led me to take the right action. If we want to be granted a miracle, it is that voice we must all strive to listen for and to follow. And we can be certain of only one thing: We will have *no* premonition that we are hearing the prerequisite step for a miracle, that what we are actually doing is following God's lead and demonstrating our trust in him. The Teacher will give no advance warning of the pop quiz. In fact, we won't even know that the brief assignment is the final examination. So stay alert! Keep your wits about you and your ears tuned in to the right frequency.

These then are the five conditions that I believe must necessarily be fulfilled if one wants to ask the cosmic life force for a miracle of growth.

I refer the reader to Dr. Scott Peck in *The Road Less Traveled* for further elucidation of the subject of miracles.[4] I also wish to thank Dr. Peck for helping me to complete this book. For I wrote the first half of it almost eight years before the second. I started writing about one month after my initial meeting with Peter Johnston and wrote with great inspiration for about three weeks. I then developed a serious block, at the point of my admission to hospital. I simply could not go on, not fully comprehending the reasons why until now. I am indebted to Dr. Peck for helping me to understand those reasons.

The main factor was that, although truly freed from the chains of my anorexia in 1983 and fully acknowledging God's role in that release, I failed until reading Dr. Peck's book to understand completely my own role in it. I failed to realize that in the final analysis I was *responsible* for my illness, and I am *responsible* for my wellness, not in the sense of causing it but in the sense of *owning* it, as all adult humans own their pasts, their feelings, their needs, their choices, and their actions. And lacking this knowledge, I felt vaguely threatened when I tried to describe even the initial phase of my healing. For it was of course this same failure of total acceptance of personal responsibility that caused my second fall, as described in part four of this story. My initial hospitalization resulted in some important and essential insights, allowed me finally to acknowledge the depth of my repressed anger, showed me the dreadful pain I still felt over the loss of my father, enabled me to let go of my unconscious irrational rage at my parents, and so forth. But all of these insights were insufficient to prevent my slipping back into the pseudosecurity of my illness when life began to challenge me again.

It was not until nine years later at the Marian Center that I was finally able to use the grace God gave me to say, in effect: "Here I am, Lord. This is my disease, for which no one is to blame. I don't know how to change my behavior, but I accept myself fully, including this disease that is part of me. Take me as I am and draw me into you. Help me to stop trying to direct the play. Teach me to desire, for once, that your will be done. All I ask for is integration of my spirit so that I can stop living a lie, knowledge of your will for me, courage and strength to act upon it, and the peace of spirit that only you can give." And as soon as I made that ultimate admission of personal responsibility, God said, "Ask and you shall receive," and I knew that my prayers were answered, that I was whole again in a way more marvelous than I could have dreamed.

A second reason for my eight-year writer's block is the fact that I had a good deal of growing up to do. During those years of illness, my emotional development came to an abrupt standstill, as it does in any human enmeshed in the cobweb of deception and illusion known as addiction. I was paralyzed, frozen at the emotional level of an average thirteen-year-old child, although chronologically I was nineteen when I became sick. My disease rendered me utterly incapable of further maturation. When I recovered at the age of thirty-three I had to "catch up" before I could do anything as difficult and profoundly challenging to the newborn adult in me as the self-examination required to write this book. As Henry Thoreau observed: "It is easier to sail many thousands of miles through cold and storm and cannibals ... than it is to explore the private sea, the Atlantic and Pacific Ocean of one's being alone."[5]

Finally, the reader is entitled to know what has occurred in the nine years since this story ended. Was my miraculous recovery "real"? Did it last? What happened with Peter Johnston? Briefly, Peter did call me three days after our first meeting. The following evening we went out for dinner together. My amenorrhea of fourteen years' duration ended spontaneously three weeks after that. Eighteen months after we met, we were married, and the following year, 1985, I gave birth to our first son, Ben. David followed in 1987 and Chris in 1989, one month before my fortieth birthday. Miracles? What do you think?

By this time, I suspect you are burning to ask the final question, the most critical one: Has my anorexia recurred? This is the first thing asked by all the anorexic and bulimic women, recovering and sick, whom I work with today. All of them nod with comprehension when I give them my answer.

The answer is yes and no. No in the sense that I have never again become obsessed by an irrational fear of fat. I have never again undertaken the "relentless pursuit of thinness"[6] that is the hallmark of the disease. Nor has the "calorie cash register" described in my story ever dominated my consciousness again as it did during the years of my active disease. This does not mean that I do not bear scars. I survived with an unhealed fractured leg, with the flesh over the fracture site torn and bleeding, for fourteen years. I lost a lot of blood. The blood has now been replaced, the bone and flesh healed, the scar tissue very strong indeed, as scars usually are. Yet I walk with a limp. And when the weather changes the scar aches. During periods of stress in my life, particularly the interpersonal stress that invariably accompanies one's most intimate relationships, I hear distant echoes from my scar. I feel twinges of pain, old memories haunt me for a time, I remember what the ancient days were like. This is all to the good, for it serves to bring me to my knees in gratitude and praise for the One who healed me. It allows me to recall just who I am and who he is. And I lift my face to him but close my eyes, for who can look into the face of God and live?

But the answer is also yes, as I will discuss in detail in part six. For I have been required to come to terms with the reality that anorexia nervosa will always lie within my psyche, in a more or less deactivated condition. I liken it to a videotape that has been ejected from the videocassette recorder. The old tape in all of its not-so-tragic insanity is stored in the cupboard now. But I have had to learn what I must do to keep it there. I must turn daily to my God. I must remain centered in him, connected with him in the most secret space within me. I must ask him for the gifts I need: humility, compassion, daily surrender to his will for me, courage, wisdom, fortitude. And, above all else, honesty. Honesty with myself, with him, with others. Honesty to admit my neediness. Honesty to admit my many failures as they occur. Honesty to seek forgiveness and further healing every time I run from him, trip and fall, and scrape my knees.

My life since 1983 has not been smooth, nor has it been painless. Rather it has been a struggle to keep growing up and embracing the changes that life has asked of me now that I am whole. At times I have almost forgotten about God, but I keep coming back to my commitment to my spirit's growth into him, as I recall with awe and wonder the mysteries recounted in this book.

For ever since my consciousness emerged from whence it came, I have been blessed with the absolute knowledge that God exists. At too many times along my life's journey I have tried to reject this knowledge, but it refuses to go away. As I mentioned above, I am a great fighter against growth. He must drag me, kicking and screaming, every inch of the way. But eventually, through the seemingly endless maze of my illness, I have come to know of God's existence within me, to discover that the God within and the God without are in fact one and the same, one living Energy undivided, and that my mortal being is merely the flimsiest veil between the two. And I have come to know that my life here in time has but one terrifying but unspeakably joyous purpose: To continually thin out the veil to the point where, as I exhale my final breath, the veil shall be rent and my consciousness shall dissolve into my God.

Part Six

Finding Recovery

I will lead the blind on their journey;

by paths unknown I will guide them.

I will turn darkness into light before them,

and make crooked ways straight.

ISAIAH 42:16

Chapter 31
ANOREXIA, AN ADDICTION?

Eighteen months have elapsed since I completed the first five sections of this book. During this period I have experienced a time of further growth that leaves me in a state of almost perpetual astonishment as I see more and more how God works in our lives. I have been led to some startling insights regarding the nature of the disease anorexia nervosa and the nature of my recovery from it. And, perhaps even more important, I have been given the opportunity to develop and refine these ideas in the crucible of clinical experience: in actual work with a number of individuals suffering from eating disorders. This work has been and continues to be a walk of faith for me, as much of the time I feel myself blindfolded, walking in the dark with my hand in God's.

I preface this section with a strong caution that I am yet in the earliest stages of exploring the uncharted territory to which my insights lead, that all things in the cosmos including myself are in a continuous state of flux, that I have no messianic delusions about changing the face of therapeutic intervention in eating disorders, and that I am the first to admit the fact that I do not have all the answers to these baffling, powerful, and deadly diseases. Rather, I see this book as a seedling work, one that I hope will lead readers to understanding and to a process of recovery for themselves and their loved ones. To the professional therapist reading this work, I make an impassioned plea to keep an open mind.

Recently, I've begun researching the current literature on addiction, and particularly on alcoholism, in a quest for greater knowledge to assist certain individuals in my practice. In the course of my reading I have been struck forcibly in the solar plexus by the realization that the books are talking about *me*. That the critical dynamics of alcohol addiction and anorexia are identical.

I am surely not the first to make this observation. Some workers in the field of eating disorders have advocated this approach. And many people who work in the field of addiction and recovery have identified anorexia, and the other eating disorders of bulimia and compulsive overeating, as addictions.[1] But the addiction model is *not* widely accepted in psychiatric and other medical circles. This fact is highly significant, because it is generally to the family doctor or pediatrician or psychiatrist that a young anorexic or bulimic woman first presents. *And the first encounter with the therapeutic community is critically important in determining the eventual outcome for the victim.* She and her family will either embark from that point forward on their journeys of recovery, or else they will end up mired in a murky and often lethal quicksand of confusion, frustration, desperation, and despair.

The principal objection of the medical world to the use of the addiction model in approaching anorexia is that the true clinical meaning of addiction is lost if one applies the term loosely. That is, true addiction involves not only *psychological dependency* (an overwhelming inner sense that "I need this in order to survive," and that "I am completely powerless to do anything about this need. It controls me."), but also both *psychological and physical tolerance* to the abused substance, which means that progressively higher doses are required to obtain the desired effect as time goes by. And, most important, *physical dependency* occurs, meaning that definite observable and measurable ("objective") *physical withdrawal symptoms* occur if the substance is withheld from the addict. Where is the addiction in anorexia? the experts say. Certainly not to food! Where is the withdrawal syndrome? And with one sweeping pooh-pooh they discard the entire concept as unworthy of further consideration.

I beg the experts to listen, to open their minds to one who has been there, behind the mask, inside the skin of the anorexic, through fourteen long agonizing years. Those of us who suffer from anorexia know, if we can admit it, that the addiction is real—not to food, but *to the rituals of starvation*. The *psychological dependency* on these rituals is real. If we attempt to break free from them the obsession swells like a malignant tumor until it takes over so completely that all other activities become impossible until the craving is met. *Tolerance* undeniably develops: In the early stages of the disease only a small portion of our waking hours and mental energy are diverted into the rituals, but as it progresses more and more time and energy are taken up with these activities—planning what to eat, how to not eat, how to exercise, drooling over food in supermarkets and magazines and calorie-counter books, preparing elaborate meals for others that we can vicariously enjoy.

Furthermore, real *withdrawal symptoms* occur—both psychological and physical. I have described both in telling my story. The *psychological* ones are intense craving, ceaseless preoccupation of the mind, endless obsession with ideas about calories, food, fat, exercise. Even while we are conversing with you or doing our jobs, one level of our consciousness is centered on our starvation and the service we must pay to it. Outwardly we will appear cheerful and smiling and do outstanding work. You will love us for our apparent selflessness and admirable dedication to the task at hand. But beneath the surface, we are one screaming hellhole of pain. The addiction rules our lives and poisons our relationships, for the guilt and shame we feel over our profound disconnection from you causes us to huddle in dark corners, sneak about while you sleep, and construct elaborate lies to hide our madness from you.

The *physical* withdrawal symptoms are also present and just as powerful. Any anorexic, whether she admits to her disease or not, will recognize them. If the ritual behaviors are prevented by external circumstances the panic-stricken heart pounds, the breath quickens, the gut cramps up, we sweat and tremble and are literally consumed with longing. We find no peace until the rituals are resumed, and the physical relief is glorious, albeit brief.

Additionally, the anorexic shares with the alcoholic a familiar cycle of addictive behavior: remorse and "swearing-off" with passionate vows to change after a drinking episode, the temporary abstinence during which the physical and psychological craving for alcohol mounts to a critical point, followed by the seemingly inevitable relapse as the addict recalls only the euphoria of indulging in the behavior and forgets the painful soul-destroying aftermath of guilt and worthlessness that follows. Therein lies the truly diabolical nature of addiction: The abused substance eventually presents itself to the mind of the addict as the *only* way to relieve the increasing anguish of the disease. Catch-22? Believe it!

The physical deterioration, which often proves fatal, is present in both anorexia and alcoholism. Current studies suggest an average mortality rate of about 10 percent in anorexia nervosa, ranging up to 20 percent in some series.[2] Statistics are difficult to obtain in alcoholism, especially in view of the increasing recognition of early alcoholism in our society and the escalating recovery rates.

Perhaps the most critical—and the most neglected—analogy between anorexia and alcoholism is the effect on the families of the victims. It is well recognized in addiction circles that alcoholism is a family disease,[3] that all of those close to the alcoholic become themselves "infected" by it in predictable ways. It is essential to deal with the suffering of these individuals as well as with the alcoholic himself. (Note that my use of the masculine terminology is for convenience only, just as referring to the anorexic as "she" is for convenience. There is no sex discrimination in addiction, but gender differences in incidence rates do exist. Approximately 10 percent of anorexics are male.[4] A clear but not overwhelming majority of alcoholics are male.)

The reason behind the necessity for dealing with the effects of the disease on the whole family is not merely to relieve the family's suffering, but also to unburden the addict sufficiently for him or her to make the turn to recovery. I can assure you that the drama played out in the alcoholic's home is identical to that which unfolds in the anorexic's. The tears and begging by parents and other loved ones, the accusations and recriminations, the desperate attempts to control the sick one's behavior, the punishment, "the silent treatment," the heaping of blame on the addict's head—all are identical. So are the unspoken themes, the lies and cover-ups, the denial, the mixed messages, the distorted communications. And so is the assumption of irrational guilt by the family—the haunting conviction that it is all their fault, that somehow if they had loved better, the victim would not be sick, or at the very least would recover from the disease.

Notice the critically important element of guilt that runs like an insidious and malignant melody dominating the tragic symphony of this disease: The reaction of loved ones to the addict's behavior further fuels his or her guilt as on a deep, hidden level he or she assumes responsibility for the suffering of everyone involved. The more their pain is in evidence the more guilty the addict feels, and the greater the drive to turn to the only means of effective pain relief ever found: further indulgence in the addiction!

So the vicious cycle continues, sucking in everyone involved in a downward spiral of suffering and despair, paralleled by the physical consequences of the addiction, frequently ending in death.

IS ADDICTION A "REAL" DISEASE?

It may be obvious to the reader that there is one shining, beautifully simple fact that can cut through this vicious cycle, paralyze it at its center, and lead to positive change for all involved. This fact is: *Addiction is a disease.* Alcoholism is a disease. Anorexia is a disease. This may sound ridiculously self-evident, and most people involved in these dramas will probably say, "Of course it's a disease. I know that, but ..." and then proceed to further comments that demonstrate that they have not truly, deeply accepted the concept. If they had, there would be no "but."

To the professional reader, I must add an important aside here that my agreement with many experts that addiction is a disease does not lead to a corollary conclusion that its management is best approached using the medical model. My views about this are in fact the exact opposite: *The medical model simply does not work* for assisting addicts to true recovery. More about this in part seven.

The reasons why the disease developed are similarly unimportant. Naturally none of these conditions emerges from a vacuum: There is always a vulnerable personality, always low self-esteem and a fragile and poorly defined sense of self, always a set of stressful circumstances that triggers the entire entity. But in general the early life histories of the victims are no more or less pathological than those of other human beings who succeed in negotiating the adolescent passage to adulthood in a somewhat more sane condition. And understanding how our disease came about does not allow us addicts to automatically recover from it.

Lest I be misunderstood, I must add here that understanding how I came to be anorexic was not irrelevant to my recovery. It was in fact necessary to understand the deep psychic forces involved and work them through one by one during my therapy with Dr. Runions before I could eventually recover. Yet I clung to my disease for *another full nine years* after I attained all of this intellectual, and even emotional, *understanding* of the origins of my disease. Something more was needed.

What is important, then, is not why the disease developed but the reality of the present: The disease is. It exists. It is present. And it is a disease. It is not "all in our heads." It should be obvious that a condition that is capable of killing 10 or 20 percent of those afflicted is a real disease. I can assure the reader that no one of us chooses to develop an addiction. No one chooses to become anorexic or alcoholic, and we sufferers have not caused our disease. Nor has anyone around us. It is more accurate to say that the disease "chooses" its victims from those among us who are "set up" by underlying personality and precipitating factors to get it. Just as cancer "chooses" its victims from among those genetically predisposed who are subjected to certain environmental agents at a time when their immune defense mechanisms are weakened.

Once this disease concept can be accepted at a very deep level, irrational guilt must evaporate. For it makes as much sense to feel guilty about being an addict as it does to feel guilty about being diabetic. Similarly our families have as much reason to blame either themselves or us for our disease as they have reason to blame us for developing cancer. And once the driving force of irrational guilt is defused, there is a greater likelihood that we may reach the point of accepting responsibility for what *really* belongs to us: The choice to go on being sick or to take the steps necessary to recover.

Much has been written about anorexia, and I am certain that many of its victims have been assisted to recovery by approaches quite different from my own. I believe there is room for a variety of psychodynamic frameworks and therapies in this challenging field. Professionals, family members, caring friends, and those of us who suffer or have suffered from anorexia can all be instruments of healing by developing the unique talents and insights we have each been given and applying them willingly and effortfully toward helping ourselves and others. We must not lose sight of the fact that we are literally engaged on a mission, involved in a ministry of healing to fellow human beings deeply wounded and in need. I believe that to be effective we must become willing to extend ourselves radically and even to be wounded and healed ourselves. We must personally *participate* on an equal basis with the suffering victim in the recovery process. In short, we must love.

ANOREXIA: PHYSICAL OR MENTAL?

In the midst of the eclectic approaches to healing, I also believe one unifying thread must run through all effective frameworks. I am referring to the undeniable fact that eating disorders are *primarily* spiritual and mental diseases that only take on physical dimensions as they unfold.

It is probably unnecessary to point out that the physical side of anorexia generally comes to dominate the spiritual one and, therefore, becomes the critical concern for the anorexic and the therapist. And well it should. The anorexic does not die from the spiritual hell in which she lives, but from the grim physical realities of starvation: marasmus, kwashiorkor, attendant electrolyte imbalance, and their deadly effects on vital organ function. The kidneys become unable to concentrate or dilute the urine to balance the body's internal chemical milieu. Potassium levels fall, causing muscular weakness. The blood sugar level drops, becoming inadequate to supply all of the body's organs with the energy they require. The brain tissue gradually shrinks, causing profound psychological consequences such as decreased concentration, indecisiveness, mood fluctuations, and sleep disturbances. The salt and water imbalance in the brain may trigger convulsions. The bone marrow is starved for nutrients and cannot manufacture red blood cells to carry oxygen or white blood cells to fight infection. The stomach is slow to empty and the bowel becomes sluggish. The liver cells are damaged by malnutrition and leak their enzymatic contents into the bloodstream. The heart is slowed down, blood pressure falls, and the heart muscle cannot pump blood effectively and may develop a fatal rhythm disturbance identical to the one that kills the victim of a heart attack.

Long before death, the skin becomes dry and shriveled. The teeth may undergo extensive decay. A fine velvety blanket of hair grows all over the body's surface in a primitive but pitifully inadequate attempt to warm up the uninsulated and hypothermic central core. The skeleton becomes depleted of its calcium content and may fracture like that of an elderly woman. Nerves throughout the body are no longer cushioned from external pressure and may be pinched, causing paralysis. Cataracts may develop in the eye. The menstrual function has long since ceased and the ovaries shrink, forcing hormone levels to prepubertal levels. Reproduction is impossible. Sexual libido is diminished.[5]

Because of these tragic biological realities, the physical side of anorexia *must not* be ignored. Any physical complications must certainly be treated using a medical model, *before* any psychological or spiritual recovery is possible.[6] Although true deep recovery from these diseases occurs in the mind, as I have described in the story of my personal healing, such recovery is impossible if the victim is dead.

But neither can the spiritual side be ignored. Mind and body are one inseparable unified whole, as all physicians know. Treatment must be directed to the whole person. So often have I listened to the frustrated anguished cry of my anorexic patients, "Dr. X says all I have to do is eat and everything will get better. He doesn't understand!" She is right, of course, even ignoring the fact that giving this advice to an anorexic patient is roughly as sensible as telling a paraplegic to stand up and walk. A person can eat and even be of stable weight for long periods of time, and still be actively anorexic.

The essence of anorexia is *the obsession* that drives the victim in her relentless pursuit of thinness, the siphoning away of 95 percent of her mental powers into the continuous unceasing preoccupation with fat, calories, control, rituals, secrecy, exercise, planning and scheming, hiding, lying, deceiving. Furthermore, on one level the victim *knows* what she is doing: She knows that she has allowed this disease to become her god, that it takes precedence over everything else in life. And she is all too painfully aware that she is choosing to live a lie. The guilt that results from this awareness—in a person who is essentially honest and carrying from early childhood the burden of an overdeveloped conscience—is indescribable. It is shattering, devastating, fragmenting. It is hell. This spiritual suffering is immeasurably worse than any of the physical suffering involved in the starvation process. To the anorexic it often seems worse than death itself.

Guilt can, of course, be rational or irrational. The anorexic's guilt might be rational in some small measure: It may result from harm she has intentionally inflicted on another. Just because people are sick does not mean they are incapable of sin, of doing deliberate wrong. But at least 90 percent of the anorexic's enormous burden of guilt is irrational. And this irrational guilt is the driving force of the entire disease. What the victim, and all or most of the people in her life, do not realize is that this guilt is the fuel that the disease "uses" to keep her sick, for it further erodes what little hope, what little capacity to make the choice to recover, that she still possesses.

I would like to conclude this chapter, then, with a poem about the guilt we addicts experience in our disease. A clarification is in order at this juncture. The reader will note my frequent references to the "demon" of anorexia. My use of this word implies nothing about actual possession by an evil spirit. I do not for a moment believe that we anorexics or other addicts are possessed by a devil, if indeed such a phenomenon exists. Nonetheless, I can assure the reader that in our sickness we truly *experience ourselves* as being controlled and "possessed" by a perverse power that leads us to act in ways abhorrent to another, healthier part of our psyches. Again and again we do what is contrary to that which our healthy side really *wants* to do. We feel controlled by the very force that we initially welcomed to provide us with perfect control over our own bodies and our behavior. So my use of the term *demon* is not merely poetic, but deeply descriptive of the reality of the addict's experience.

Before you read this poem, or skip past it, let me say something important about my poetry. I urge you not to be frightened by the passion in it. Poets are a strange lot, but we are also just ordinary human beings, as any of my patients will testify. If you came to my office you would probably find me an atypical physician, but most certainly you would find me quite, quite human. My patients declare that I am an easy person to talk to, that they are quite amused by my antics at times.

I love my patients, and I love surprising them sometimes with unexpected gifts, which brings me to the second reason for offering you my poetry. If a particular experience in my office with an individual patient triggers a chain reaction in the creative side of my brain, I must sit down that night and write a poem about it. Otherwise I can't sleep. I almost always send a copy of the poem to the individual who sparked it, reasoning that the connective force flowing between us in my office gave birth to the poem for some reason other than my personal pleasure. Invariably the recipient of my gift is at first taken aback, but then moved by it in unexpected ways in his or her personal spiritual journey. The outcome is always a surprise.

So please read my poetry, slowly and gently and without trying to force any sort of response within yourself. Poetry is a completely different art form from prose, and can communicate with a different part of your mind than the rest of this book. If you can become still in the deepest part of yourself, emptied of preconceptions and prejudice and fear, then the energy that flowed out of me into the poem may flow out of it into you, generating something unexpected and growthful within you. Possibly even something wonderful. Please try this. It is my special gift to you.

THE ANOREXIC'S SCREAM

For all who have known this anguish

"Have pity on me, O Lord, for I am in distress;
        with sorrow my eye is consumed;
        my soul also, and my body.
For my life is spent with grief and my years with sighing;
My strength has failed through affliction,
        and my bones are consumed.
For all my foes I am an object of reproach,
        a laughingstock to my neighbors,
        and a dread to my friends;
        they who see me abroad flee from me.
I am forgotten like the unremembered dead."
Psalm 31:10–13

I
Disease of magic
        smoke and mirrors
Deception incarnate
        lie of lies
Mother father sisters brothers
Hear her for she's dying in it
alone
Won't anyone listen hear comprehend?
This sickness is real it possesses her
She needs your acceptance
She could use a friend.

I hear you saying it's all her fault
        it's all her selfish way
You say that she is punishing you
        for failing her one day

You say all she must do is eat
 and all would be okay
Don't you see that she can't?
Don't you see she is dying to?
Don't you see that she's victim and prey?

The most pathetic part is that
 the goodness in her cries out
With the selfsame message she hears from you
 in all of your pleas and shouts
She tells herself she could control it
 if she really wanted to
She tells herself she is sinful and weak
 she beats herself up for you.

She struggles she fights she resolves she swears
 to change her way, to begin
She succeeds for an hour a day a week
 before despair sets in
Then the demon can suck her back into hell
 spiraling deeper than before
For she hears in its ghastly mocking sneer
 that she never will change the score
Each failure of willpower proves that fact
 to her shrinking spirit and body
Each failure of intellect to control
 adds another nail to her coffin
A little bit more of her dies.

II
Don't you see it's all a tissue of lies?
 a cobweb spun of alibis?
The whole bloody thing?
You see the obvious ones but
 can't you see those concealed?
The idea that she can control it is lie

it's planted there by her disease
Dread whisper in her heart that it's all in her head
that she's rotten right down to her core
that she loves no one round her
not her God
not her family
that the world should be rid of her sore
These falsehoods they goad her
corrode her and
load her
The guilt further tears her to shreds.

The demon convinces
It's cunning and clever
It deafens it blinds it distorts and it finds
every way to lure deeper its prey
Every angle is covered, no refuge discovered
by victim or family—all pay
Coming and going she's caught
in a trap of illusion
It binds it entangles in webs of delusion
Her spirit is bled in a fog of confusion
She grows finally too weak to pray.

Fragmented and bleeding, shattered and needing
release from the torturing rod
She longs for her death, for freedom to rest
The disease tells her there's no other end
possible
And the lie most malignant seeps into her soul:
that she's outside the help of her God
Outside of his mercy
Outside his compassion
Outside of his power to heal.

III

And in a wild, mysterious place
  far beyond the brief paragraph of her knowing
God's volumes cry out in her pain
He suffers with her, weeps with her
  watches helpless in weakness
  for he's given her freedom to choose
To endure and to suffer, or take steps to recover
Having given he can't take it back
But he never abandons
He cannot abandon
  the creature who bears, blind, his being.

The specter's chill laughter from out the night rings
  it rules for its hour
  it still holds the power
  it fancies itself quite the king
It bloats up with pride
  and weaves on the lies
  the shadows smoke mirrors it brings
Deceiving the victim the loved ones the healers
Eventually deceiving itself.

For that's not the end of the story, you see
This strange God who appears to be weak
In truth is much greater, stronger than the Deceiver
He waits for his hour to be.

And when the sad creature has filled her cup of suffering
  when her blood spills out and overflows
She descends to rock bottom
  to the end of the road
  to the place where there's nowhere to go
but up.

And as her agonal spasms cease
    when the execution is complete
And her poor broken body lies
    spirit emptied
    at his feet
Then can the fire of his justice blaze
    His passionate rage drive demon back
    reverse the letters of e-v-i-l, raise
    her, invite her now to live.
At that moment he sends her
    a messenger prophet
    a song or a dream or a voice
The lyrics are clear to her still, silent place
He woos her surrender and floods her with grace
    makes it easy for her to trust him and rejoice
Then he waits with breath held for her choice.

Chapter 32

AA AND THE TWELVE STEPS

If we accept that anorexia is a form of addiction, what are the therapeutic implications? How do we get better? How do we rid ourselves of the obsession that rules our lives? And how do we help others heal? Following the analogy with alcoholism to its logical conclusion, we arrive at the concept of Alcoholics Anonymous (AA). *AA works*: This is the most compelling reason for paying it due attention and respect. In the last sixty years it has helped millions of alcoholics worldwide to achieve and maintain sobriety. Most other effective treatment programs incorporate AA methods into their approaches and conclude by connecting the recovering alcoholic with an AA group in his community.

AA is a *wholly spiritual* approach to the disease of alcoholism, though not a religious one. Its basis is the Twelve Steps to recovery, which the alcoholic voluntarily embraces, accepting full responsibility for achieving his own recovery, with the intensive support of the group for assistance. In the early months of sobriety, most individuals find that they need at least one meeting a day for their spiritual sustenance.

AA assists its members to a belief in a Higher Power greater than themselves that can deliver them from the insanity of their addiction, over which they have first admitted a total powerlessness. Some members call this Higher Power "God." For others who cannot believe in a God, the Higher Power may be the organization or the group itself or some other abstract force like Truth, Beauty, Compassion, or Love. What is critical is the admission of the existence of *something* greater and more powerful than themselves. Eventually, recovering individuals come to know that the Higher Power is not outside themselves but rather deep within. Yet paradoxically the Higher Power is still something greater than (as in "more than") themselves alone. It is essential to the fullness of recovery to arrive at this knowledge. I trust this will become clearer to the reader as we go on.

It might be helpful at this point to name the Twelve Steps that form the essence of the AA journey to recovery:

1. We admitted we were powerless over alcohol—that our lives had become unmanageable.

2. Came to believe that a Power greater than ourselves could restore us to sanity.

3. Made a decision to turn our will and our lives over to the care of God *as we understood Him.*

4. Made a searching and fearless moral inventory of ourselves.

5. Admitted to God, to ourselves and to another human being the exact nature of our wrongs.

6. Were entirely ready to have God remove all these defects of character.

7. Humbly asked Him to remove our shortcomings.

8. Made a list of all persons we had harmed, and became willing to make amends to them all.

9. Made direct amends to such people wherever possible, except when to do so would injure them or others.

10. Continued to take personal inventory and when we were wrong promptly admitted it.

11. Sought through prayer and meditation to improve our conscious contact with God, *as we understood Him,* praying only for knowledge of His will for us and the power to carry that out.

12. Having had a spiritual awakening as the result of these Steps, we tried to carry this message to alcoholics, and to practice these principles in all our affairs.[1]

While conducting the research into alcoholism for this book, a "light" suddenly flashed on in my mind and I made the connection between these steps and my recovery from anorexia. I used the Twelve Steps to recover! Although I had not heard of them at the time, I, in fact, followed their path in every detail in coming to my dramatic recovery and in continuing my recovery work to this day.

Step One: In the eight weeks prior to the day of my abrupt recovery I had finally admitted my powerlessness over anorexia. I had reached my rock bottom, my end of the road. I came face to face with the reality that I could no longer carry on with my life—practice medicine, maintain the superficial appearance of a normal lifestyle, be capable of offering anything to others, truly enjoy anything, or even experience authentic emotions—while still remaining sick. My life had become "unmanageable" because of my disease.

After I left the obstetrics residency program in December 1982, I was forced to confront the emptiness of my life as an anorexic. Denial was wholly gone at last. I died spiritually as I experienced the void at my center, which consisted in my having allowed anorexia to be my god for fourteen years, allowing it to determine my behavior as it took precedence over every other consideration in life. I knew in my heart that if it came to a choice between my addiction and *anything* else—a patient's well-being, my marriage, God himself— the addiction would win, and indeed had done so. A shattering admission. Truly it annihilated my spirit. During the weeks prior to the Marian Center experience I felt like an empty shell, a body without a soul, a bag of skin walking on the earth that, if punctured, would reveal a black hole just beneath the surface. During my meditation at the Marian Center on February twenty-fourth, 1983, I admitted both the reality of the emptiness my disease had caused and the fact that no one, including myself, was to blame for it. Guilt fully evaporated at this point.

At only one previous time had I fully completed Step One, and that was during my hospitalization in 1974. In 1978 when I left Eric, I made only the first *half* of Step One, an admission of true powerlessness, by saying to myself, "Yes, I am an anorexic and I can't do anything about it." But I still believed that my life was *manageable*, that I could go on practicing medicine, that I could continue to effect good in the world while still keeping my disease.

Step Two: At the Marian Center for the first time in my life I "came to *believe*"—absolutely, totally, without reservation—in God's healing power. There was no shadow of doubt in my mind, no wrinkle in my trust. I was filled with faith, which is in itself a gift from God, as I discussed in chapter 30. During my hospitalization in 1974 it is debatable whether I completed Step Two. Perhaps I did truly believe in God's power, perhaps not. There certainly was an element of doubt, at least at the beginning of my hospitalization: "It's no use, Dr. Runions. It's never going to be any different ... How can you change a person's thoughts?"

Furthermore, it makes no real difference whether I completed this step in 1974 or not, for recovery is truly a *process* in which any given step may need to be completed many times before moving on to the next one. In addition, we never truly finish with any given step, for once we have completed it we essentially go on completing it for all time. Recovery never ends.

Let me reiterate that perfect faith is a miraculous gift from God.

Step Three: On that critical day at the Marian Center I made a conscious decision to submit myself totally to the will of God, as I recognized clearly that he knows better than I do what is best for me, what I need in order to be drawn closer to him. Never before had I made this decision. Even during my hospitalization I had insisted on asserting *my* will much of the time, never fully letting go of what I thought was best for me.

Step Four: My "searching and fearless moral inventory" may not be immediately apparent to the reader. It was not a catalog of the sins I committed through my anorexic behavior. Rather it consisted of an acknowledgment of the profundity of the disconnection from myself and my own emotions, from other people, and from my God, which was the inevitable consequence of my fourteen-year acceptance of my spiritual fragmentation and my refusal to let go of it.

A moral inventory is not an unending beating of one's breast and saying, "What a horrible person I am. Obviously worse than anyone else on earth" (which is really a form of inverted pride) but rather a quiet, gentle, and ruthlessly honest examination of one's person and one's behavior—good and not-so-good, bad and not-so-bad. This involves a realistic assessment of both strengths and weaknesses, of talents and flaws in one's God-given personality, of what comes easily and what comes with great difficulty, of the things that are flowing well in one's life and the things that are blocked up and need attention. In my own case, I had to clarify in my mind *precisely* what needed to be changed in my psyche in order to achieve wholeness and integration of spirit.

Step Five: I "fully admitted to myself and to God" the exact nature of my wrongs that day at the Marian Center. I did not admit them to another human being, however. I had no AA sponsor and no group to connect with. This is an important difference between the way I worked the steps and the way most recovering addicts work them. During my reflections I made the final admission of personal responsibility for my disease and for my wellness. In effect, I said to myself: "This disease belongs to me, not to anyone else. Although I did not cause it, I do possess it, totally and completely. And I cannot live any longer in the pain of this disease as it now stands. I have a choice. I can ask God for healing, for spiritual integration—here, right now. I can ask him to take the obsession away from my mind, or to take away my desire for change. Either option would bring spiritual integration, would free me to take up the threads of my life once again." This acceptance of personal responsibility was a necessary part of my "moral inventory."

Step Six: It should be obvious to the reader that as I entered the chapel that momentous day I was "fully ready to have God remove my defects of character." My inventory was complete, my trust in him absolute.

Step Seven: I sank to my knees and formally asked him for healing of the terrible schism within myself, for integration of my spirit, that my will would at last be in accord with my behavior. I gave him the choice of which way to effect this integration. I submitted myself to his will at last, surrendering myself without reservation to whatever he wanted for me. I untied his hands for the first time in fourteen years. I think I can imagine his joy at that moment.

He didn't give me time to have any second thoughts about my surrender. Five minutes after I asked him for healing, with perfect faith in his power to effect it, he responded in all the magnificence of his mercy and compassion. All was forgiven as though it had never existed, I was liberated in the blink of an eye from my obsessions. I have tried to put into words the fullness of my joy as I experienced that moment of healing, and I have failed. No words can capture it. I "saw" him face to face. He was there. He heard me. He loved me. He wanted me. Everything I had professed to believe for thirty-four years was really true. It was stunning, exhilarating, overwhelming, awe-inspiring. It was heaven.

Step Eight: Immediately following my healing I experienced an urgent need to contact everyone who had known me throughout my illness and share my joyful news with them. I now believe this need was the same force that compels all recovering addicts to make a list of everyone they have harmed, intentionally or unintentionally, through the course of their active addiction. Please recognize that this includes *everyone*, even those harmed during drug-induced "blackouts." The recovering addict *knows* that he is morally responsible for all this damage, regardless of the fact that he was suffering from a disease.

Once he is at this step in recovery, he no longer attempts to shift the blame outside himself. For example, he knows the fact that he was sexually abused when he was four does not mitigate his responsibility for his actions now. He can with deep sorrow say to himself, "I ran down and killed a child last year when I was drunk. My not remembering the incident because I was drunk does not cancel out the reality of the killing. Nobody except me is to blame for this action. I lifted the bottle to my lips. No one held a gun to my head. I did it. I was sick, but I did it. My God, forgive me." And in this acknowledgment there wells up a profound peace and joy—yes, I said joy—that a God whose mercy knows no bounds has now led him to the sanity of being able to state the truth. I cannot emphasize enough the inner serenity, tinged with sadness though it may be, that accompanies Step Eight, and the permission it brings for the addict to admit that he is not perfect, to name and own *all* the harm he has inflicted on others in the past.

Step Nine: After I had completed my "list," I directly approached everyone on it whom I could possibly contact and shared the story of my healing. Everyone who was enmeshed in the web of my anorexia: my mother, my stepfather, my brothers and sisters, my ex-husband, my friends. I believe this was my way of "making amends" to them.

Many of my patients also had suffered, some of them grievously, and making direct amends there was more difficult. Many had borne the brunt of my irritability and impatience during my lengthy depressed periods. All had been deprived of the deep compassion I was incapable of entering into as long as my emotional life was frozen as it was during those years.

Writing this book is one way of making indirect amends, I suppose, for I ask all reading it who knew me during my sick years to forgive me for whatever injury they suffered at my hands. But all I could really do, and still do to this day, is know that even as I acknowledge my failures I *am* forgiven—which allows me to forgive myself and move on to make the only true reparation possible: becoming all that I can be, birthing the divinity that lies within me as a created being made in the image of God, and with this empowerment creating among my fellow human beings all the beauty and justice and love that I am capable of bringing into being. In short, furthering the spread of the kingdom of God within my world.

One thing that is poorly understood by outsiders looking at the Twelve Steps is the fact that Steps Eight and Nine are done primarily for the benefit of the recovering addict himself, not for those who were harmed. All of us who are in the process of making these steps know this truth. Schaef explains this beautifully:

> The amends process, I believe, is a process of claiming our own lives, relinquishing our defensiveness, and doing what we need to do to become *right within ourselves*. Making amends is a personal act. We make amends for ourselves. Amends are not made to make others feel better, to change others' attitude toward us, or to elicit forgiveness. We make amends because *we* need to ..., because we know that our recovery, our growth, our

development, cannot proceed unless we claim those things we have done of which we are not proud that have harmed others.[2]

Step Ten: "Continuing to take moral inventory" has been and still is a real struggle for me, a creature imbued with enormous pride and arrogance as well as with a powerful propensity to deny reality and blind myself to the truth. I believe that a holdup at this step has been the principal reason why I have failed until now to accept at the deepest level of my self the fact that anorexia is an addiction. I wanted to believe that I was cured, you see, once and for all; that my anorexia is a thing of the past, a demon that has been exorcised from my mind forever; that my continuing wellness need not require any ongoing painful effort on my part.

And I have always known that this is not the melody sung by recovered alcoholics. No truly recovered alcoholic ever says, "I was an alcoholic." Rather he or she affirms, "I *am* an alcoholic ... I have a disease that I must remain aware of for the rest of my life, lest I fall into its clutches once again ... I need my Higher Power and my fellow human beings to keep me on the right track, one day at a time, until the day I die."

I had no desire to unite myself with the poor in spirit who sing this refrain, day in and day out. Until now. Now God has given me the courage to admit it. I am an addict. *I am an anorexic.* Recovered, certainly, but still carrying within myself the memory traces that could reactivate and cause me to sink into the fullness of addiction once again. I need God's help daily to keep me growing, to keep me moving toward him through my fellow creatures in healthy ways. Without him I am lost. And I revel in my weakness, in my neediness, for it is only in admitting it daily to myself and to him that I can tap into his strength, there finding all the power and joyous liberation I could ever desire. The truth sets me free.

The reality of my continuing potential for addiction has been brought home to me on innumerable occasions in the nine years since my recovery. I am one who clings to routine, who has enormous difficulty letting go of any pattern of behavior—good or bad—once it is established. I hold fast to routines in my work, in recreation, in my reading and my writing and my parenting. This is not always detrimental, but at times it can be: It often gets in the way of experiencing life fully and interacting with others in the healthiest ways of which I am capable. I must be constantly on guard against my tendency to allow a ritual of behavior to become *too important* to me.

Step Eleven: My prayer life has become immeasurably richer in my recovery, and particularly since I wrote the bulk of this manuscript eighteen months ago. I have learned to find the time to converse with God in prayer and meditation at least twice a day, surrendering to his will for me over and over again. Since I have been exercising this discipline he has begun speaking to me a good deal more, both during the prayer time itself and throughout the day and the night following. Often he speaks through other people and through events during the day, through apparently random thoughts that come to me "out of the blue," and occasionally through dreams. Or perhaps it is more accurate to say that I have begun to listen to him more. I suspect he has always been attempting to make himself heard above the din of my personal chaos! Sometimes, of course, I don't like what I hear—that is the risk involved in listening to him at all. I can still choose to reject what I hear, but the problem in that lies in my certain knowledge that I do so at my own peril, that following my own way instead of his invariably leads to negative growth and deep unhappiness.

Step Twelve: Writing this book and speaking to groups of people about anorexia is twelfth-step work. So is "coming out of the closet" with selected individuals in my practice, sharing with them my personal experiences with anorexia/addiction with a view to assisting them in their own, often similar, struggles. The most exciting facet of doing this is that our exchange invariably becomes mutually beneficial, framed as it is not as a conventional doctor-patient relationship (a hierarchy I rejected many years ago in my work), but as two human beings on an equal footing participating in a process. We both benefit in unexpected ways through the sharing of our common experience. We assist one another to grow while celebrating our interconnectedness.

The entire practice of Step Twelve was impossible until I came to accept at a radical level within myself the fact that I *am* an anorexic. With this acceptance comes true humility. It is no longer possible for me to place myself on a pedestal, on a different plane from the rest of suffering humanity. It is no longer possible for me to see myself as one specially favored by God, as one to whom he granted the miracle of recovery for my own personal happiness and salvation. For we are *all* specially favored by our Creator!

The admission of my ongoing addictive potential explodes the vacuum in which I might prefer to place myself. It throws me right back into the blood and guts and sweat of the human condition, where I rejoice in pleasure and in pain, in giving and receiving, in speaking and listening, in laughing and weeping. In other words, it has awakened my dialectical consciousness and allowed me to begin celebrating the paradox, the mystery inherent in my very existence. I am a divine being who must eat and sleep! I am an anorexic and I am recovered. I am capable of the heights of ecstasy and of the grim reality of deepest sin. I am a spirit with infinite and eternal dimensions, and I am an animal who must first possess and then relinquish everything material and temporal, including my own life one day.

I conclude this chapter by stressing again the *most* important truth about Alcoholics Anonymous and the Twelve Steps. *It works!* Every AA meeting around the world on any given day concludes with all the individuals present rising, joining hands, and chanting, "Keep coming back. It works!" Even the most vocal critics of the recovery movement reluctantly admit this fact. Working the Twelve Steps on a daily basis, sharing specific problems with others at the meetings and with one's sponsor, using ancillary avenues to work at resolving underlying issues that have been buried deep in the psyche, one step at a time, brings about the miracle of recovery from addiction.

THE AA MEETING

For KATIE, RICK, and the Others

"To rejoice at another person's joy
is like being in heaven."
Meister Eckhart[3]

I saw your birth today, my God
Not in a midnight stable with angels singing
But in a shabby sundrenched room with smoke stinging
    my eyes
With twenty grace-drenched persons allowing it
Twenty men and women birthing you
    as I shed silent tears
    the silent observer of holiness
    watching
    listening
    seeing.
Their costumes were all different
    blue jeans business suits black leather
    nurses' uniforms muscle shirts
    housedresses workboots
Their bodies were all different
    fat skinny short tall young old fit decrepit
    white black yellow red
    dainty and rough-hewn
    all beautiful
    beautiful all
Their eyes were all the same
    glowing flowing knowing eyes
    all seeing the same thing
    growing
Their tales were all different and

all the same
pride deception self-pity rock bottom despair
now acknowledged
now transformed by
you in them
into
them in you
Their attitude was all the same
all were sitting drinking coffee
all were dancing naked wakened
all were on their knees.
All spoke of you and of your work
in their gritty lives
in the persons they were
had been
were becoming
All spoke of love trust spirit
of the group which sustained them
sustained by
you
One spoke of surrender
of paradox
of losing everything to gain
everything
I thought I was complex one said
but I am simple and
so was my disease
so cunning and so
simple
I fought hard to kill myself one said
the hardest part was having to look good
while I did it
fourteen years forty years wasted
but not wasted for
birth is so sweet to one who has tasted
death

The miracle one said is that I am here
    alive
    sober
    sitting around a table with twenty drunks
    laughing
    and there is no bottle in sight
    I need all of you my friends and God to keep me
    laughing
    at the night
A tough soft man in leather jacket
    maybe nineteen maybe ninety
    pony-tail tattoos earring intact
    spoke of finding you
    spoke of needing you
    spoke of loving you
I wept in his joy.
All rejoiced and praised and thanked
    you
    in each other
Their thankfulness was mine, mine theirs for
    we were
    one
    in you.

The echoes of their gratitude resounded in the room
Humility and joyfulness shone forth there, nowhere gloom
No quiet desperation any longer set the rhyme
They sat embracing life and birthing
    one day at a time.

Chapter 33
ANOREXICS ANONYMOUS

Anorexics might benefit from a group approach structured along the same lines as AA and using precisely the same principles. Might it be possible to organize a self-help group to which anorexics come voluntarily and anonymously, having admitted their powerlessness over their obsession and their need of a Power greater than themselves to restore them to sanity? Might it be possible to meet together frequently (probably at least daily in early recovery) as AA members do, to begin working through the Twelve Steps as individuals with the healing power of the group as their fuel and foundation?

I am not the first to propose an AA approach to eating disorders. Far from it. In fact, such an organization was established for compulsive overeaters in 1960 and has been flourishing worldwide for decades. Overeaters Anonymous (OA) works for these addicts and for bulimics (discussed in the Appendix) in the same way that AA works for alcoholics, as I can definitely attest from the numerous OA meetings I have attended while doing the groundwork for this book. OA opened its doors to anorexics and bulimics many years ago, but I have yet to meet another anorexic there. And as I've shared my personal story in the meetings and confessed my "ulterior" motive for being there (to research the organization for its potential usefulness to us anorexics), I have heard a chorus of agreement that a separate organization is desperately required for us "starvers" (as the overeaters affectionately nickname us).

Although only about half of the men and women I've seen at any given OA meeting have been obese (many have been attending for many years and in their sobriety have shed their excess poundage), I can virtually guarantee that I will never convince any of my sick anorexic patients even to walk into the room. The sight of even one obese individual is so terrifying to the unrecovered anorexic that all rational thought evaporates instantly. The meeting will merely serve to reaffirm her resolve to stay thin and to cling more tightly to her own addiction as the surest way to achieve that goal. As psychoanalyst Susie Orbach has observed, from the point of view of the sick anorexic, "the anorexia is *not* the problem, it is the *solution*." [1]

In order to recover, the anorexic must make a 180-degree turn in this deep-seated attitude about herself and her condition, to truly see her disease as "the problem." She must make this initial step (in essence the equivalent of Step One) before she will ever begin attending Anorexics Anonymous.

I am utterly convinced that Anorexics Anonymous can be established and can function to assist us to recovery, but I also have a few important reservations. The first of these is that such a program is not appropriate as the *initial* approach for any of us trapped in the clutches of full-blown anorexia. The physical effects of starvation on the brain itself [2] are such that spiritual recovery is impossible until physical recovery is at least well under way, lean body mass is significantly restored, and electrolyte imbalance is corrected. The same situation is seen in alcoholism, where it is seldom possible for a drinking alcoholic to begin attending AA without first obtaining treatment in an inpatient detoxification center, usually for several weeks, to eliminate the bulk of the *physical* effects of alcohol on his body and mind.

Thus, for the very sick anorexic, initial therapy will always need to be conducted along more traditional lines aimed primarily at restoration of weight and optimization of nutritional status, both of which can be achieved most effectively in an inpatient setting. The Anorexics Anonymous approach I am here proposing can be initiated in hospital, but on a *strictly voluntary* basis, and then continued following discharge. In hospital there will be an opportunity to educate the anorexic about the nature of addiction, about how her disease fits into the addiction model, and about the Twelve-Step approach to recovery, so that she will clearly understand how it is aimed at the deep spiritual/mental recovery that every anorexic intuitively recognizes is the *essence* of true recovery.

Reflecting back on my own story, I suspect that had such a group been available to me in 1974 following my discharge from hospital, I might have reached my own recovery point much earlier than I did. The intensive group support, the ongoing healing experienced there, might have assisted me in cutting through the denial that so quickly resurfaced when I left hospital.

It is worth emphasizing what the critical differences will be between Anorexics Anonymous and traditional group therapy as presently practiced by conventional therapists. In the former each member will be present for only one reason: to accept the *personal responsibility* for her own recovery, having recognized that this is difficult, painful, and effortful, and that no other human being can do it for her. The goal, clearly identified at the outset, will be to recover *spiritually* from the essential "demon" of anorexia, which is the obsession about food, calories, fat, and so forth.

The means to this goal will also be clearly identified at the beginning of each meeting as the Twelve Steps are read aloud by the members. The group will have no leader, and the members themselves will take turns chairing the meeting, the format of which will be stylized as in AA. No psychotherapist will be present (unless of course she is anorexic herself and attending for purposes of her own recovery). No one will be there to counsel or direct or practice therapy on another, but rather to work on her own problems, at her own speed, and in her own way. In short, to follow her own process to recovery. The group, like AA, will become a "safe" place of mutual acceptance and sharing of a common struggle. Any infiltrator with a hidden agenda to exert power or domination over others will be quickly taken to task by the group as a whole. I cannot emphasize enough the healing power that is generated within such a climate. At the open AA meetings I have attended, I have felt this power in the deepest sensors within me. It flows around the room from one individual to another like an electric current. It is mysterious and awe-inspiring and uplifting. It is God.

As in AA there will be no fees or dues, no solicitation of outside financial support, no advertising or promotion. Each group will be fully self-supporting as a "hat" is passed around at each meeting for small voluntary donations to cover the cost of coffee, any rental fees for the meeting place, and so forth. A body of literature and pamphlets analogous to AA literature will need to be developed also, and it will be essential for persons interested in organizing Anorexics Anonymous in their community to become thoroughly familiar with AA by attending a number of open AA meetings and by studying in depth the AA literature and dialoguing with AA.

I am intensely interested in establishing an Anorexics Anonymous network in North America, and wish to invite any anorexic readers who share my interest to contact me. Perhaps we can organize an initial brainstorming meeting at which we can pool our ideas and God-given talents to hammer out a plan of approach. I do promise to respond to all inquiries received. Contact information can be found at the conclusion of this book.

Just as AA requires that members arrive in a sober state at meetings, the anorexia group will require that members have eaten before walking through the door of the meeting place each day. For us anorexics, abstaining from starvation is entirely equivalent to the alcoholic abstaining from alcohol. "Abstinence," of course, is *not* the same thing as "sobriety," as any alcoholic who has tried being a "dry drunk"[3] will attest, but it is an essential precondition and must be worked at on a daily basis. There will be no need to "police" this requirement of abstinence, for the whole essence of AA is the ruthless and fearless honesty demanded of all those present, the end of denial. If the anorexic is deluding herself about her eating behavior, she will feel so intensely uncomfortable that she probably will not return. In any event she will not experience authentic healing in her heart if she is lying, so as in the case of the alcoholic, there will be nothing to motivate her to persevere in the program. This is the real beauty of AA: All present experience healing if they are there with hearts open to receive it. If they are not, they experience nothing, so there is nothing to draw them back to further meetings. Thus only those, and all those, ready to recover do recover!

I can hear in my mind at this time the objections that may be voiced by several of my anorexic patients: "It wouldn't work! I have to get rid of the thoughts inside my head in order to recover. How can I do that by going to a meeting?" To them I say: I did. By working through the Twelve Steps I was able to arrive at the point where I could turn to my Higher Power with *absolute* faith, ask for inner healing (Step Seven), and receive it. This will not occur quickly or easily in the majority of cases. It may require years of work before this step is reached. It took me nine years to move from the termination of my original denial until my recovery was reached. (Although, as I mentioned above, in a group such as I have described, knowing *what* I was striving for, I venture to say that I might have done it a good deal faster.)

Recovery is a *process*, and even when one has "arrived" at what is regarded as full recovery, as I have, one has *not* arrived. It is necessary for me to begin each day with the admission of my weakness, asking God for the grace to keep me free of the clutches of my addictive process, in *all* its cunning manifestations during the hours ahead. Any AA meeting you attend will have a number of individuals in the very early stages of recovery—look into their eyes and you will know. The desperation and near-despair *is* all too painfully evident. I say *near*-despair because if they were in total despair, had *no* hope, they would not be in the room.

All the individuals present must have taken Step One in order to cross the threshold of the meeting-place, but some may be no further than that. Many may be uncertain that a Higher Power exists, yet they will discover that coming to believe in a Higher Power is the next step to be taken. I daresay that many alcoholics in the early months of their sobriety crawl along from one hour to the next filled with the compulsion to drink, spending countless hours obsessing about it, yet finding the courage in AA to continue the struggle, knowing that they are not alone and that their victory is assured as long as they remain connected to the only Power that can conquer such a powerful, cunning, and baffling enemy as their disease.

Does the depth of this hell sound familiar? Anorexia is right down there too. In any Anorexics Anonymous meeting there will certainly be individuals in this early stage, those who ate their meal that morning for the sole reason that they might attend the group meeting with a pure heart, even while making the despairing assertion, "Eating this food is *not* going to make me well. It is not going to turn off the demon inside my head. But I can see that eating is necessary for me to stay alive and to keep my brain functioning optimally in order that I might eventually *really* recover. I will make an act of trust in the healing power that I have seen working in others in my group. If it happened to them, it can happen to me. I will eat."

Liberation from this hell begins in the earliest stages of recovery and truly is a process. I suspect that instantaneous transformation such as I was granted is rare. Perhaps God knew I needed such a dramatic healing because I did not have the support of an AA group and its meetings to turn to, nor did I have the blueprint of the Twelve Steps planted in my mind. In the recovery program I am proposing, I can envision anorexics coming gradually and gently to Step Seven, and experiencing the healing move through it so slowly that they are unaware of the miracle that is transpiring until it has occurred and is past. For example, one day they may suddenly realize, "Good heavens, I ate that meal without counting the calories!" or "Good grief, I actually watched that movie and truly enjoyed it without thinking about my anorexia for one moment!" or "My God, I was able to drop my plans for exercising this afternoon when my friend called to invite me over for coffee."

Realize, too, that growth and progress in AA is not linear and steady. Plateaus occur when nothing seems to be happening for long periods of time. Setbacks and relapses also occur at times, including resumption of drinking. These are called "slips" in AA and are not a cause for despair but for renewed humility, for ruthless honesty, and for picking oneself up, dusting off one's knees, and setting off on the journey once again, by the grace of God. It might be useful to the reader to learn that I experienced a serious "slip" in my own recovery in 1986, during a period of intense personal stress. At that time I actually began a new ritual of unhealthy secret eating on a daily basis. On my way to work I began stopping at the Dairy Queen where I ingested a large ice cream cone and a package of chocolate-covered peanuts (which I had concealed in my handbag before leaving home) as a substitute for breakfast and lunch.

The healthy part of my mind clearly recognized the danger in what I was doing and whispered to me urgently to wake up and admit it, but the diseased side had regained sufficient power to allow me to deny reality once again, rationalize away my action, and enable me to continue the pattern for about six or eight weeks. This slip was not all the way down into the full-blown hell of my former state. I continued to eat a normal dinner, and I lost no weight, nor was I continually preoccupied with calories and fat as I had been before. But it was close enough that, looking back on this time, I break out in a cold sweat.

I had no AA group to help me see reality and break through my denial, no AA literature or Twelve Steps burned into my soul to rescue me. So what happened? It is with a sense of wonder that I can relate to you that God in his infinite mercy intervened once again: I became pregnant with our second child, after a period of nine months of infertility and fruitless attempts to conceive. In my exultation at carrying new life within my body, the slip came to an abrupt halt. The temptation to eat candy and ice cream lost every vestige of its power the moment I discovered I was pregnant. I nurtured my unborn son with irrepressible spontaneous generosity. Without a backward glance, I began eating normally, all longing for control and for ritual evaporated, and life moved forward once again.

I have never disclosed this incident to a living soul until now (perhaps because to do so would have been to admit that I *am* still an anorexic), but I think it important to record it here. For we must never overlook the real source of the healing that occurs in AA and similar Twelve-Step programs. It is the Higher Power, God himself, working in the hearts of each of the individuals present.

WHAT ABOUT THE FAMILY?

I alluded earlier to one area of anorexia research that has been sadly neglected to this point: the nature of the family's involvement. There is an urgent and pressing need for this oversight to be addressed, for just as the alcoholic's family plays into the disease, fueling it with predictable reactions to the alcoholic, so the anorexic's family is enmeshed in the dynamics of the illness and unwittingly plays a part in driving the anorexic further and further away from recovery.

The families of anorexics suffer enormously. I have listened to their pain and seen their despair countless times in my office and in the hospital. Generally by the time they reach my practice they are bewildered and desperate, having exhausted every resource they can think of to help their anorexic. I see a huge void in the psychotherapeutic approach to date in that the pain of these individuals is, by and large, not even being acknowledged, let alone being relieved as it could be through an approach such as I am about to propose. With the exception of a few family-oriented therapists and treatment centers, most professionals working in the field ignore the family once the initial history has been taken and the family dynamics superficially explored.

I believe that if an AA approach to anorexia is to achieve success, there is a compelling need to establish a support group for the families and friends of the victims, one that operates along the same lines as Al-Anon and Alateen for the families of alcoholics. These groups serve three purposes. First of all, they relieve suffering by teaching the participants to let go of irrational guilt and by leading them to stop attempting to exert control over something they cannot control: the disease of alcoholism. The families slowly learn to *detach* from the disease, to let the alcoholic have his disease all to himself—including all of the painful consequences that his sick behavior brings about for him. They learn to have compassion for the sick one, to go on loving him, while knowing that they cannot choose for him whether he is to recover or not.

Second, the families also learn to address their *own* part of the problem, to see how the addictive process in the loved one has affected them, and to stop letting the alcoholism control *their* behavior. They do all of this by following the same Twelve Steps that AA uses, beginning with an admission of their own powerlessness over the disease and of the insanity they have allowed to develop in their own lives. In the addiction and recovery literature, the disease that "infects" those close to the alcoholic or other addict is termed *codependence*. It is estimated by Wegscheider-Cruse to affect 96 percent of the population of the United States![4] Schaef believes that codependence is better viewed as a disease in its own right; it is latently present in those afflicted long before they become involved with the addict and then emerges when the addict's disease triggers it. Furthermore, she sees codependence as merely another cunning manifestation of the same *addictive process* that leads to substance abuse.[5] I believe this is enormously important, for it allows the families and friends of addicts to claim *their own problem* and to actively work at recovering from it. I also see related issues surrounding codependence that have profound significance for the health care professional. I discuss the entire subject in greater depth in chapter 34.

The third purpose served by the support groups is to be a possible indirect help to the alcoholic himself. By putting an end to the heaping of guilt on him from all sources in his life, they can free him sufficiently to choose to recover. Remember my earlier comments about guilt being the driving force of the disease, the fuel it "uses" to keep the alcoholic sick. When he sees that his loved ones are detached from his sick behavior, that it no longer brings them the suffering that it once did, then he is more likely to be free to address his own problems and accept responsibility for himself. He can no longer use his family's negative reaction as an excuse for drinking.

Precisely the same dynamics apply in the case of the anorexic and her family. My own family and close friends were able to achieve this detachment from my disease without any support group to assist them, but it required many painful years for this to happen. In the interim all of us suffered greatly. For at least five years before I recovered, my mother had let go of my disease completely. I knew that she loved me and was available to me whenever I turned to her, but she had abandoned all attempts to control me, even by facial expressions or body language. I truly felt that she was no longer emotionally involved in my illness, that if I died from it she would grieve but then move on with her own life, feeling no responsibility for my death. I cannot express what a sense of relief this gave me. I was able to relax in her presence, to stop being on guard against doing something that might cause her pain. I knew I was not dragging her down with me into hell. The same can be said of other family members and intimate friends after Eric and I separated in 1978.

Many years later, in my recovery, my mother shared with me the process of her achieving detachment. She told me that through reflection, prayer, and discussion with others she was able to arrive at the point where she could face without unbearable agony the almost certain knowledge that I would never live to practice medicine, and that *there was nothing she could do about it.* Yet she never stopped loving me with a miraculous depth of true maternal love. Nor did she ever stop praying for me. She truly recovered from her disease of codependence.

I am convinced that this detachment on the part of others was a *prerequisite* for me to make the turn to recovery, and in my work with anorexics now I spend a good deal of time with their families and friends discussing this and nudging them along the paths to their own recovery. My "ulterior" motive, of course, is to unburden my anorexic patient. Again and again I find myself longing for an Al-Anon support group to which I could refer these individuals, if only to free up my time a little!

I wrote a poem following one recent session with the parents of an anorexic, and I would like to conclude this section by reprinting it here, as it may illustrate something of what I am attempting to say about the family dynamics.

THE ANOREXIC

For JENNIFER and for her parents

"The spirit of the Lord God is upon me,
because the Lord has anointed me;
He has sent me to bring glad tidings to the poor,
    to heal the brokenhearted,
To proclaim liberty to the captives
    and release to the prisoners,
Recovery of sight to the blind,
To announce a year of favor from the Lord."
Isaiah 61:1–2

I
Beautiful child my beautiful baby your mother cries
A gash of pain between her eyes
How can you do this to yourself to me to us
It makes no sense this disease that is no disease
    I can see and cannot see
How can it be?
Says she.

What was the cause calm father asks
The furrowed brow belies the mask
There is no cause that I can see therefore
    there is no cause
But what have I done wrong?
I was right here all along
Says he.

You're doing this to punish us it's obvious to see
For crimes unknown invisible to everyone, to me
You say you can't control it but that's ludicrous you know

It's all inside your head this devil why not cast it out?
If you loved us you would do so, mother father scream and
     shout.

Doctor can't you see that she is acting like a child?
Perhaps we should have spanked her more, perhaps we were
     too mild
Perhaps we gave her far too much, perhaps deprived her so
Perhaps her toilet training was too lenient too harsh
Perhaps our love was not enough to keep away the dark.

II
You look at them and I watch
the anguish in your sunken eyes
     and I bleed with you
     need with you
to relieve their pain
to release them from their guilt to
     release you from your guilt
For I know this web in which you're caught
I too have looked on daylight from behind the bars
     manacled strangled enclosed in a space too small for me
     tried to grow smaller—lunatic attempt to break free
     succumbed to the lure of the quicksand
     the shining quicksand
     the mirage
     it swallowed me alive
     I thought.
I am in you, starving one
Your wound mine your blood my own
I have tasted of your death, been consumed in it with you
Won't you celebrate this truth with me
     rejoice in our connection?
For sorrow shared is sorrow divided
But joy shared is joy multiplied.

III
I speak to the three they listen but
        do they hear?
Search for the words to make them comprehend that
        they cannot comprehend what cannot be
        comprehended
To let them know there are no
        answers to these questions
To help them see the questions must die
To show them they cannot control so
        why struggle to control?
        why seek logical solutions to the logically insoluble?
        why not let it go?
This evil is a tornado
        a real tornado
        sucking in victim family healers
        all who would befriend
destroying in a noisy terror of confusion tears and rage
It kills and all is silent desolation in its wake.

But yet there's hope I say to you, fragmented one and lovers
Recovery truly can occur, not just more masks and covers
Mother father trust me for I am one from death arisen
But first you must let go of all, as everything must be
Allow the darkness to unfold, for with the dawn you'll see.

Admit you're wholly powerless to gag this ghastly voice
Yes, your daughter still may die but she must make the choice
Fueling guilt will never help—it shores up more the prison
You cannot give her life to her, not now or then or ever
But there is One more powerful who can, and he is clever.

More clever than this demon which is ruling in its season
And furthermore he loves your child beyond all bounds of reason
Mysterious and foolish God, he shares with us his mind

He made her body, gave her spirit, formed her in his image
He died for her, he cries for her, he'll fight right to the finish.

So turn to him with all your hearts
    your spirits to him lift
Believe that he can heal all wounds
    and change them into gifts
He transforms weakness into strength
He does so with delight
Entrust yourselves into his hands
Know that his will is right
Surrender to his love for you
There'll be no peace this night
until you let him win the war and let him calm the din
For we can fail but he cannot if we allow him in.

Part Seven

Transformation: When Famine Becomes Feast

*"He who walks in the way of integrity
   shall be in my service.
He shall not dwell within my house
   who practices deceit."*

PSALM 101:6–7

Chapter 34
FILLING IN THE
BIGGER PICTURE

I assume that you have reached this point in the book because you have some interest in eating disorders. This section, although it is addressed in large part to health care professionals, is important for the interested lay reader as well, whether a person with an eating disorder or a concerned member of his or her circle. First, I strongly believe that an informed patient is a better patient. And it has been my experience that, given the array of possible treatments and the low success rate of many of them, people with eating disorders who are desperate to recover have already learned a great deal about their disease. But, more important, it is my profound conviction that no treatment for eating disorders works unless the patient and the therapist work together as a team in the healing process.

Whether your background is in psychiatry, general practice, pediatrics, gastroenterology, surgery, other medial specialties, psychology, nursing, social work, family therapy, dietetics, occupational therapy, or some allied discipline, I assume that your interest in this book relates to your professional experience with eating disorders. Some of you may, of course, have both a professional and a personal interest. You may be thinking right now of individual patients or clients with whom you have had either brief or extended contact. You may have spent most of your professional career working with the victims of these diseases. You may still be energetic and passionate about your work, inspired by the healing you are seeing in your patients, enthusiastic about the approach you currently use.

Or you may be tired. You may be frustrated, baffled, confused. You may be burning out. You may be valiantly flogging your sagging spirit, struggling to conjure up the fervor you once felt for this work, wondering whence it has vanished. You may even have given up, overwhelmed with despair at the paltry measure of positive results you have obtained and the wrenching pain you have endured as you enter into the hell in which your patients live.

If you are the person who suffers from an eating disorder or her family member or friend, you no doubt know that I do not use the word hell lightly or with any sense of literary exaggeration. You, too, know the demoralizing effect of treatments that don't work. Most assuredly, you know despair.

Wherever you are on this spectrum of being, I wish to address you. I wish to console you, to bring a breath of hope, to introduce a new direction that you might choose to explore further, bringing your own talents and visions and insights to bear on this journey.

Please accept the concluding section of my work in this spirit, as my gift to you. It is uniquely mine, and comes from the center of my reality as a woman, as an anorexic, and as a physician who loves her work. Realize that it has required ten years of "complete" recovery from my disease before I could pen these words. As recently as two years ago, I was just as baffled by these patients as you may be right now. Because of the gift of my personal experience I could understand them, empathize with them, and diagnose them accurately, yet I hadn't the faintest notion of how to assist them to healing, despite knowing how I had recovered. In fact, I referred all of them to psychiatrists or psychologists for therapy.

For I, too, am a scientist, you see, trained in that paradigm. Unless I could formulate a problem in a logical and linear fashion, break it down into its component parts, hypothesize and test my hypotheses, and collect "objective" data for analysis, I was deeply suspicious of myself. I lived in the left side of my brain, viewed with skepticism anything I could not understand rationally, and judged harshly the opinions of anyone whom I perceived to be "unscientific."

Over the last two years I have moved to a new place, yet bearing all of my past with me. I invite you to enter into my new home, to sniff the air, to peek in my cupboards, to make your own decision about whether or not to carry a souvenir away with you.

You now have to make a choice. By my own admission I am an accomplished liar, a highly successful con artist. I may be lying now. Or I may still be as deluded as I was during the fourteen years recounted in my story. You must decide whether to hear and possibly even believe what you are about to read, or whether to reject it outright as the ravings of a manic-depressive, obsessive-compulsive neurotic, who has even been psychotic in the past. A religious fanatic. A lunatic. The choice is yours to make.

THE CURRENT "STATE OF THE ART" IN ANOREXIA AND BULIMIA

If you are baffled and confused by your eating-disordered patients, you are in good company. In my extensive review of the literature, I was struck forcibly by the consistent note of confusion that runs like a poignant refrain through almost everything written about anorexia and bulimia.

There is no agreement about therapy, and this divisiveness has undergone little change over time. Bassoe and Eskeland note that "throughout the centuries many types of treatment have been advocated in ... anorexia nervosa: psychotherapy, behavior modification, isolation, bedrest, drugs, acupuncture, endocrine therapy including pituitary transplantation, shock therapy, lobotomy, dialysis and exorcism."[1] Similar conclusions were reached by the Canadian experts Garfinkel, Garner, and Goldbloom, who noted that there is little factual knowledge to help determine the best treatment regime or setting for anorexia nervosa patients.[2]

An excellent study by Herzog et al. found that less than 50 percent of medical doctors and psychologists attending an international conference on eating disorders in 1988 and 1990 believed there is a consensus regarding treatment of eating disorders. Furthermore, the results indicated "that clinical decisions are not influenced primarily by treatment studies in the scientific literature," particularly in anorexia as compared to bulimia, and that "patients [themselves] play an important role in determining the type of treatment received,"[3] not in the sense that the therapist tailors the approach to the individual, but rather that the patient requests a specific type of treatment in many cases.

I was shocked and appalled by this finding, for in my clinical experience patients are as bewildered by their disease as are their therapists. Again and again in taking treatment histories I hear of multiple therapies by multiple practitioners using a variety of approaches. Patients appear in my office floundering in a vast sea of confusion and despair. Do we really expect the blind to lead the blind?

I believe the principal reason behind this lack of uniformity in therapy is the correspondingly profound lack of uniformity in the framework clinicians use in viewing these diseases. In the recent words of Lunn, "anorexia nervosa has been categorized as a hysterical disease, as a compulsion neurosis, as a phobia, as a specific kind of the manic-depressive disease, as schizophrenia, and in recent years as a borderline state. It has been compared to the addictive diseases, and recently it has been regarded as a special variant of the sexual perversions." She noted that therapies currently used can be divided into somatic, somatic-psychiatric, and psychotherapeutic. The latter approaches vary enormously, from suggestive therapy and behavioral therapy, through classical psychoanalysis, analytically oriented psychotherapy, and cognitive therapy, to body therapy, regression therapy, systemic therapy, and family and group therapy.[4] Small wonder that as clinicians we have all been filled with "helplessness and confusion,"[5] and are often "frightened, bewildered, or repulsed"[6] by these patients.

I do not mean to imply by these observations that there has been no progress in *understanding* the etiology and pathogenesis of these diseases. On the contrary, volumes have been written on this subject, and the analyses are frequently brilliant. Intricate and beautifully logical formulations have been made of the psychodynamics by analysts, feminists, behaviorists, family therapists, sociologists, historians, and cultural anthropologists. The problem is that these advances in intellectual understanding have failed to make any real impact on outcome for the individuals and families affected. This does not surprise me, for I agree with Schaef that understanding a problem is not the same thing as solving it,[7] despite what many professionals seem to think. I believe this because I remained sick for nine years after I achieved full "understanding" of my disease. Yet, using the medical model, we have all been trained to believe that if we can just test extensively enough, gather data accurately enough, and analyze the results cleverly enough, we should automatically be able to prescribe the "fix" for a given disease.[8]

Thus the most tragic result of the therapeutic confusion and lack of uniformity in basic approach to these disorders has been our failure to significantly alter the prognosis for afflicted individuals since anorexia nervosa was first accurately described in the early 1870s.[9] In all studies regarding outcome and prognosis of anorexia, the same gloomy conclusions are reached, possibly best summarized by Ratnasuriya and his colleagues at Maudsley Hospital in London: "After twenty years, almost 40% of the patients were still gravely ill or had died. ... Perhaps even more striking is the high level of dysfunction in other areas of life. Of those still alive at follow-up, one third led a socially isolated and restricted life, and reported a high dependence on their families of origin. Attitudes to sexuality, marriage and childbearing were still problematic for at least half."[10]

Noted authorities Hsu, Crisp, and Callender made an observation in 1992 that is highly telling and of great relevance. They describe the "grim" prognosis in anorexia and conclude that "greater understanding of the process of recovery from this distressing and potentially fatal illness is clearly important. Surprisingly, very little has been written on this topic and *almost nothing is known about what facilitates recovery* even on an experiential level."[11] (Italics mine.)

Sibley and Blinder note the difficulties in comparing outcome studies, which are plagued by methodological limitations and are therefore often suspect.[12] In my literature review regarding prognosis and outcome I was additionally struck by the studies that carefully examined in depth the patients reported as experiencing a "good" long-term outcome—roughly one third of the total in most series.[13] The *majority* of these individuals in one study continue unusually restrictive eating patterns,[14] a large number suffer from anxiety and mood disorders, close to half persist in excessive preoccupation with thoughts of food and weight and body shape, a significant number become alcohol-dependent or socially isolated and unhappy, and some are even episodically bulimic.[15] I therefore seriously question how many of these patients were *truly* fully recovered. When interviewed, a large number were unable to identify how they had recovered.[16] I am not alone in my suspicion that the reported "complete recovery" rates of 30 to 40 percent may be overly optimistic.[17]

After reflecting on all these considerations, what can we conclude about the current status of the professional's approach to anorexia and bulimia? All authorities agree that "nutritional rehabilitation" must assume top priority in initial management,[18] although precisely how this is to be achieved in a critically ill individual who remains recalcitrant and uncooperative is less certain. But beyond the initial phase of nutritional repletion and electrolyte restoration, there appears to be a therapeutic jungle in which lives a disconnected population of experts each beating their individual drums in a dysrhythmic cacophony sufficient to strike terror into the hearts of all listeners. Why? Why are the experts so vociferous in putting forward one approach or another? Why are so many of us skeptical of one another, unwilling to listen to one another, and defensive about our own particular method of managing these patients?

THE ADDICTION MODEL IN EATING DISORDERS

I examined at some length in part six the question of the validity of viewing eating disorders as addictions, in the true clinical sense of the word, and have no intention of repeating the discussion here. Rather, I wish to move on to explore some more subtle facets of the issue, ones that may not be immediately apparent to the naked eye.

It is no secret in medical circles that approaching anorexia and bulimia using the framework of addiction is largely regarded as sentimental hogwash at best and deluded fanaticism at worst. In wading through the voluminous scientific literature on eating disorders, I encountered an air of deep suspicion wherever the addiction model was mentioned (usually in passing). I was able to find only one reference to a study that apparently supported the use of this model, and that was to an obscure German journal that has not been carried by the medical library of the University of Alberta (one of the finest reference libraries in North America) since 1982.

I found this situation puzzling. Why are the experts in eating disorders so unanimously skeptical about a reality that I have known in my bones for virtually all of my adult life? Why is there such an aura of rigidity, closed-mindedness, hostility even, surrounding the entire issue? Why? Are we not scientists? I asked myself. Is not the essence of the scientist to open oneself to every avenue of learning, provided it does not violate the personhood of oneself or another? To use every morally acceptable tool one can find to explore every possibility, to turn over every stone in the universe? Are not human persons created to be such cosmic explorers, to learn, to think, to choose, to share in the knowledge of the Creator herself?

It has required months of reflection and further study for me to move beyond my initial puzzlement into glimpsing a possible answer to these questions, an answer that leaves me trembling in terror, dry-mouthed, and stunned as I sense the enormity of it. One part of me wants to run away, to pretend that I have not seen what I have seen, to talk myself out of my horror, to forget it. But a deeper, truer part of me, a part that has been nourished and strengthened by my passage through death and resurrection, will not allow me to run away anymore from what I know to be true. I must stand and face it. I must give voice to my Truth regardless of the cost. Otherwise I will die.

Before I share this terrifying answer with you, I must weave the background of a tapestry. There has been a recent burgeoning of fashionable treatment centers specializing in eating disorders, modeled on those that have been operating for many years for alcoholics and drug addicts. Chemical dependency and eating disorders are now big business, you see.[19] With so many of the rich and famous either dying from these diseases or emerging from the closet to share their secrets with us while they are alive, "healers" are now appearing in droves to cure them of their malady. "Recovery" has become a billion-dollar word.

I do not mean to imply that all such centers are the evil offspring of human greed and that all of the individuals staffing them are wicked charlatans. I have no doubt that many people working in these centers are compassionate individuals who truly care about the sick ones who come to them for help.

My point here is rather that the profit motive and the power motive cannot be ignored as we reflect upon the booming recovery movement in North America. Human evil thrives in every quarter of society, even in churches and in social movements. We cannot afford to blind ourselves to this reality. We must develop our powers of discernment. When we see television evangelists and faith healers making millions of dollars out of their careers, or "recovery experts" whose compassion hinges on the thickness of their clients' wallets, we must allow our suspicions to be aroused. We must listen to our guts. Otherwise we will be led like sheep to the slaughter.

But let us not lose sight of the fact that the recovery movement originated as a grass-roots phenomenon, in the sick ones themselves yearning for wholeness and opening up their arms to one another. Alcoholics Anonymous was founded sixty years ago as a tiny seed by two drunks turning to one another for solace in their shared pain and remains to this day an *anonymous* fellowship out of which no one makes their living. Anonymity and volunteer labor are two of the AA traditions, and there is a critically important reason for that. Their "leaders are but trusted servants; they do not govern."[20] No one earns money or climbs to power and prestige through AA. Observing such wisdom in these guiding principles of AA lets me know in my gut that the true spirit of Compassion was leading those two sick men and still lives and breathes today in the organization they established. Furthermore, the naming of the Twelve Steps emerged out of the actual experience of healing that these men had, not from an outside expert designing a rational "figured-out solution"[21] for their disease.

Similarly, my clear identification and naming of the steps I followed in recovering from anorexia occurred a full nine years *after* my actual *experience* of healing. This is of crucial importance in our reflections on the recovery movement and the use of the addiction model in eating disorders. In writing this book and suggesting that other anorexics consider the possibility of using the Twelve-Step program in their own way, I have no desire to join the ranks of proclaimers of models, to lock myself or anyone else into a rigid magic formula for cure, which would be nothing but illusion anyway. All magic is illusion.

Six months ago one of my colleagues, a gastroenterologist, asked me to see a very sick anorexic in his practice. After he read my consultation report, in which I consented to work with her to facilitate her "deep spiritual recovery," he turned to me and said, "How do you recover from this disease, Joan? Give me the formula!" I replied that there is no formula, Twelve-Step or otherwise. There is no magic.

Are you confused by this assertion, following as it does upon part six, in which I urge the foundation of Anorexics Anonymous? If you reflect upon all that I have said, you will discover there is no conflict here. I knew in 1983 that my recovery had occurred through a radical surrender of my will to that of my God. I knew it in my gut and in my bones. I knew it. Nine years later I discovered AA and its Twelve-Step program. The identity between these steps and my own recovery process was undeniable. It struck me like a lightning bolt. I knew that the Twelve Steps were *naming the reality of my own already-experienced healing*. I knew it in the same way that I knew I had reached a turning point in January 1974, in the same way that I knew my experience of Rachel's transfiguration was real, in the same way that I knew I could and must let Eric Thomson go in 1978, in the same way that I knew the "tape" of my anorexia had been ejected from my brain at 5:25 P.M. on February twenty-fourth, 1983. All of my subsequent experience has validated the truth of that knowing, has led me to trust my deep knowing and to begin to admit to myself and to others, clearly and honestly and humbly, in all circumstances, that I know what I know. I believe this deep knowing resides in each one of us, in our right brains and our guts and our hearts and our bones. I believe it is identical to the "collective unconscious" named by Carl Jung, to "Wild Woman"[22] named by Clarissa Pinkola Estés, and to the "Living Process"[23] named by Anne Wilson Schaef. I believe it is the Truth within us. I believe it is God.

What is the point of all of this? Simply that knowing what I know about my recovery, I am compelled to share my knowledge with you. I must do so—not for you but for me, for my own integrity and health and wholeness. I stand before you stripped of all my lies. I want nothing from you. I want only to be whole within myself, to live in my Truth and my reality. I have no way of knowing what you will do with my offering. You might think about it. You might scorn it and mock it. You might file it away for future reference. You might throw this book in the garbage, or return it to the bookstore and demand a refund. You might write me a letter. You might enclose a letter bomb. You might praise me. You might kill me. It doesn't matter. I have nothing to lose and nothing to gain anymore, for I live in a place where winning and losing are simply irrelevant.

I have met in my travels an astonishing number of Spirit-filled individuals who live in this same place, and those meetings have been priceless gifts, for mine is a lonely place in many ways and the discovery of others here brings some of the deepest joy I have ever known. Some of these men and women are writers, and I have connected with them only through their words. They emerge from a variety of backgrounds. M. Scott Peck comes from psychiatry, Anne Wilson Schaef from psychology. Matthew Fox comes from theology, Clarissa Pinkola Estés from storytelling and the land of mythology and archetype. Adrienne Rich is a poet. Meister Eckhart was a mystic, C. S. Lewis a professor of medieval and renaissance literature. If you are intrigued by some of my ideas, or have thought the same thoughts I have, I urge you to explore some of these writers, and to discover more for yourself. Explore. Nurture yourself. And trust your *own* deep intuition as you proceed on the voyage.

MISCONCEPTIONS ABOUT ADDICTION

In continuing to fill in the background of my tapestry, I address some common misconceptions about the nature of addiction and recovery from addiction that appear to be rooted deeply in the minds of most people, professionals included. So deeply that we cannot even fathom the possibility that they are misconceptions, for we have simply accepted them as "facts" and relegated them to that region of the mind that harbors such concepts as gravity, the atomic nature of matter, and the chemical basis for the functioning of the human brain.

Some of the more obvious myths about addiction I have dealt with in earlier sections of this book: "Addicts are weak-willed." "Addicts are bad/evil/sinners." "Addicts don't care about anybody else." "Addicts are just trying to escape taking responsibility for their actions by whining that they are sick."

There is a subtle thread running through all of these misconceptions, and it is a truly evil one. It is the lie/sin of objectivism, of making oneself the subject and the other person an inferior object to be scorned or judged or punished or otherwise used. The person who buys into these myths is declaring, in essence, "I am better than the addict." I, of course, know this lie well, for I embraced it and lived it for many years.

I shall spend no further time on these more obvious misconceptions, because I need to explore at some length a much more important, pivotal, and far-reaching one. My ultimate goal in this discussion is to complete the tapestry that will, I hope, allow you to begin to grasp why my mouth went dry with terror when I saw the answer to my question about the unwillingness of my colleagues to even consider the addiction model for eating disorders.

The pivotal, and critically important, misconception about addiction was voiced succinctly by a dear friend who helped with the research for this chapter, a graduate student in family studies who will shortly be working as a family therapist. He is a brilliant and compassionate man who is about to be unleashed on an unsuspecting public, as I was in fourth-year medical school when I lay around for three days with appendicitis without making the diagnosis. When I mentioned my acceptance of the addiction model for my disease, Henry looked at me with deep kindness and gently said, "But we'd like to think that anorexia can be *cured*, Joan, not merely accepted and 'coped with' for the duration of the patient's life."

Aha! Does this ring a bell in your mind? Does it sound suspiciously like the concept in my own mind which I discussed in chapter 32 when I explored the reason why I was held up in my recovery at Step Ten? Henry's reservation was echoed boldly in a recent bulletin published by the National Eating Disorder Information Centre (NEDIC). This body is a powerful dispenser of information and "facts" to professionals and interested lay people alike (principally individuals suffering from eating disorders who have admitted the reality of their disease). In discussing the addiction model, this influential body declared in bold type, "While we recognise that some people have *felt* supported by 12 Step programmes, NEDIC does not endorse groups intended to support sufferers or significant people in their lives which adhere to addiction models. ... The belief that 'eating disordered' behavior can only be *controlled*, not cured, is damaging to the self-empowerment of the sufferer and creates a sense of permanent disability or pathology."[24] (Italics mine.)

Once again I say, "Aha!" When I read this I began to see the profound misconception about addiction that is inherent both in Henry's gentle statement and in this bold warning issued like an edict by NEDIC. Both had failed to grasp a fundamental truth that all addicts *know* in our bones once we are well advanced in recovery. *We don't "control" our disease!* We can't! We can *only* recover from it by letting go of the attempt to control! We can never be "cured" of our addiction, yet admitting this fact is the only way in which we can *in effect* be cured for the rest of our lives, one day at a time. Although not cured we are cured. By admitting our weakness we become empowered.

Paradoxical? Absolutely. Yet that is the nature of the spiritual realm and of the cosmos. To deeply enter into our spirituality, a place of bottomless mystery, we must make a radical paradigm shift in our thinking so that we can grasp the paradoxical. We must move from a dualistic "either/or" way of thinking to a dialectical "both/and" way.[25] Henry and NEDIC were both hung up on a dualism: The patient is *either* incurable (an addict) *or* she can be cured. They could not see the trap in their thinking. All dualism is like a seesaw. It keeps us stuck. We will vacillate back and forth between the two ends of the seesaw forever, impaled on the horns of a dilemma. *The only solution is to leave the seesaw.*[26] To leap off and embrace a completely different approach, the dialectical way of thinking: The patient is *both* incurable *and* curable. By accepting her "incurability" she is in effect "cured." The operative words here are "in effect." By living one day at a time, by doing what is necessary for her sanity on a daily basis, she is empowered to live without the starvation, without the "fix" that numbs the mind and separates her from the Truth within herself.

Dualistic thinking attempts to break down a highly complex, multifaceted cosmos into two oversimplified opposing poles and makes us believe we must choose between them, thereby keeping us static and preventing us from seeking other alternatives. The whole thing is an illusion anyway, because the universe cannot be reduced to a pair of opposites.[27]

Dualism in action is occurring at this very moment in thousands of psychiatric units in the civilized world, and we need to realize the extent of the devastation it is causing. I am referring to the common practice of treating the anorexic or bulimic patient by "taking control" of her. Nurses sit and watch her eat. The bathroom is locked. She is closely observed for two hours after meals and confined to the ward lest she escape to the outdoors to exercise. Punishment is inflicted if she fails to eat the prescribed food. The underlying dualistic principle is that *either we have control or she has control.* And since she is incapable of exercising control of her disease, we must take control. As she gains weight and appears to be getting better, we gradually let her take over the control. We encourage her to do so, tell her she is in control now, tell her she will be fine.

Tragically, the patient, who is already embroiled in the sick dualistic thinking generated by her disease, is reinforced to continue in this mode by the dualism of her therapists. So although she feels uneasy about their reassurances, since she *knows* that she is not "fine," she sees no alternative but to go along with the majority opinion. After all, we are the professionals. We are the experts. Progress appears to continue for a time (more illusion), until one day: "Gotcha!" The disease rears its ugly head when she least suspects it, and she is caught in its teeth once again, this time even more demoralized and hopeless than she was before.

What is the alternative to this vicious cycle, which is all too familiar to every anorexic and every professional working with her? There is only one solution. *The therapists must jump off the seesaw.* She is too sick to let go of the illusion of control. We are the sane ones, remember? It takes two to play the game. We must come to grasp the alternative to the dualistic seesaw and embrace the reality that *no one is in control.* No one *can* be in control. This disease cannot be vanquished by control. The patient must eventually recover, if she does recover, by a *total surrender* of control to her own healing principle/Truth/God/Higher Power, which she will come to discover lies deep within herself. She must get in touch with it and let it flow. She must love it as it loves her and stay connected with it at all times so that it can empower her to choose life over self-destruction. In such a state of true recovery, "control" is an irrelevant concept, a word from a foreign language. It is an illusion. It does not exist.

WESTERN DUALISM AND ADDICTION

I believe it is of crucial importance for all of us living in Western societies to study the concept of dualism if we hope to keep our planet around for our children to grow up on. Two thinkers have clarified the subject for me, and I invite you to peruse their ideas for yourself. Psychologist Anne Wilson Schaef explores the concept extensively in her pivotal work, *When Society Becomes an Addict,* and extends it in *Beyond Therapy, Beyond Science.* Theologian/historian Matthew Fox discusses dualism in *A Spirituality Named Compassion,* in *Original Blessing,* and again in *The Coming of the Cosmic Christ.* He sees it as the most basic of sins, "the sin behind all sin,"[28] and I believe this concept is at least worth thinking about.

Western civilization has been steeped in dualistic thinking since Descartes, and Isaac Newton solidified it for us, as Fox lucidly explains,[29] and Schaef agrees.[30] Fortunately, twentieth-century post-modern scientists, beginning with Albert Einstein, in virtually every discipline from physics and astronomy to the biosciences, are waking up to this fact and making the paradigm shift to dialectical thinking. Physicists no longer have difficulty accepting that light is both particle and wave, for example. Albert Einstein further demonstrated that the particle itself can no longer be seen as a static object, but as a form of energy, and that the particle world (matter) is dynamic and forever changing. Mystics in all of the world's religions have long accepted the existence of paradox, of dialectic, as the driving energy of the cosmos, and in the twentieth century, scientists have come full circle to arrive at the same conclusion. Matthew Fox explains it this way. "The basic force of the subatomic world is the force of electric attraction between the positively charged nucleus of the atom and the negatively charged electrons. ... Harmony does not mean a balance-at-rest but a vibrant, bi-polar energy force that urges on all other energy. Dialectic becomes the basis of all reality!"[31]

So in our lifetime the long-awaited reunion of science and spirituality, which Peck describes as being artificially split in the seventeenth century in the time of Galileo,[32] is actually taking place. In the words of Blair, "The schism between the two worlds of science and religion is beginning to heal and to merge into a single majestic river of vision."[33] Or, as Griffin observes, "A reenchanted, liberating science will be fully developed only by people with a postmodern spirituality, in which dualisms that have made modern science such an ambiguous phenomenon have been transcended, and only in a society organized for the good of the planet as a whole."[34]

If the other sciences have been capable of making this critically important shift from dualism to dialectic, why has medicine—the science that touches humankind so profoundly and intimately and that most of us would regard as more art than science anyway—been so slow to follow suit? Why have we as a body been dragging our collective heels to make the only change that is capable of rescuing our entire planet from destruction as it rescues the individual walking upon it from the insanity of a disease process (addiction) that leads to self-destruction? Why?

The answer to this question is the same as the answer to my earlier question about why my profession refuses to look at eating disorders as addictions, the answer that cast me into the terror I earlier described. For this refusal *stems directly from the dualistic thinking* embodied in my friend Henry's statement and NEDIC's edict. Therefore the answer to both questions is paradoxically contained in the question itself: *Because we as professionals in the "helping sciences" of medicine and psychology are entirely and utterly and blindly "stuck" in the congealed stasis of dualism.* We are slow to abandon dualism because we are stuck in dualism! We are so stuck that we cannot even see our own stuckness! We have embraced, and continue to embrace, a now outmoded way of viewing the world from a nonparticipatory science that is dualistic, reductionistic, objectivistic, mechanistic, linear, and empirical.[35] We have fossilized ourselves into a paradigm that the other sciences have been outgrowing for most of the twentieth century, a paradigm which will destroy us all if it is not changed.

The enormity of this concept is almost overwhelming, for it strikes at the very heart of my life as a physician. It is staggering and terrifying. Consider the implications! If Fox and Schaef and Peck and countless others are correct in their conception of Western medicine and psychology as being enmeshed for centuries in a dualistic worldview, it means we are *all* affected by it. It means we must *all* make the paradigm shift if we are to save ourselves. For, as Fox makes clear in his inspired work, *The Coming of the Cosmic Christ*, it is dualism (an entity unique in all the universe to *Homo sapiens*) that has resulted in the current state of a planet hovering on the brink of nuclear annihilation and ecological catastrophe.[36] Dear God, where do we begin?

BRIDGING THE SCHISM WITHIN

Let me answer that question on a somewhat calmer note, one that emerges from my hope. We begin with ourselves. For our universe is a hologram, which means that each particle within it, including every living creature on our planet, contains the whole of the universe in microcosmic form within itself.[37] We must each begin to look at our selves with honesty *and with compassion*. We must allow ourselves to know that we have done nothing to *bring about* this evil other than to be born human. We must accept that we are not God, can never *be* God as long as we continue to exist as humans, and do not ever *have* to be God during our sojourn on earth. For *all* humans fall into the sin/evil/lie of dualism. It is inescapable. We are not born in this state ("original sin"—a Catholic doctrine that I, like Fox[38] and many other Catholics, reject). Can anyone look at a newborn baby and believe it is sinful? Hogwash! No, Wordsworth was on target when he wrote that we are born "trailing clouds of glory ... /From God, who is our home."[39] But we all become sinful as we mature. Anyone who denies this is living in delusion. With the possible exception of sociopaths, we all know in our hearts that we have done things we are ashamed of, deliberate willful actions that we took or actions that we willfully failed to do, that harmed ourselves or another. That is sin.

We are human beings. We are limited. We cannot ever be God, all-seeing, all-knowing, all-loving, all-just, all-true. Nor is all-ness required of us. So when we fail to be all-anything we have not sinned. Rather I must define within myself (as you must define within yourself) what the essence of being *fully human* is, for me. That is what I am required to be. And failing to be fully human is what constitutes my sin. Only I can know what the fullness of life within me means. Only you can know what the fullness of life within you means. So only I and my God know when I have sinned. And only you and your God know when you have sinned. (I also believe there is only one God, but he/she presents him/herself differently to each of us.)

You may wonder what all of this theological discussion has to do with eating disorders and recovery, yet the concept of sin is critically important to those of us who suffer from addiction. During the fourteen years of my active disease virtually everything I did surrounding the issues of eating and weight *felt like a sin* to me. I now know there is an enormous difference between being sick and being sinful. During the years in my hell I did not. I had no powers of true discernment. Not too surprising, really, considering that I was sleep-walking, profoundly separated from my feelings and my knowing and my Truth by the numbing effect of my daily "fix" of starvation and "control."

A recovering teenage bulimic recently shared with me her joy when she experienced the breakthrough to her Truth, to her deep self. "I feel like I've been asleep for three years," she said, "and I've just wakened up. I'm shocked to discover what a good person I really am. I like myself! I'm so outgoing! And I see everything and everybody differently now. I see that everybody has their own problems. And I can understand them now. I don't feel mad at anybody anymore. And I don't feel nervous when I'm talking to them, afraid of looking stupid if I don't know what to say or do. Now if I don't know what to say I don't say anything, and it feels comfortable. It feels great!" She was experiencing the ecstasy of interconnectedness for the first time.

Folklore and mythology, those priceless treasurehouses of our deepest wisdom as human beings, are replete with tales of the enchanted sleeper waking up from the hundred-year sleep. "Rip Van Winkle," "Snow White," and "The Sleeping Beauty" are but a few of them. *The Chronicles of Narnia* by C. S. Lewis contain several more modern renditions of the enchantment motif, in particular *The Lion, the Witch and the Wardrobe* and *The Silver Chair*. Try reading these stories from the perspective of the anorexic/addict falling into the sleep of her disease and then waking up at last, when the spell is broken by the willing completion of a pre-ordained task by another human being, to the awareness of her deep self.

Jill in *The Silver Chair* is one such victim. "It didn't come into her head that she was being enchanted, for now the magic was in its full strength; and of course, the more enchanted you get, the more certain you feel that you are not enchanted at all."[40] Examine the nature of the enchantress or sorceress in each case. See how she always appears in disguise and tricks the unknowing and gullible heroine (or hero) into swallowing the poison that puts her to sleep. See how innocent the wicked one always appears on the surface. Her disguise is impeccable, for she *is* truly evil. She is acting out of the reality of her own true nature. So she can trick us, just as the sociopathic con artist can trick us completely. We experience no "gut instinct" that we are being lied to, because we are not. I believe the demonic sorceress in these tales, this "malevolent thing disguised as a benevolent thing"[41] is identical to what Schaef has labeled the "Addictive Process,"[42] and which she sees running through our entire civilization and through each of us living in it. I think it is also the same force that Fox has identified as "the spirit of dualism," of which he writes,

> it is part of competition which is invariably an Us-versus-Them or I-versus-You strategem. It is part of compulsion which is so often an I-It strategem, me and my bottle, me and my goal, the corporation and its rising black lines, etc., etc. The members of this trinity are not isolated but interact in a kind of vortex and tornado-like funnel that carries us deeper and deeper to where the demonic lies and lies and lies. And maybe ... dualism is the ultimate alienation, the ultimate rending of the truth of ourselves, the ultimate sin. Or, as they say, dualism is the original sin.[43]

Different names for the same entity. Schaef sees it as disease, Fox as sin, and both of these deep thinkers emphasize the presence of this malignant process in *Western* civilization. But my own view of this force is more in accord with Jung's concept of the Shadow, and with Jungian analyst and storyteller Clarissa Estés's naming of the natural "predator" of the psyche. I concur that "it is innate, meaning *indigenous to all humans* from birth forward, and in that sense is without conscious origin."[44] (Italics mine.) In *Women Who Run With the Wolves*, Estés's rendition of the ancient Bluebeard tale and her brilliant analysis of its powerful meaning for all of us psychic travelers is without parallel in its rich poetry and complex insight. Estés has undoubtedly wrestled long and bloodily with the predator and emerged victorious. I would highly recommend an exploration of this story to every reader. It will strike a chord in your deepest self and turn on dozens of lights in your soul. Although as a feminist Estés is addressing a primarily female audience, I believe that most of her stories, and certainly Bluebeard, are equally meaningful for men, for they speak to the feminine principle in *all* humans.

Estés points out that we should not be surprised by the presence of the predator but rather deeply "acknowledge that both within and without, there is a force which will act in opposition to the instincts of the natural Self, and that that malignant force *is what it is.*" It always acts in accord with its nature, which is "filled with hatred and desires to kill the lights of the psyche.[45] ... Wherever the predator lurks and works everything is derailed, demolished, and decapitated."[46] Its task is "to see that no consciousness occurs,...to check in from time to time and twist off or poison any new growth."[47] Our task as humans is not to run away from the predator or deny its existence but "to recognize it, to protect ourselves from its devastation, and ultimately to deprive it of its murderous energy."[48]

Estés voices the truth that I have learned through my own sojourn in Bluebeard's castle, that it was only through bearing the deepest of woundings, a wounding severe enough to bring me to the edge of the grave, that I could be awakened to the reality of my "blood loss and therefore ... [begin] to live."[49] The paradox again. Furthermore, the conquest of Bluebeard is a process wherein one attains awareness and awakeness, the fullness of individual consciousness, in which state one is able "to break the old pattern of ignorance and to behold a horror, and not look away."[50] The process invariably involves asking the "key questions. ... What stands behind? What is not as it appears? What do I know deep in my ovaries that I wish I did not know? What of me has been killed, or lays dying?"[51]

We will shed blood in answering these questions, but after the conquest we will celebrate the pain, for our final task in the struggle is "to allow [our] Life/Death/Life nature to pick the predator apart and carry it off to be incubated, transformed, released back into life." This *transformation* of the predator's energy leaves us

> filled with intensity, vitality and drive. ... The predator's rage can be rendered into a soul-fire for accomplishing a great task in the world. The predator's craftiness can be used to inspect and understand things from a distance. The predator's killing nature can be used to kill off that which must properly die in a woman's life, or what she must die to in her outer life, these

being different things at different times. ... What ash of the predator is left then will indeed rise up again, but in much smaller form, much more recognizably, and with much less power to deceive and destroy.[52]

The initial enchantment by Bluebeard and mating with him, followed by the complex combat to the death, is the ancient story known to every addict, and probably to every human being.

All of the writers discussed previously are correct when they say the function and purpose of the predator/Shadow/spirit of dualism/Addictive Process is to destroy life. It is the opponent of the Wild Woman/collective unconscious/spirit of compassion/Life Process, whose purpose is to enhance life and to bring the individual to the fullest experience of his or her existence as a human person. All of the world religions have, of course, concerned themselves wholly with this struggle between Good and Evil, and various names have been placed on the opposing forces. In my own tradition, the same one as Peck's, they are called God and Satan, and they wage their eternal war in the battleground of the human soul.[53]

Note, however, that Evil is not the same thing as Death. Death and Life are inextricably linked in an unending cycle, and one cannot occur without the other. Out of Death comes Life. Out of Life comes Death. I do not believe that Life and Evil are linked in this way. They are two truly opposite forces. As Peck points out, even the name of Evil is formed by reversing the letters of "Live."[54] The purpose of Evil is to destroy Life, to annihilate it utterly, whereas the purpose of Death is to transform Life.

My favorite names for the two opposing forces within me are the Truth and the Lie, for the predator is the most cunning of all liars, and the Wild Self is the ancient deep knowing of what is and what must be—a knowing that has always existed, long before any created being emerged from the void. Furthermore, I have learned that it is only by living as close to my knowing, to my Truth, as it is possible to get, can I remain whole, sane, integrated, experiencing all there is in life, flowing out to others as the person who I am, and receiving of others in joy and in pain. Even the smallest lie about the smallest thing is dangerous to my health. Withholding the truth from myself or others, failing to communicate honestly, is a lie (although at times compassion may necessitate a temporary delay in disclosure of the truth to another. We can trust our love, if it is true, to guide us in this fine discrimination).

I have never in my life encountered a situation in which lying resulted in any ultimate good for anyone, nor one in which adhering to the practice of truthfulness failed to result in ultimate good for all. This is not the same thing as saying that the truth is painless! Far from it. In fact, the most common reason why I am tempted to lie is to avoid pain. I may tell myself I am lying to protect the other person, to avoid hurting him, but that is another lie, for the truth is I cannot bear the thought of the pain I might have to endure if I speak my Truth out loud. The other person may not like it! There may be painful consequences. That is the risk. That is why the Truth is usually the road less traveled, and why the Lie appears to be the easy way out. When I feel afraid of speaking my Truth, I know the Lie is hard at work in me, for fear is its principal weapon, as Peck has astutely observed.[55]

Something I have discovered in my personal life and in my work is that truth begets truth. When I choose to connect with my courage and speak the Truth despite my fear, astonishing things happen in the other person. My Truth seems to call forth the Truth from the other, and we both change as a result of the dance of our Truths. Transformation occurs. The joy that results from this experience is so profound and so exhilarating that I now move through my life looking for every opportunity to bring it into being. I love my Truth, for he is my God.

And lies beget lies. Dualism is the ultimate Lie. Dualism is at the root of my addiction. Dualism disconnects me from the rest of the universe by providing me with the initially comfortable and warm illusion that I am separate from everything else, that I am subject and everything else is object. It is a short step from "separate" to "better," and—*voilà!* I am wholly in the clutches of my disease. In thrall to the predator/Shadow/Lie/Addictive Process. The Truth lets me know that I am not separate from the rest of the universe. I am in reality part of it, inextricably linked with it. Even when I die these atoms that

I call my body will be transformed into something else, and the energy of my spirit will dissolve into the Energy of the cosmos.

I have explored in great detail the nature of the predator in the human psyche. If you have not drifted off to sleep by now or tossed this book onto the junk heap you may be wondering why. Or perhaps you are now seeing the portrait emerging from the ground of my tapestry. You may be able to recognize the features of the face before you, the countenance of the prey of the predator. Is there something familiar about the nose? The mouth? The structure of the bones? And, most importantly, the eyes? Yes, you are correct. The face is yours.

Be not afraid, my friend. Look into the face. Open your eyes wide. See what you see. Let your heart pound. Let your terror rise up. It will not kill you. Most assuredly, it will not kill you; but blindness will. And continued deliberate ignorance will. And failing to ask the questions will. And failing to seek the answers will.

Know, above all else, that you are not to blame for falling victim to the predator. It is in the nature of the human journey to do so, for we must, each one of us, take the test set down for us, move through Bluebeard's castle. If you have not yet seen his beard, you will. If you have not yet viewed the bones and the stacked skulls and inhaled the pungent stench of blood in the dungeon, you will. It is part of our destiny as human beings. There can be no escape. We never asked to be born. But we were. We are here. Let us see what is to be done about that.

ARE WE ALL ADDICTS?

Anne Wilson Schaef, in her important work *Beyond Therapy, Beyond Science*, presents a compelling argument that all therapists among us who are still mired in a dualistic paradigm, in subject/object relationships, in a linear, rational, reductionistic, mechanistic science, are ourselves suffering from *addiction*. A full exposition of her thesis is impossible in this discussion, but I would urge you to read her work, for she offers a number of meaty bones that will keep you chewing thoughtfully for hours, days, and weeks. She believes all of us who still practice "therapy" on patients are codependents,[56] and that we are either sick and getting sicker (if we are still in denial) or sick and getting better (if we are in recovery). She sees no middle ground. She states that she is now a "'recovering psychotherapist' (as in recovering from *being* a psychotherapist)."[57] (Italics mine.) For her "sobriety" she has had to break with her professional colleagues and go her own way, moving to the beat of her own distant drummer. She is, without doubt, an utterly unique and courageous woman who is in fact helping to lead us through our darkness as we suffer the death throes that must precede rebirth. She is also, not surprisingly, an outcast from her profession.

Matthew Fox views our struggle as global villagers from a somewhat different perspective, that of a theologian and historian, but his essential thesis is the same as Schaef's. He decries Western religions for restricting their vision, since the time of Augustine in the fourth century A.D., to sin, the fall of man, and redemption in Jesus Christ, and urges our return to creation-centered spirituality.[58] The latter begins with the deep knowledge that we are, first and above all, *blessed* by our Creator and bestowed as *blessings* on the universe. *The Coming of the Cosmic Christ* is a powerful indictment of all facets of Western society—economics, education, politics, medicine, religion—and the facts he presents to substantiate his denunciation are sufficient to curdle the reader's blood. He sees our civilization, for example, as one that "devours its youth,"[59] and the figures he offers to back up this viewpoint are sobering indeed. He traces the historical route along which Western society has moved, showing how the blatant injustice suffered by the *anawim* (literally the "little ones," and encompassing the poor, the crippled, racial and ethnic minorities, homosexuals, and other downtrodden groups in our society) has been the inevitable result of patriarchy, of hierarchy, of a civilization that is in love with death. He calls us to return to naming God with his/her true name: Compassion, which includes celebration of interconnectedness and justice-making.[60] Like Schaef he is a prophet, a latter-day John the Baptist, a Spirit-led man, following with courage and humility the mission his God has given him. And like her he has been misunderstood, mocked, rejected, and crucified by his own church and other guardians of the status quo in all sectors of society.

I was at first astonished by the vituperative quality of the attacks I have read and heard on these two individuals. I could not understand how anyone reading their work could fail to see and hear their beautiful integrity, to connect at gut level with the profound truth in their messages. I was overwhelmed with rage and grief as I heard the blatant lies, half-truths, and slander that have been uttered about them, even by a few of my colleagues whom I have always deeply respected. (Most of these lies originated in media reports. My colleagues had not even bothered to read the books in question.) I have prayed for them all, attackers and attacked, and I have wept and felt their pain as my inner being experienced their crucifixion.

You may once again be wondering if I will ever get to a point in all of this. I have described in such detail the trials endured by prophets like Schaef and Fox for a very good reason. Not to sympathize with *them*, for I have discovered that the pain resulting from being misunderstood and rejected by others cannot begin to compare with the joy experienced by any human person who follows his or her own drummer and acts in accordance with the requirements of inner Truth. Fox and Schaef and I need no sympathy. I no longer weep for them, or for myself. Rather I weep for you. For any of you and all of you who have not yet experienced the blessing of having your eyes opened, of being struck by a thunderbolt, of being knocked off your horse. I weep not from the illusionary stance of self-righteous pity but from the bleeding center of my compassion, from my interconnection with you. How well I know your pain! How loudly I have howled your cry! How profoundly I ache to draw you into this place where I dwell, to share my ecstasy and my joy.

I write all of this in order that you may see my tears for you, that the light reflected in those tears may enter the dark mysterious central room of your being and trigger some ancient music written before the dawn. I write to draw you forth, to urge you on in your own journey of self-discovery and self-healing. The evil spell can never be broken by the one who is enchanted, but only by a willing action of true love by another human being, as Peck so eloquently points out.[61] This book is my true love for you in action. I offer it with a prayer that these words may be the correct ones, the key to break the spell for even a few of you.

And I write it to share my hope with you as well. For I have witnessed the blind rage of a cornered and mortally wounded bull. How he charges with bloodshot eyes at anything moving in his vicinity. How he lashes out from his agony with hooves and horns and teeth. And I have watched his frenzied efforts grow progressively weaker as he staggers to his knees, attempts to rise again one last time, then succumbs at last to his death. And I see in the macrocosm of my wounded world the same sightless rage striking out in all directions, the same writhing anguish that the bull and I have endured. And I believe that when my world falls to its knees and thence on its face in the mud, then the bottom will have been reached and the old song will be heard by the divinity within us, which cannot die. In those days the phoenix will rise up from the ashes in joyous freedom to soar to a place of ecstasy beyond our wildest imagining. For the joy always exceeds the pain, and there can be no doubt that our species and our earth are in a state of indescribable pain. I pray that our children or our children's children will live to experience the joy.

Everywhere I go these days I find evidence that nurtures my hope for *Homo sapiens* and the future of my planet. The winds of change are blowing, enlightenment is on the move, humans are awakening to our destiny to be lovers and dancers and justice makers. In my office I meet secretaries and firemen and mothers and politicians and floor-scrubbers and plumbers who have thought the same thoughts I have. At the hospital I witness instances of caring and courage that leave me gaping in awe. At professional gatherings I exchange ideas with social workers and teachers and physicians and nurses and speech pathologists who are traveling the same road I am on, who react to the voicing of my Truth with a deep knowing yes in their eyes. In every facet of my life I find individuals who are discovering their own Truth and taking the risk of giving voice to it. I estimate that 20 percent of humans are already stumbling or strolling or skipping down this road less traveled, and that the survival of our species into the third millennium will have been secured when we number 40 percent.

After reading the wisdom of original thinkers like Fox and Schaef I suffered profound doubts about my own feeble attempts to effect change in the professional world in which I live and move. Schaef confesses to similar doubts about her own ability to be a torch-bearer, which she calls her "imperfect vessel" routine.[62] When I read this I laughed, then braced my shoulders and carried on with the work I know I must do. For I believe I have one small unique contribution to offer to the debate about the rampant dualism enmeshing my profession and the entire society in which we live. This contribution relates to my earlier discussion about the predator, but I will reiterate it here in slightly different words.

I noted that Schaef sees dualism as the Addictive Process and concludes that we are all therefore *sick*. I noted that Fox sees dualism as the origin of all sins and concludes that we are all therefore *sinners*. Which of them is right? I prefer to completely abandon this dualism about dualism ("dualism is either disease or dualism is 'original' sin"), jump off the seesaw, and give voice to what my Truth is whispering about this. Dualism is neither disease nor sin, and dualism is both disease and sin. *Dualism is part of the essence of what makes us human*, for it is the predator that inhabits every human psyche from the cradle to the deathbed. Dualism is the Lie we must bear within ourselves as members of *Homo sapiens*. It is the price tag attached to our magnificent humanity, for if it were not there, deep within our psyches, the concept of free will[63] would be a joke. If there were no *real* temptation to believe the Lie, we would merely be puppets on God's string. What purpose would there be in that? We might as well be giraffes. (Not that I am implying there is anything wrong with giraffes. They are beautiful creatures. I love them and learn a lot from the way they are content to be themselves, to live and die as giraffes, without pretending to be lions.) Dualism is the opposing force of our Truth, and the internal battle between them is what generates the heat and light for our growth in creativity and compassion. Dualism is to be welcomed as a facet of our humanity, for it provides us with the constant challenge to outwit it, dismantle it, and transform it, to put it in the service of dialectic, of Truth, of Compassion, of God.

So to Schaef I say: Why must we name dualism as a disease? Can't we say we're human instead of sick? The concept of disease implies that cure is possible and must be constantly striven for. There can be no cure for dualism, as there can be no cure for addiction, as I earlier discussed. There can only be transformation: power out of weakness, good out of evil, life out of death, Truth out of Lie.

And to Fox I say: Why must we name dualism as sin? The concept of sin implies deliberate willful choice. Who among us chose to be born human? Sin must be forgiven by God and by the sinner himself. Must we be forgiven for being human? Can we not celebrate the existence of the dualistic predator within us, and even as we dance lay out the steps for using this predator to the ends of our Truth, to the glory of our Creator? The predator can never be expelled from the human psyche, not until we no longer must pitch our tents east of Eden. Let us learn to live with it, opening wide our senses to all of its wily tricks. Let us not expend energy on attempting to banish what cannot be banished. Let us instead allow our Truth to outfox our Lie. And that is possible, for Truth is more powerful than the Lie. The ultimate downfall of the Lie is assured by that fact. We need not fret about it. The Lie will in the end be defeated by its own lie, by its own pride, by its own blind narcissistic belief that it can vanquish the Truth. Our destiny as humans is but to facilitate that defeat, within ourselves and within our small circles of influence, one day at a time.

Chapter 35

A "New" Therapeutic Approach to Eating Disorders

In this final chapter I would like to share with you the new paradigm I am in the process of evolving as I work with anorexic, bulimic, and chemical addicts in my practice. If you can glean something from it I will rejoice with you, for these individuals and their loved ones are enduring unspeakable pain as we experts flounder about in our confusion. Although a few are recovering under our traditional ministrations, I believe this is largely occurring *despite* our help rather than because of it. I beg you to let go of any flareup of defensiveness that occurred within you as you read that last sentence. Please take my hand and come with me now as you recall that I attach *no blame* to any of us, you or me, for we are merely human (thank God!). We must allow ourselves to make mistakes. We must also allow ourselves to *see* the mistakes, to claim them as our own, and to proceed with the work of change.

I must first express my gratitude to Anne Wilson Schaef for her assistance in my work. In her latest book, *Beyond Therapy, Beyond Science*, she has given *names* to the concepts I too have been evolving. Her lucid formulation of the work she does with addicts has helped me to crystallize my own mission into a framework that now makes "sense" to my left brain. Before I read her book I was working almost completely out of my right brain and my gut, out of my Truth. But without the correct names for what I was doing I stumbled a lot and endured the agony of total blindness, relying solely on prayer most of the time. (This initial phase has been a blessing to me because it has connected me more solidly with my Truth than ever before in my life.) As Peck has observed, "to name something correctly gives us a certain amount of power over it."[1] I still spend much time in prayer and reflection, connecting with my Truth, experiencing his love for me and returning it in a prayer that has no words. For I must be in tune with my Truth if I am to be his instrument in my work. My Truth is the Center of my being, the Hub of my wheel, and he lives in my solar plexus.

If my ideas stimulate your interest, or if they echo your own original thoughts, read Schaef's recent work, as well as one of her earlier books, *When Society Becomes an Addict*. I believe these two books are of fundamental importance for anyone who is working, or wishes to work, with eating-disordered individuals or other addicts. If you experience some emotional difficulty with Schaef's premise that everyone in our profession, and indeed in our society, is sick, try tempering your response with a gentle injection of compassion for yourself, using Estés's concept of the innate predator as discussed earlier. Remember at all times that you and I are guilty of nothing but being human and that we can never be "cured" of our Lie.

I will now sketch a general outline of my approach to my patients, dividing it into *The First Encounter*, *The Second Encounter*, and *Subsequent Encounters*. Please bear in mind that I *never* follow this plan rigidly, but rather adapt it to the individual and her particular circumstances. Nonetheless, I think it will help to clarify for you the key aspects of my work if I discuss it in this framework.

THE FIRST ENCOUNTER

Rarely is this a diagnostic encounter. Most frequently these days I find patients have long since accurately labeled their own disease and are coming to me as their "last resort" after failing to heal through other therapists or other approaches. Nonetheless I first take a complete history and do a thorough physical examination as I would with any patient in my practice. I use this vehicle to allow us to get acquainted with one another and also to assess where she is in terms of denial of her disease.

Following the examination, I invite the patient to join me in a comfortable room for a discussion about her disease and my approach to it. Realize that the relationship between us, *which is in itself my most powerful tool* in working with her, begins from the first moment we lay eyes on one another. (Sometimes it even began weeks earlier on the telephone.) My attitude and approach throughout this visit (and all subsequent ones) emanates from my Truth, and is the same as that I strive for with all of my patients: one of deep acceptance and respect. If any of you has a different attitude to patients emerging from your Truth, I would suggest that you train for a new occupation.

The **first and foremost issue to address is that of control.** To do this work I have had to leave the seesaw of control. ("Either the patient is in control or I am in control.") In my Truth I know that *no one* is in control, including God, nor can anyone *be* in control, of any disease of addiction. The disease *is.* It is the spawn of the predator within, and it is far more clever than any feeble human intelligence. So it cannot be controlled. It cannot be cured. It is far too cunning to ever be tamed. It can only be dismembered and transformed. So I leave the seesaw on my initial encounter with the patient. I tell her that I cannot control her disease, and I sketch out the framework of my approach, including my gut knowledge that she, too, will never be able to control her disease, although generally she is still laboring under the illusion that she can. At this juncture the patient usually looks either baffled, startled, or relieved. The first two responses generally arise because what I am saying is diametrically opposed to everything she has heard to date. The third emerges from a profound instantaneous connection with her own gut-level knowledge about her disease. To hear someone validate her own deep knowing provides some immediate relief of her suffering.

This gut-level connection between us, and the pain relief that it affords, opens the door to the second critical issue to be discussed. I tell her that **I use only a fully participatory model,** an interplay of two equal human beings doing our own work—not the work of the other. I tell her why I "know" so much about addiction. I fully disclose the fact of my anorexia and briefly summarize the pathway I have trod to date. I outline how I must work with my patients: as a wounded and now-healing healer still on my own journey of self-discovery (where I will be until I die). I tell her that my professional work is one of the vehicles I use in continuing my journey, and that if at any point I find myself spiraling backward into my disease and am unable to reverse the process, then I will have no alternative but to terminate my work with her, at least temporarily. (This has never happened yet, by the way.)

I go on to discuss the third, and related, truth that I have no agenda for her (or for myself, for that matter), that I have no idea how to "make her better." I emphasize that **she will heal herself, or she will not heal at all**. I tell her that I don't know how she is going to recover or when, that only she "knows" how to do that, although as yet her knowledge of the process is not conscious. I advise her that if she wants a doctor who will claim to be able to "fix" her, or if she wants a doctor who is a superior being dispensing wisdom to the lowly masses, she must find another doctor.

I don't want to leave you with the false impression that this initial meeting with the patient is a twenty-minute monologue by yours truly. It is anything but that. Rather this encounter is a dynamic, two-way, highly flexible, fully alive, and always unique exchange of words, body language, tone of voice, and unspoken communication of understanding and acceptance of one another. Should it fail to be that, then invariably I never see the patient again.

The patient frequently reacts to my assertion that she must heal herself by wailing, "But I don't know *how!*" After the wails have subsided I move through this doorway into the fourth important truth: **my radical trust that she bears deep within herself a healing power** that *wants* her to recover and that can and will lead her (and me) through the dark twisting corridors of her sick mind to the place of wholeness and peace. I tell her that I can probably facilitate her getting in touch with that power if she decides to work with me. The choice is hers. She is a totally free human being, and I have no intention of taking away her freedom or her power. I will not be a policeman. I will not be a magician. I will not be her keeper. I will not take care of her. But I will care *for* her. I will care *about* her, always, whether she decides to see me again or not. She will remain in my prayers until the day I die. I go on to tell her there is only one person in the entire universe who can take care *of* her. Often at this point a light appears in her eyes, and she nods with comprehension and breathes the word, "Me!"

There are frequent periods of silence in this work, often long periods, and an important part of my preparation for doing it has been learning to be comfortable with silence, learning to allow it to be without fidgeting or breaking eye contact. There is no book that can teach you or me how to do this. You probably already know this is an art that must be patiently and painfully acquired by actually *doing* it, and this requires courage. I'm not very brave, so I just pray a lot. You may have found other routes to courage, and if they're working for you, I applaud you and urge you to carry on.

Silence is critically important. Connecting with my own deep Truth during the silence is important, just as important as tuning in all my senses to what the patient is revealing (or not revealing) of her own Truth through facial expression and body language. One thing I've learned is that if I don't have a clear sense of what to say at any given point, then the best course is to say nothing. I have never gone wrong by following this rule of thumb, but I've certainly made plenty of mistakes by opening my mouth and jumping in!

At the end of the initial encounter I invite the patient to **think about everything before deciding what she wants to do**. I tell her my door will always be open if she decides to return. I virtually always give her my home telephone number and tell her, with complete honesty, that she may call me anytime. (Rarely in eighteen years of active practice has anyone abused this privilege, and almost never has the culprit been an addict.)

Being available on a twenty-four hour basis, seven days a week, is important when dealing with anorexics, bulimics, and other addicts, because usually they must "hit bottom" before they are able to admit defeat and reach out for help, and in my experience this bottom rarely occurs during normal working hours. A common time for bottoming out is the evening hours, especially on a weekend. Anyone reading this who is serious about working with these individuals must address the issue of availability, and if in your Truth you know you cannot allow your patients to reach you in this manner, then I strongly urge another line of work. Otherwise you will be dealing with a lot of dead bodies. This issue is similar in the practice of obstetrics, surgery, pediatrics, family practice, and a number of other specialties, of course, and perhaps similar arrangements for sharing a call system could be made, provided that *everyone* who is taking your calls is thoroughly briefed in how you wish crises to be handled and is prepared to do it. The main problem with sharing call is that, in my experience, a suicidal, profoundly depressed anorexic or bulimic may simply not possess the energy and hope required to reach out to a total stranger from her despair.

The initial encounter usually ends at this point, at least with a medically stable patient. Exceptions occur, naturally, if the first contact is during a period of critical physical illness. In that instance I always stabilize the patient's condition before broaching *any* of the above issues. It's difficult to communicate meaningfully with a dehydrated, acidotic or alkalotic, hypokalemic, hyponatremic, hypoglycemic, hypotensive, convulsing, or unconscious patient. First things first. Save the patient's life. Ask questions later.

A word about the family. Frequently if the patient is still living at home a parent is the first one to call me, and often one or both parents turn up in my office with their daughter on the first visit. This is a golden opportunity to begin working with them as well. My usual approach is to see the patient alone first, and then to invite the parents to join us for the discussion that I outlined above, provided the patient is agreeable to this. (**She is in charge of what transpires at all times in my work with her.**) I have found that in most instances the patient not only agrees to have the parents in the room but in fact *welcomes* my offer to "educate" her family about the disease. She is so accustomed to being misunderstood by her family that it is an enormous relief to find a professional who is willing to enlighten them.

I think it is crucially important for the family to "unhook" from the patient's disease, as discussed in part six, and I see this as generally prerequisite for her recovery. If the parents are present at this session, I include a direct plea to them to begin working on their process of detachment. It will be necessary to discuss this concept a number of times, usually over an extended period, before most people will comprehend it deeply. I warn them that it will take time, and usually offer concrete suggestions that I think may help them. These vary with the individual family, but may include reading books like Toby Rice Drews's *Getting Them Sober, Volume One*, joining a Twelve-Step group like Al-Anon, and further discussions with me or another person who is knowledgeable about addiction.

One note of caution here. I have learned the hard way that it is impossible for me to work with the parents in separate sessions from their daughter. Although my goal in attempting such direct work with them is to relieve *everyone's* pain by mediating between them, it is very difficult for me to remain in my Truth at all times while using this approach. Invariably, because the parents are still mired in their blind codependency they attempt to suck me into the family dynamics of lies, half-truths, second-guessing of others, keeping secrets from others "for their own good," mixed messages, confusion, and insane thinking. I have fallen into the trap unwittingly once or twice and "awakened" days or weeks later to discover that I'm in the clutches of my own Lie again.

This flaw in my nature as a "healer" may be unique to me, a reflection of the fact that I still have a long way to go on my journey. Others who are more spiritually advanced may be secure enough in the embrace of their Truth to withstand the lure of this spider's web, but I am not, at least not yet. Having been compelled by my Truth to recognize this and to admit it, with great pain, to myself and then to all of those whom I have harmed by my action, and made what amends were possible, I now choose not to play this game in the first place. So I tell the whole family at this initial encounter, with all present, that I will keep no secrets from my patient, that my first allegiance lies to my own inner Truth and, moving out from there, to my patient. I advise the parents that anything they reveal to me, verbally or nonverbally, in subsequent private encounters (by telephone or in person) will be passed on to their daughter immediately and as honestly as I can. I will keep no secrets for anyone's good. Secrets are lies for me. Should it become necessary to work with the parents directly, I now always do this with my patient present, or at least with her full permission beforehand and with a debriefing session immediately after, in which I fully disclose to her everything that transpired. I urge all of you to examine what you are doing with ruthless honesty to ensure that you are connected with your own Truth every step of the way.

THE SECOND ENCOUNTER

This may not occur for a long period of time after the first encounter, and I have come to expect this delay in working with addicts. I no longer berate myself for having "scared them away"! I know I can only be an instrument in someone's healing if she allows the process, and I know I can't actually heal *anyone* (except myself), let alone everyone. That's OK. God has many instruments in his tool kit besides me. If I am to facilitate someone's recovery, it will occur on her timetable, not mine. I have radically let go of agendas in my life, except at committee meetings.

The patient usually needs to hit "bottom" before she enters my life again. My aim is to be available when this occurs and in the meantime to hold her before my God in prayer on a daily basis. Prayer works, and if you have not yet discovered this truth, I urge you to try it!

At the second encounter the patient is generally in a state of profound despair. She thinks she is ready to surrender. Whether she really *is* ready or not remains to be seen. In any event there are a number of key issues that must be addressed at this meeting. Once again, top priority belongs to dealing with any critical physical realities that will block communication.

I briefly review with the patient the points covered at our initial encounter, to ensure that they are fresh in both our minds. I then move on to the core of this encounter: **the therapeutic contract between us.** I clarify the terms of the contract in specific detail, stating what I am prepared to do and what I expect her to do. I introduce at this time what I have labeled my "Siamese Twin Theory" of healing from addiction. This concept is beautifully clarified by Schaef. In brief, it involves the concept that for true deep healing from addiction to occur, *both* "recovery" and "transformation" must happen.[2] They are inextricably linked. They are Siamese twins. And these twins are not joined at the hip. Rather *they share one heart.* There is no surgery that can separate them. They are two but they are one. They are one but they are two. One can go nowhere without the other. If one dies, they both die. For one to live, both must live. They are identical to one another, but paradoxically they are different, for *they are mirror images of one another.*

"Recovery" means the addict must deal with the substance or behavior to which she is addicted (alcohol, drugs, starvation, bingeing, and purging) on a daily basis, one day at a time. It involves her abstaining from the daily "fix," using whatever tools she finds are effective for her. One such tool is the Twelve-Step program. There are many others. Joining other groups, telephoning friends, meditation, prayer, writing in a journal, painting or working with clay, exercise, reading books, standing on one's head—whatever works. The list is probably endless. The addict must do whatever she needs to do to get through her day, crawling along from one hour to the next if necessary, without indulging in her addictive chemical or behavior. Schaef states that "the best tool we have for recovery is the Twelve-Step program of Alcoholics Anonymous and its satellite programs."[3] I agree with her. We both could be wrong. I am open to other suggestions.

The second twin is "transformation," which I have discussed a great deal already. Briefly, it involves "a complete paradigm or system shift"[4] deep within the self to allow the Truth to take over from the Lie. It means learning to tune in to the Truth, *to trust it radically,* to follow its lead wherever it will go, to love it and experience its love for the self. In transformation, the addict will discover that the Truth yearns for her to be wholly herself, to be sane, to be fully awake and alive, to be utterly free yet profoundly connected with the rest of the universe, to be empowered, to create, to have faith in the deep knowing within herself, to be capable of acts of great love, to trust her moral outrage when something is intolerable in her world, to bring justice into being around her. The Truth longs to bind up all her wounds from the past, to stop the bleeding, to replace the blood, to turn weakness into strength, to bring deep joy out of her pain, and to be born into the world today through her willing cooperation.

How does transformation come about? It is a mystery and outside of my or anyone's control. How can I facilitate transformation in the addicts I work with? By allowing it to occur in myself. By sinking my roots deeply into my own Truth and following its lead at all times. When I allow the Truth to transform me, miracles occur in front of my eyes. As I said before, I believe the Truth in me calls forth the Truth in the other, and their dance together transforms us both. Truly it is a mystery. I know it happens. I have seen it happen in myself and others, but I cannot explain it. I hope many of you reading these words know what I am talking about for the simple reason that you have experienced it yourself. There is no other way. If you have not yet been blessed with transformation, ask your Truth for it with all your heart. The prayer will be heard; the prayer will be answered. But remember that transformation *never* happens without recovery, without doing one's own work in blood, sweat, and tears.

Schaef elaborates on what I call my Siamese Twin Theory in this way (note once again she uses the word "process" or "living process" to identify what I call my "Truth" and "addictive process" for what I call the "Lie"):

> When I am still enmeshed in and operating out of my addictive process, I cannot live my process. Wanting a quick fix or a quick transformation without facing my addictive process will not work. Wanting to recover without being willing to change my life will not work. There is no recovery without transformation, and there is no transformation without recovery. The two processes, by necessity, *go together and paradoxically are the same*.[5] (Italics mine.)

Yes, they are the same and yet they are different. This paradox will not be grasped by the sick one for a long time after she begins walking down the road of recovery. Schaef's experience with addicts is that most people must *do the work of recovery* for two to five years before they experience transformation. I am able to see now that I had to do it for eight years (1983–1991). God is merciful. He saw that I was destitute. My personal tool kit was empty. He had to give me a very powerful tool indeed to get me doing my work. So he did. He "ejected the tape" of anorexia out of my inner VCR. Only when this happened was I able to begin eating normally and to proceed with the remaining tasks in my life. I of course thought that I was "cured" in 1983. Ha! It required eight years of doing the work of my life until the scales fell from my eyes in true transformation. Transformation means being fully connected on a conscious level with my Truth. In 1991 it occurred in tiny glimpses. Now it occurs for increasingly long periods of time, often for many consecutive days or even weeks. I look forward to the day I die, when it will occur without end for all eternity.

How does all of this relate to the contract I strike with the addict? I explain my Siamese Twin Theory to her. I say the words, although I know she cannot fully comprehend them. I know I will have to repeat them many times, changing them somewhat each time, on many occasions over the course of our work together. I go on to explain that **her side of the contract is to do her daily work of recovery**. I cannot do it for her. (In fact I cannot "do" her transformation either. Only *her* Truth will do that, but my Truth can facilitate, since paradoxically they are the *same* Truth.) She must eat a "normal" diet and/or abstain from the binge-purge cycle, on a daily basis, one day at a time, using whatever tools she finds work for her. The tools will probably change as she goes along. If Anorexics Anonymous is established, that will be one very powerful tool for many people. In the meantime she must find alternatives for herself. I may offer some suggestions: attending OA if that is feasible (it may be for some bulimics), attending open AA meetings where she translates the word *alcohol* to *anorexia* or *bulimia*, adopting me or some other human being as her sponsor (someone to do reality checks with, someone to bolster the flagging spirits when required, someone to assist her in discerning the Lie in her psyche on an hour-to-hour and day-to-day basis). But in the end, the decision as to what recovery tools she will use is hers to make, just as the daily work is hers to do. Not mine.

And it *is* work. Painful, arduous work. She will sweat. Her feet will be bloodied when the road gets rocky. She will be tempted to despair at times. For her Lie will be fighting for its life, and it will use every trick in the book to win her back to its deceptive embrace. I warn her that "slips" will occur and tell her how they are to be handled—as spurs to move her forward rather than as occasions for indulging in despair. *She will learn through her slips*, if she allows herself to.

My side of the contract is to facilitate transformation. This I do by the only route there is: doing my daily work of recovery and allowing transformation to occur within me. I pledge to remain connected with my Truth during our time together, to give voice to it as honestly as I possibly can (even when this brings pain to both of us), and to stay with her on her journey by allowing my path to parallel hers during our work together, so that we may stretch out our hands to one another and walk in unison for an unknown time. Sooner or later this walk will become a dance.

I warn her that just as she will slip in her part of the contract, so I will slip in mine. For we are both human. I will be unable to execute my side of the contract flawlessly. I will fail. I will disconnect from my Truth. I will lie to her sooner or later. I will need her assistance to spot my lies. I will need her to forgive me, just as she will need me to forgive her.

The patient may express fear at this time, the fear that she will be unable to do her own daily work, let alone spot my lies. I reassure her that she need have no fear about that, for my trust in the Truth is radical. I know the Truth loves us both and will never let us down if we are both sincere about seeking healing. If either one of us is not sincere (is lying), no healing will occur until the Truth is allowed to flow again. I promise her that if she is ready to heal, if she truly has hit bottom and endured as much suffering as she is presently capable of enduring in her disease, then she will begin to heal if she adheres to the contract. Her trust in this promise is rarely as profound as my own, but that doesn't matter for now. If she trusts me, then the process can begin. If she doesn't, then we will part with a hug and a prayer for the time being.

So healing is the payoff of the contract for her. What do I get out of it? Healing. Ongoing and progressive transformation (a potentially boundless process limited only by death). Ongoing and deeper connection with my Truth. The joy of this is worth any amount of pain I will be required to willingly embrace in my work with her. And there is a good deal of pain. Let me not mislead you. Whenever I take on the task of catalyzing the healing of another human being I shudder for a moment as I recall what I know: She will not heal unless I too heal, and in order to do that I will have to *experience* all of her wounds with her, in addition to accepting fresh ones of my own. Precisely what these will be I never know in advance. Invariably it comes as a shock to me when I wake up one day and discover I am bleeding from some new region and crying out in my pain. Sometimes it takes me a while to recognize this bleeding for what it is: the cost of being transformed.

But just as the suffering is always a surprise, so are the tangible fruits of transformation. The new joyous energy created by the deeper bonding between me and my Truth flows out from me to others and brings about astonishing and unexpected changes in the world of my relationships. Old rifts are healed, seemingly hopeless situations reverse themselves, happiness abounds everywhere as miracles happen.

Do I get paid in dollars and cents too? Yes. A lot? No. Do I ever do this work without financial compensation? Yes, frequently, when the circumstances require it, provided that I have enough "paying guests" to feed and clothe and shelter me and my family. Would I do this work only for money? No. Never. There are far easier ways of making money. Looking at sore throats and rashes is far more comfortable. Boring and, for me, soul-destroying, but comfortable. Just like my anorexia.

What will be the penalties for breach of this contract? Halting of growth in *both* of us occurs *immediately,* as soon as the Lie poisons the flow of Truth between us. It may take us a while to realize that growth has stopped, but sooner or later one of us awakens to this reality and must then make a decision: to go on playing the lying game; to painfully confront the other with her knowledge that she is either lying herself or being lied to, and see where that leads; or to terminate the contract forthwith, with or without explaining why.

This works on a completely mutual basis. I have not yet had to "fire" a patient. One day I may have to. I have once *been* "fired" by a patient, although this was only a temporary layoff. When I reconnected with my Truth and admitted my wrong action to myself and to her, she was able to forgive me for the betrayal and renew our relationship. Someday I will probably screw up so badly that someone will be unable to forgive the pain I inflict on her through my deception and will fire me permanently, with or without kicking me in the teeth first. When that happens I pray that I will eventually admit my lie, endure the pain of my guilt and shame, prostrate myself before my Truth and repent, then forgive myself and go on to make whatever amends are possible.

So at the time of striking the contract with my patient, I emphasize the only key word in it that she and I must remember. **Honesty**. Total, ruthless, and absolute honesty, with ourselves and one another, about *everything* at all times. There can be no secrets between us, no hidden agendas, no attempt to control the other by guarding our speech. Everything relevant to our relationship that comes to the surface of consciousness must be shared as soon as possible with the other. This includes niggling doubts, sudden thoughts or questions that arise "out of the blue" in our minds. As you can imagine, remaining honest is exhausting work!

With regard to honesty, I remind my patient that I practiced her disease with great vigor and a modicum of success for fourteen years, and that it is hard to con a con artist. I tell her that she will be unlikely to be able to deceive me for long, as long as I am doing my own work of remaining connected with my Truth, because I will know in my solar plexus that something is not ringing true. I emphasize that I have no intention of checking up on her, snooping about to see if she is lying about anything. Instead I will *check up on myself*. If I cease to grow in the relationship, and I am *certain* that I am not the one doing the lying, then I will conclude that she is lying and confront her with that.

On a less philosophical note, **the issues of diet, body weight, and weight gain** must be agreed upon as well, right at the outset of the contract. I stress to the patient that I am prepared to commit myself to being her true friend, but I am simultaneously and inseparably a physician as well. I cannot split myself. I *am* a physician. So part of my Truth emanates from my medical training and clinical experience, from the scientific facts I have gleaned from books and from twenty years of practice. The physical realities cannot be ignored during our work together. We are mind and body, inextricably linked—Siamese twins again. Body affects mind. Mind affects body. If one dies to this earthly life, they both die. For one to heal, both must heal. So it will do her no ultimate good if her mind appears to be growing and expanding through our journey together if her body is shrinking. If this happens we will discover, too late, that her spiritual growth was all an illusion, for when her body dies our spiritual work will be terminated as well. The dance will be over.

By way of an aside, note this is not strictly accurate. The patient may secretly wish to begin working with me in order to "expand her mind" and advance spiritually while slowly committing suicide. Remember that there are two questions the addict must answer when she hits bottom: "Do I want to die?" and "Do I want to live?" Schaef correctly explains how these are two entirely separate and different choices that must *both* be made before full recovery is possible.[6] I can only strike a contract with a patient who has decided she does not want to die. I will never assist anyone to commit suicide. My Truth will not allow it. As to the second question, my patient may be incapable of answering it at the outset of our work together, but for the work to begin she must be able to say either, "Yes, I think so," or "I don't know." If her answer is "No," then we cannot strike a contract, for we are contracting to proceed on the journey of recovery and transformation, the goal of which is to awaken us both from our enchantment and render us *fully alive*. If our work *works*, then we know she has decided to live. If it doesn't, then we can conclude that she (or I) is not yet ready to decide to live. That's OK. She cannot heal until she is ready to heal. Once we discover this, we will terminate our contract for the time being.

To return to the main point here, I explain to the patient the physical reality that her mind cannot work if her *brain* is critically ill from starvation. I think the human mind lives in the whole body, but especially in brain, heart, bones, and gut. So all of these organs must be working in a healthy manner if her mind is to become healthy. I broach the subject of optimum body weight, and I discuss the needs for electrolyte balance, normoglycemia, and freedom from starvation ketosis and catabolism of lean body tissue. The patient is invariably hung up on the numbers when I mention the concept of ideal weight. I usually leave this issue for the time being, stating that we will involve a knowledgeable dietitian to help us set her goal weight and to design an appropriate dietary plan in collaboration with the patient herself.

Let us now summarize the therapeutic contract. The patient agrees to do *her own daily work of recovery*. I agree to remain *connected* with her, to facilitate transformation by *doing my own work* at all times. We both agree to practice ruthless and fearless *honesty*. We agree on the *provisions for breach of contract*. After spelling out the clauses of this contract, I remind the patient that she is a free agent. If she has truly hit bottom she generally stretches out her hand at this time, and we *seal the contract with a handshake*, usually followed by a hug. If she is not yet at bottom she generally asks for more time to think about it. That's OK. I am prepared to allow her as much time as she needs, for I know I cannot make this or any choice for her. I will not talk her into it. I will not coerce her. I will not attempt to trick her into agreeing. Lies beget lies. Violence begets violence. I will spend the rest of my life striving to practice these truths. I would rather die than abandon them wittingly.

Am I ever afraid that she will die if she doesn't agree to the contract at this time? No, for my trust in the Truth is absolute. If she cannot enter into the contract at this time, she will get another chance at healing, either with me or someone else. Once again, I know I am not God's only tool. If the patient is in danger of imminent death I intervene, of course, to save her life, just as I would with any other human being. But once the immediate danger is past, I stand back and remind her of her freedom. I have found no other approach that works.

This generally concludes the second encounter. Let me address here the issue of hospitalization versus outpatient therapy. In my experience it is very difficult or impossible to begin working with a *very sick* anorexic or bulimic as an outpatient. She is generally too devastated physically and too profoundly depressed to be capable of entering the contract and adhering to it. So I advise hospitalization for a time to break the vicious cycle of her disease. Physical complications can be rapidly addressed in hospital, a good dietitian is available daily, and the change of surroundings usually induces dramatic improvement in the patient's mental status. I think one of the greatest benefits of hospitalization is the "permission" it affords the patient to see herself as *sick* instead of sinful. We professionals are acknowledging that patients have a disease when we admit them to hospital, and we are implicitly assigning a certain level of severity to it. Thus a portion of the addict's burden of irrational guilt is immediately lifted. Furthermore, the intimate contact with other human beings in hospital, including nursing staff and other patients, is of enormous benefit to these profoundly alienated individuals. All in all, inpatient treatment at the outset of therapy is of great value.

I will not broach here such issues as cost of inpatient treatment, availability of beds, and third-party payment, because they cannot be covered briefly in any depth. These are real problems of great importance, and in glossing over them I do not mean to minimize them. But they are social, economic, and political issues and are beyond the scope of this discussion.

SUBSEQUENT ENCOUNTERS

In a hospitalized patient subsequent encounters occur daily, seven days a week, in my solo practice. In outpatients they take place anywhere from three times weekly to twice in a month, depending on the severity of disease, amount of progress being made and its rate, and other individual factors that vary from patient to patient and over the course of time in a given patient.

I shall discuss **inpatient management** first. I do not intend to address the details of intravenous therapy, gastrointestinal management, monitoring of blood chemistry, and other aspects of lifesaving treatment. These have been covered thoroughly by other authors, and I can add little that is new to these topics. What I can do, however, is discuss the *new paradigm* I am using in my work, for it may be new and potentially useful to some of you as well.

Following initial lifesaving measures I shift the balance of power immediately back to my patient. She is in charge of herself and everything about herself, including her own disease, the course it will take, and whether and when she is to recover. This guiding truth is in my mind at all times. I review the therapeutic contract, clarify it as necessary, and we verbally agree to it once again. I remind her that the daily work of recovery is hers alone to do. I will not monitor it. She may weigh herself as frequently as she needs to (very few patients can refrain from weighing themselves less than once a day in the beginning). She may eat any balanced diet she chooses and exercise as she chooses, provided that she continues to gain weight at an acceptable rate (usually two pounds per week) or maintain it, if she is already within 5 or 10 percent of ideal body weight, and refrains (in the case of a bulimic) from bingeing and purging. Initially compromising on a lower goal weight than ideal is often necessary in order to find a number that both of us can live with. I know it is a compromise, and I tell the patient that. The weight we agree on may not be sufficient to start menstruation functioning again. But it is one that I know as a scientist is adequate to allow her to function in a reasonable state of health. Later on, as the patient progresses in her healing process, she is usually able to let go of her fear and set a more realistic goal weight.

Caloric and protein requirements are worked out by the dietitian, and adjusted as necessary. The dietitian meets daily with the patient to design a menu plan acceptable to them both, one that meets reasonable nutritional standards. Once I have communicated these general guidelines to the dietitian, I withdraw from this arena. I ask the patient daily what her weight is and how her eating behavior is going. She tells me. If she lies I usually know this in my gut and confront her with it immediately. If she succeeds in deceiving me for a time, she is generally so consumed with guilt that she confesses the lie quite soon, and we deal with it, learn from it, and move on. Or else further growth in me halts and, as soon as I realize that, I confront her with it. I cannot emphasize enough the vital importance of the fact that *if we are not both growing, at least one of us must be lying.* It is an infallible rule of thumb, so I use it as my "lie detector" in this work. It is the crux of my entire approach. I benefit spiritually from the work I do. If I am not growing in the arms of my Truth, something is wrong, and I must acknowledge that and address it immediately, usually with great pain. Otherwise neither of us can benefit.

I have had to spend a great deal of time educating other hospital staff about my approach to these patients. This necessitates openly revealing why I "know" so much about eating disorders and other addictions. I must be honest with *everyone* directly concerned with my patient, or else I get in trouble. (Actually, I've learned that I must be honest with everyone in my entire life, or else I get in trouble! This doesn't mean I must burden everyone I meet with the story of my life.) I have found nursing staff and psychiatrists to be amazingly open to allowing me to continue to work in my own way, and eager to cooperate with me, as long as I am perfectly honest with them. Truth begets truth. This gives me enormous hope that many of you reading this may be open in the same way.

I always warn my patient that, because my paradigm is new and radically different from that of most professionals, she will probably experience some difficulties in her interaction with at least one or two of them in hospital. This will really be a blessing in disguise, for we will both be able to learn from such incidents. I discuss this frankly with her, tell her that I respect almost all of my colleagues even though we hold differing viewpoints, warn her that I have no "hard data" as yet to prove that this new approach works, and remind her that she is a free agent and free to terminate her work with me at any time. I advise her to stay in touch with her gut. If her interaction with a nurse or other professional triggers a hard knot of anger in her solar plexus, an urge to punch the other person in the nose or to begin starving or bingeing, then she will know that she has a problem she can learn from. I advise her to discuss it with me as soon as possible, and we will work through it to see what is to be done. Sometimes I must speak to the other professional about the problem. Sometimes my patient is able to let go of her rage and not allow the person in question to get under her skin again. Often we end up laughing it off together, sharing the ironic joke that because we have been blessed by having this disease, we can understand things that others who have never experienced addiction are unable to. There is a lot of laughter involved in healing, for our disease is in reality outrageously funny when seen from a sane perspective. Schaef also makes a point of mentioning this laughter.[7]

You may be wondering at this juncture whether I am implying that you must be a recovering anorexic or bulimic or addict of some other kind in order to be able to work with these patients. I do not believe this is essential, but if you are it will certainly give you an edge that will expedite your movement into working in the way I've outlined, if that is what you decide to do. There is only one prerequisite for facilitating the healing of addicts, and that is *to have wrestled with your own inner predator to the point of at least beginning transformation*. You must have discovered *for yourself* the paradox of the blessing hidden in human suffering, and embraced it with all of your heart. The predator within has at least a million ways of attacking us humans. It is a master of disguises and illusion. There is none better. As Peck has observed, "perhaps [the Lie's] best deception is its general success in concealing its own reality from the human mind."[8] If you have not consciously identified the predator within yourself who seeks to destroy you, then you are still sleepwalking, still enchanted. "And of course, the more enchanted you get, the more certain you feel that you are not enchanted at all."[9]

How do you know you have reached the stage of beginning transformation on your life journey? Here is an infallible test. Look directly into your eyes in a mirror one day for five minutes when you are alone in a silent room. Do you know the person staring back at you? Do you love this person? Are you staring at your best friend? Do you break into a wide irrepressible grin? Do your eyes sparkle and dance with laughter? Does your heart shudder deeply with joy? Do you want to jump up and down with glee because this person is alive?

Transformation is always apparent to others. It shows in the eyes. They glow with deep fire and life. A perpetual grin lurks at their edges. A passionate interest in others and in everything going on around him or her is apparent. Spontaneity and utter lack of self-consciousness about revealing emotions to others is invariably present. (Notice that only by first truly loving the self and defining the boundaries of the self can one let go of the self and allow those boundaries to collapse in a joyful, painful orgasm of interconnectedness. Another paradox.) The observer simply knows this person doesn't care in the least what others think of him or her. The observer usually finds himself wanting to laugh with the transformed one, and feels very warm and comfortable and totally accepted in their interaction. He often feels awed by this person. He may not know what to make of him or her. The transformed one may appear to be a lunatic, yet the observer knows this is not the idiocy of naïveté and inexperience, but rather the mysterious wisdom of one who has suffered deeply. The maturity in the lines of the face proclaim that fact.

Common observations made about transformed people are: "He's so natural." "She doesn't put on any airs." "He's a good person." "I like being around her." "He's so easy to talk to." "She makes me feel special." "I wish I could be like him." "*She's a different person than she was* five years ago." "He's different than most people I know." "She scares me a little." "He laughs a lot, and his laughter is *real!*"

If you do not identify yourself in the above description I urge you to halt and think deeply about where you are in your life journey. What do you think about death? Do you look forward with an eager tremble of anticipation to the end of your journey? If not, why not? Examine the eyes that look back at you from the mirror. Why are they so sad? Why do they appear to be on the brink of tears? Why are they lifeless? Why do they appear not to give a damn about anything? Why are they angry and bitter? Why do they want to destroy something?

These questions must be answered, my friend. It is never too late. There are many routes to healing. Explore them. Read. Talk with others. Pray. Think back to the days of your youth. Think of teachers you met who inspired you, who made you feel you were powerful and could change the world. What has happened to you? Or perhaps whatever happened occurred so early that you have no recollection of ever feeling joyful or inspired by another human being. What was it? Can you remember? We all need help to answer these questions. We all need other people. "It is not possible to heal in isolation."[10] Take a chance. Stretch out your hand to someone you can trust. If there is no such person in your life, then consider my description of a transformed person. Have you seen someone like that? Your barber? Your plumber? Your office mate? Your doctor? Your teacher? Your supervisor? Your pastor? Your student? Your grown-up child? Take a risk. Go and talk to that person. Reveal your pain. I promise you will not regret it. But you must make the choice whether to believe me or not.

I have discussed at length the sole prerequisite for this work because it is vitally important. If you have not identified your own wounds and begun to heal them, you should not be doing this work yet. Great harm may befall others if you are still asleep in the clutches of your predator. Enchantment is often contagious. History has proven this reality time and time again. Auschwitz and My Lai[11] and Watergate and the street gangs in Los Angeles are but a few examples. We must be ruthlessly honest with ourselves. But remember, to not have reached the stage of transformation in your life journey does not mean you are bad. It means you are still young. It means you have not suffered enough yet. None of us needs to search for suffering. Believe me, it will come to you and to me without our seeking it! Our only choice is whether to admit we are suffering when we are suffering, or to pretend we are not. Or, as Fox phrases it, whether or not to "let pain be pain."[12] The choice is there for each of us humans. We cannot *not* choose. It is part of our destiny.

To return to the subject of my work with the hospitalized addict, I spend an hour to an hour and a half with her about four times a week, making myself available to her in whatever way she needs me: for my version of what Schaef terms "deep process work"[13], for reality checks and summarization of and debriefing from work she is doing with other hospital staff and fellow patients, for exploration of slips as they occur in order that she may learn from them, for deepening connection between us by my sharing my struggles with her. Whatever is needed. Whatever comes up. Great flexibility is required. I "fly by the seat of my pants" much of the time. Or perhaps it is more accurate to say I fly by the wings of my Truth. On the other three days, my visit will be briefer, usually twenty or thirty minutes. This time commitment means that I can usually have only one or two addicts in hospital at a time, since I am a family physician with obligations to other patients as well. Your circumstances may be different.

A word about scheduling. To work effectively with the addict in the way I've described you will need to be enormously flexible about the time you make available for her. *Crises will occur*, both in the hospitalized patient and the outpatient, and your willingness to be available at times of crisis is paramount. If that willingness is lacking, you will not be able to work in the way I do. Again, be honest with yourself. We must each do what we must do. We have been created as utterly unique beings for a reason. Find your own path and walk it in deep fulfillment of yourself.

What about psychotropic medication? The only type I ever use anymore in these patients is antidepressants, and I use far less of them than I did in the past. *All* anorexics and bulimics and other addicts who have hit bottom are depressed. How could they not be? But the depression is undoubtedly secondary to the illness in the majority of cases, not the other way round. Some do need medication for a time, but not all. Hospitalization alone, with daily work as described above, will frequently suffice to lift mood in order for real progress in recovery to occur. Whether medication is needed as well will rapidly become apparent, usually within a matter of days. Medication is required "to take the edge off" in a patient who is profoundly depressed, where insomnia and sleep deprivation becomes a problem in itself. I find the sedating tricyclics most useful in this situation. I also use serotonin reuptake inhibitors, particularly Prozac®, but certainly not in every patient. The patient whose insomnia worsens on this agent gets sicker, and I have grave reservations about adding a benzodiazepine to counteract insomnia, because of addiction potential. *It makes no sense to me to ever prescribe an addictive drug for a patient dying from an addictive disorder*, and indeed I have acquired patients with eating disorders who came to me heavily addicted to sedatives prescribed by other well-meaning physicians.

Then we have two massive problems to deal with instead of one. Interestingly, Schaef thinks Prozac® may interfere with deep process work,[14] and I believe she may be right.

I prefer to transfer my patient from a medical bed to the psychiatric unit once her medical condition is stabilized, since the duration of admission will rarely be less than one month. Furthermore, intimate contact with other psychiatric patients and nurses trained in this specialty will almost always prove beneficial. Deep processes often surface at night, so having a skilled listener like a psychiatric nurse available to sit with her means my sleep is interrupted less often. But whichever ward she is on, open communication and cooperation between all professionals involved is vital. Weekly team conferences are routine at my hospital's psychiatric unit, and these work well.

Let us now move on to **outpatient management**. The essential principles are identical to those discussed earlier regarding the contract, the patient taking responsibility for her own day-to-day recovery, in-depth process work with me and others in her life, my availability during crises, medication, and so forth. The main differences are the lower frequency with which I see the patient, and the unavailability of nurses and other professionals. It will be necessary to arrange for outpatient dietitian services. Usually my patient sees the dietitian once a week for assistance with her dietary planning, since "normal" eating is the core of the gritty recovery work she undertakes on a daily basis.

A Twelve-Step program as a recovery tool will be of incalculable benefit for most addicts, and I highly recommend this to my patients. The decision rests with her, of course, and I often encounter resistance to my suggestion. I think much of this resistance originates in a poor understanding of what the Twelve-Step program actually is and how it works, and this misunderstanding is fed by the slander one reads in many recent books and periodicals. The recovery movement certainly has its share of critics today whose verbal skills are surpassed only by the depth of their misinformation and bigotry.

In all fairness to these critics, I also think some of the responsibility for this backlash against it must be claimed by the recovery movement itself. I agree with a number of thinkers that immeasurable harm has been done to AA and its spinoff bodies by a *trivialization of the concept of addiction*. To suggest that everyone "addicted" to peanuts or chocolate or swimming is suffering from a devastating, chronic, progressive, fatal illness goes beyond the bounds of what is reasonable, in my opinion. It is unlikely that such an "addiction" will ever destroy human lives in the same way as alcoholism or anorexia nervosa. I think we must allow the pendulum to swing back from the present "addiction craze" toward a more balanced viewpoint. A good place to start is to return to the basic meaning of addiction, as discussed in chapter 31, including the presence of physical tolerance and physical withdrawal symptoms.

Schaef offers a good working definition of addiction.

> An addiction is any process over which we are powerless. It takes control of us, causing us to do and think things that are inconsistent with our personal values and leading us to become progressively more compulsive and obsessive. A sure sign of an addiction is the sudden need to deceive ourselves and others—to lie, deny, and cover up. An addiction is anything we feel *tempted* to lie about.[15]

In the final analysis the patient must *find her own tools of recovery*, whether they have twelve component parts or thirty-nine. It doesn't matter. What matters is that she continue doing her work, and that I continue doing mine. What is my work in relationship to the outpatient? It is essentially the same as in relationship to the inpatient: to remain centered in my Truth, doing what I know I need to do to stay there at all times. This begins with attending to my own needs for food and sleep, for prayer and reflection, for connecting with my spouse, for laughing and weeping with my sons, for listening to my employees and opening myself to other patients.

Finding the balance in my life will probably always be the most difficult aspect of my journey, and it is from my failures in this area that most of my pain is generated. I have come to accept this reality, so I aim to spend a few minutes each day meditating on the question, "Have I got my priorities straight?" and striving to listen to the Truth whispering the answer instead of allowing myself to be confused by the shouted half-truths of the Lie. When I feel "frazzled" in my solar plexus, experience a pressure there and a feeling of, "There's not enough of me to go around. Why can't there be twenty-eight hours in the day instead of twenty-four?" then I know I've got a problem. Somehow I've screwed up again. And the process of naming my failure, feeling my pain, repenting, and making amends must begin again.

During my actual time with the outpatient, the precise work I do is the same as with the inpatient: whatever comes up. My patient leads at all times, and I strive to follow wherever she needs to go and stay with her there, to be fully present with all my senses tuned, to suspend preconception and abandon hidden agendas lurking in my mind that attempt to convince me I know what she needs. My slogan is: "I can never know what *anyone* needs except myself. She is the only one who knows what she needs. Let her tell me."

Something very interesting to me is the remarkable similarity between my guiding slogan and the advice I heard repeated often throughout my years of training as a medical student and young physician. This advice emerged time and time again from the lips of my best teachers and clinical preceptors, men and women who filled me with awe, and whom I now identify as transformed individuals. Regarding the art of diagnosis, their unvarying refrain was: "Listen to the patient! *He will tell you* what is wrong with him!" Do you recall hearing that too? Do you recall the integrity of the individuals who spoke those words? The goodness shining in their eyes? The genuine caring they exhibited in their interactions with their patients? Let's think deeply about that. Let's remember it.

Schaef devotes a substantial portion of *Beyond Therapy, Beyond Science* to a highly detailed description of what she terms "deep process work."[16] This term is exactly right, and I had been unable until I read her book to find the correct name for what I do with addicts. There are a number of similarities between her methods and mine, except that most of her work is now done in groups, using a number of facilitators, whereas to date all of my facilitation has been done with individuals. My work is also far less structured than hers, and my setting is not a large room with mats and pillows but wherever I happen to be with my patient: in her living room or mine, in my office seated on comfortable chairs, in an examining room with my patient huddled on the examining table clad in a paper gown, walking in the park with her, in a café having a cup of coffee, seated in a hospital sunroom with light flooding through a bank of windows beside us. The possibilities are endless.

What exactly is a deep process? Schaef explains it thus:

> Things happen to us as infants and children that are unfinished because we just do not have the strength, maturity, awareness, or integration to deal with these unresolved processes. ... As long as they are rumbling around inside us, we have to expend energy to keep them at bay. One of the ways our inner being (process) "loves" us is that it keeps these old processes alive and waiting inside us until we are ready and in a safe place (internally and externally) to work them through. ... One of the major functions of addiction is to keep these deep processes at bay so we don't have the opportunity to heal.[17]

In deep process work Schaef facilitates others getting in touch with their unfinished deep processes, one by one, at their own pace, and "finishing" them in their own way, in order that they may heal their own wounds. "When we stop trying to control, we have this marvelous internal mechanism on alert just waiting for healing. Deep process is not catharsis; it is not relief; it is not just getting feelings out. It is much more than any of these and includes all of them."[18]

I begin this aspect of my work by explaining to my patient my "Green Garbage Bag Theory" of human development. Here is how it goes. Every one of us born into the species of Homo sapiens is given a "gift" when we exit the womb. It is a very large green plastic garbage bag, neatly folded up, with a sturdy twist-tie to accompany it. We are compelled, by virtue of being what we are—human beings—to carry this gift with us to the end of our days. We leave it behind on our deathbeds, but not before.

What do we do with our bags? Beginning in infancy and continuing throughout our lives, each of us will have things happen to us that we are not ready or able to deal with at the time they occur. The nature of these things is as varied as the number of individual members in our species. Being neglected when we are three months old because our mother is suffering a postpartum depression. Being overindulged when we are eighteen months because our parents were deprived by their own parents and are determined that "our kid is going to have it better than we did!" Being ignored when we are two because our parents are struggling with their own problems: death of a loved one, serious illness in themselves, disappointment as their dreams fail to come true, conflict in their own relationships. Being accidentally or deliberately locked in a room when we are three. Being molested when we are four. Experiencing the terror of a war when we are five. Failing in school when we are six because no one notices our reading disability. Feeling abandoned when we are seven as a result of our parents' marital breakdown. Being rejected by peers when we are eight because our skin is the wrong color or our nose is too long. Being responsible for putting Mommy to bed when we are nine and come home to find her drunk and passed out in her vomitus on the kitchen floor. Being rendered paraplegic when we are ten because a man drove after getting drunk or because a woman at the wheel was momentarily distracted or because there was an unexpected pothole in the road. Being told we are fat at eleven by someone important to us. Being orphaned at twelve by a boating accident. Being afflicted by severe diabetes at thirteen. Being gang-raped when we are fourteen.

And so on and so on. Do you get the idea? Such experiences and countless others occur to all of us. It is the way things are. The important point is that all of these events take place at a time when we are too young or too inexperienced or too ignorant to know how to handle them. So we stuff them, and the emotional response accompanying them, into our garbage bag, seal the bag, sling it over our shoulder, and carry on walking down the individual road of our lives.

What's wrong with that? The problem is that by the time we humans reach the age of twenty or thirty or forty, our bags are getting very heavy. So heavy that we are sweating and panting and growing very tired "for no reason." The bag is on our back. We cannot see it there. We plod along from one day to the next, too weary to lift our face to the sky that we might watch the flight of a bird or see a cloud shaped like an elephant or feel the sun pouring its blessed heat to drive the chill from our bones. Furthermore, some of the garbage in our bags is oddly shaped, with sharp points on it. These points poke out through the plastic and begin digging into the tender flesh of our backs. We begin to bleed from these wounds. We feel the pain and experience the weakness resulting from uncontrolled hemorrhage, but we still don't know where it is coming from. And the tiny hole in the bag allows the putrid odors of rotting garbage to reach our nostrils. The stench becomes unbearable. Our eyes stream with tears. Finally our knees give out, we stumble and fall and lie there face down in the mud. At this point we finally whisper, "I can't do this anymore. Something's wrong."

What happens next? We have a number of alternatives. We can lie there in agony until we die. We can try to get up again. We can take a drug or a drink to ease the pain temporarily. We can put a gun in our mouth and exit the planet. We can pretend we are on a beach in Hawaii enjoying ourselves. We can hope someone will come along and rescue us. Or we can take the bag off our back and see it, admit its reality, and pray for the courage to open it up. When the courage comes we can undo the twist-tie, reach into the bag, grasp the first thing we touch, pull it out of the bag and look at it. Oh my God! We will be horrified, flooded with pain, and burst into tears. We may cry for a long time. But when every poisoned tear attached to that piece of garbage and bottled up within us has been allowed to pour out, then a great calm will come upon us. We will feel very still, strangely empty, and quite exhausted. But it is a good exhaustion, akin to that felt after a long mountain hike or after giving birth to a child. We will feel serene and at peace, and we will look again at what is in our hand and say, "Why, it's only a piece of garbage!" Then we can drop it on our path instead of putting it back in the bag. The bag will be lighter. We will be able to move on. The next day we may choose to take out another piece of garbage and lighten our load even further, for once we discover that we didn't die from the pain, we feel greatly encouraged to try it again. Eventually the bag will be so light that we will be leaping and dancing down the path. At any time we can look back and see the garbage strewn along the road and sing out with deep pride, "Yes, that's *my* garbage, no one else's, but it's not so bad really. And I've left it behind me instead of bringing it along."

Emptying out the garbage bag piece by piece is deep process work. And it *is* work. Hard, slow, painful labor. But the payoff is very great. I like being there while others do their work, for if I fully participate in their pain then I fully experience the payoff, too, and I continue emptying my own bag at the same time as well. So I offer to facilitate my patient in doing her work. I reassure her that nothing will ever emerge from her bag until she is ready and able to handle it. I've never seen anyone die from looking at garbage. But the choice remains hers, and she determines the pace and direction of the work. It is hers to do, not mine.

No one fully heals from an addictive disorder without emptying out her garbage bag. It is an essential part of transformation. Sometimes my patient says, "But what's the use in looking at the past? It's over. I can't change it. It happened. So what?" My reply to this is that I believe we *can* in fact change our past, by reentering it fully and reliving it and emerging from it with a different outcome this time. By altering the impact of it on our spirit we in effect *change the past*. This is transformation indeed!

Schaef also suggests this is possible.

> There seems to be a collapsing of the time-space continuum, and I have come more and more to know from my own experience with deep process work that time is not linear and it may well be possible to change our past. This ... will not happen if we are trying to change the past, (but) by going through the feelings that are present right here, right now; it is possible to alter what we thought was real, alter our experience of it, and alter its effect on us. We cannot, however, predetermine the direction of that change. We have only to take a leap of faith and trust the outcome.[19]

Sometimes my patient fears that she will be unable to remember what occurred in the past. I reassure her that this cannot happen, for the human brain is the most marvelous super-computer in existence, far more powerful than any constructed by man. Everything that has ever happened in our lives is recorded in that capacious data bank, the unconscious mind. Those records will go with us to our deathbed, or until we are rendered brain-dead. And the healing power within us that loves us and wants us whole and happy and fully alive "knows" which unfinished records need to come to the surface and be completed. That power will *never* let us down. We can run away from it (and all of us do), but it will never run away from us.

So deep process work occupies a substantial portion of the time I spend with my addicted patient. What I have discovered is that once the work has begun, she does a large amount of it outside of my presence, on days when I don't see her or during hours when I am not with her. Frequently other individuals will be wittingly or un-wittingly filling the role of facilitator—a nurse or a friend or a family member or a stranger she meets on a park bench. Then our hour together becomes a "debriefing" session in which she describes the process, names the truth she has learned, and shares her joy with me so that we may laugh and dance together. On rare occasions deep process work is done while completely alone with the Truth, with others merely standing in the wings. In retrospect, I think that is what I did during those four hours of reflection while I ironed altar cloths and scrubbed floors at the Marian Center on the day of my healing. Transformation? What would you call it?

My role as facilitator is very simple and very difficult: to be *totally present* to my patient, to *listen* with great concentration to all that she communicates verbally and nonverbally, to *allow her process* to flow wherever she needs to go, to *do my work* of staying in touch with my Truth at all times, to *confront any lies* that I hear without giving in to my fear of the consequences, to *name the Truth* when something comes to the surface within me, to *resist the temptation to analyze* and interpret what she says for her, to *refrain from pushing* her where I think she needs to go. I listen most of the time. What I do say is usually very straightforward: asking for clarification, checking out the accuracy of what I think I have heard, stating my Truth in simple brief terms, telling a story that comes to my mind. Schaef states that she has learned to refrain from touching her client during deep process work,[20] and I have discovered that is usually wise.

I love doing this work. As Schaef rightly points out, there is no "therapist burnout" in it,[21] because I know I am not in charge, and I trust the one who is: my patient and the healing power, the Truth, within her. Our whole interaction is a graceful minuet of deep respect, which becomes transformed into a boisterous jig!

I would like to conclude this chapter by reprinting two poems that I wrote last year. Each of them resulted from interactions with patients who were very sick and very sincere in their quest for healing. "Karen, Clean and Sober" emerged from about three months of work with a young alcoholic and drug-addicted prostitute who walked into my office one February day and whom I loved from the moment my eyes rested upon her. This was not something I had any control over. It simply occurred, and I could do nothing but respond to it. She is now in another city, still sick and still suffering greatly. Please pray for her. "The Demon" was the result of a midnight exchange with another of my patients, a recovering alcoholic and bulimic woman, slightly older than myself, who is in the process of healing from the childhood wounds of systematic sexual abuse at the hands of her alcoholic father. I hope that one day we will work together with other individuals suffering from eating disorders and other addictions. Please pray for us.

KAREN, CLEAN AND SOBER

For my beautiful friend, KAREN A.
and for the One who brought us together

"Only the children know what they are looking for,"
        said the little prince.
"They waste their time over a rag doll
        and it becomes very important to them;
        and if anybody takes it away from them,
        they cry."
Antoine de Saint-Exupéry [22]

"Love was looking into the eyes of the other;
and forgetting the dark void between you
and forgetting that no one can walk in a void,
you start boldly across,
your arms outstretched to give of yourself
and to receive of the other."
Murray Bodo [23]

I
When first she came into my greening spring
        I saw her careful smile
        I saw her midnight pain
I welcomed her to me as one who is
        I listened to her words
        I listened to her silence
Hearing what she said and what she said not.

Will you speak to me of what is not? I said
Will you speak to me of your black void?
I cannot speak for I cannot see your face she said
        gazing at the floor

I got my glasses smashed last night in a barroom brawl
I picked the fight, slut that I am
I got what I deserved.

A shaft of sunlight set her head aflame
Myopic squint shattered all remaining shell
My center exploded into her pain
        into her blindness
Come close I said when I could speak for you must see my eyes
Come close I said that you might tell me all that is, no lies.

We sat knees touching, shadows embracing
Eyes locked and fused in a time of our creating
        of our gifting
        of our receiving
Slowly then she spoke of what had been
        of a childhood unforgettable
        of a childhood unrememberable
I was beaten she said and raped
Many times? I said
Yes she said and grinned
How old were you?
Maybe three, maybe two
        She smiled
        I wept.

There was only ever one who cared for me
My grandfather a holy man
He died when I was ten you see
I can't forgive God for that
        She wept
        I waited.

I'm bad she said a drunk and a whore
I'm into drugs I've lost my son
I've been to jail I'll go again

I hope I'll die soon now I'm twenty-one
        It's my only hope
I lie a lot. She stopped
Are you lying now?
No she said I don't know why
Perhaps because you know it's safe here
        your truth is safe here
        your shadow is safe here
In my silence.

II
When next she came into my April rain
Despair hung about in her booze-filled breath
        in her coke-filled death
Why have you come? I said
Did you need to prove your words?
        to make me believe?
        to make me grieve?

Maybe she said
Or maybe just to say thanks for the glasses
Why did you do it? I can't pay you back
You will I said you already have
You have no chance to change your path
        if you can't see where you're going
        if you can't trust the shadow.

She looked through me with vacant eyes
        with naked lies
I am the shadow she said why trust me?
Why indeed.

III
When next she came into my perfumed May
It was dead of night
        maybe three

maybe two
The telephone shrilled
I woke, I groped, I heard
I'm drunk she said
    I'm stranded
    I'm alone
What can I do? I said
Why have you called?
There is no one else I'm out of dimes
    out of options
    out of time
A cop picked me up we had a little fun in his back seat
He dumped me here at this hotel
    I'm not scared
    I'm sorry I called.

I lay in my silence as book knowledge screamed at me
Tough love is needed you know it must be
Doctors are suckers, enablers all
Let the addict suffer her own consequences
But what of my consequences?
Stay where you are I said I'm on my way
I have no tough love in my soul this day
    only clouds of softness
    the softness of the mother you never had
But you may have it now if you want it friend
    a soft flight to my home
    a soft bed near my own
    a soft journey tomorrow
I will give this little to you it's all I have
    it's probably not what you need
I'll pray he will multiply it
    transform it somehow
Sometime.

IV

When last she came into my blessed June
I'm clean and sober she said
        for five days—soon
I hate AA
I hate this fucking world
I hate myself
But I don't hate you
I'm glad you've come I said
You bring substance to my empty spaces
You bring lyrics to my song.

There is no magic is there? she said
No. Only the mystery
Only the unknowable
I have no magic wand I said
I have only him
        in me
        in you
Who are you? she said. Her eyes pierced mine
I am but a rattler of chains I cried
He holds the keys
        in me
        in you
And yet I cannot think of a better jailer.

Her tears dissolved into my own
Her wrenching shudders danced with my own
Her shadowy death embraced my own
As we became our joy.

THE DEMON

For KAREN, DORA, BETH, MICHELLE, and All the Survivors

"My ravenous enemies beset me;
>they shut up their cruel hearts,
>their mouths speak proudly.
Their steps even now surround me;
>crouching to the ground, they fix their gaze,
Like lions hungry for prey,
>like young lions lurking in hiding."
Psalm 17:9–12

"I feel her pain and my own pain comes into me,
and my own pain grows large
and I grasp this pain with my hands,
and I open my mouth to this pain,
I taste, I know, and I know why she goes on."
Susan Griffin[24]

It's happened again
I fucked up again
I'm almost afraid to tell you
I think you might be shocked, my friend
>can't bear to disappoint you.

I held her trembling eyes in mine
I soothed her baseless fear
Oh child of mine, beloved of mine
>when will you ever learn?
There's nothing that could disappoint me
>little that could shock
For I have been inside your skin
I'll never take it off.

Her tremors ceased but still no peace
Her tears began to flow
I've stolen again, been caught again
My God, when will it stop?
I've written down the details of the days before it happened
Yes, there was stress, I was depressed
But still I had no warning
I remember every minute of the bloody incident
This was no fugue
    no blacking out
    no epileptic fit
And what concerns me most of all
    is that I felt no guilt
The shame consumed me later on
    after my arrest.
And while the charges were being laid
    throughout my degradation
The dread voice hissed within my head
    began the flagellation.
You're wicked, pervert, hypocrite, you're life's deceitful sham
You're sick, insane, you've a putrid brain
In justice you are damned
Your spirit is rotten like your body
You're evil through and through
Child of God? Now there's a goddam laugh
You belong to hell, it's where you dwell
God's turned his back on you.

Her face was drenched in sweat and tears
    yet her eyes began to glow
As she lifted them to meet my own
    far more than anguish showed.
But even through that ghastly voice,
    she went on, tried to grin,
I heard another, strong and clear, to my astonishment
It sang a different melody: a pure mysterious tone

It moved me to believe in it
        to find a blessed reprieve in it
There was no power to deceive in it
        and I listened to it, Joan.
It led me through those dreadful hours
        the questions, horrors, violation
It walked me home—not to a pub—
        away from mutilation
It allowed me to get through the next three days
        empowered to do what I must
I phoned the people who had to know
I've been moving along on trust.

From our shared rack of pain I watched her face
        melt into terror once more
The voice led me to call you to come here tonight
        my blessed and precious friend
Then it faded away into silence, to nothing
        it vanished back into the void
Now all I can hear is the other—it's near
        and it's bringing the ghosts of the past
God, I'm scared.
I'm surrounded by large men on every side
        by father so brutal, so mocking
        by men armed with spears
They awaken all fears
Their violent weapons debauch me
God, make them go away.

Her body collapsed then in animal terror
        it shrank and enfolded to fetus.
With a cry of outrage I came down from the cross
        by the power of the One who can lead us
I enclosed her in the womb of my open arms
I buried my tears in her hair
I swallowed the horror of her fragmentation

I lay shattered with her there
I absorbed the frozen tension of every muscle in her body
I heard the inhuman whimpers
    which escaped her stretched taut mouth
I grasped the hand which clawed her hair
    which strained to pull it out.

God help me, she screamed through her agony
I held her all the tighter
He is, I whispered in her ear
Feel his embrace in mine
Let's sink together into him
Let's plunge into his night
Let's spiral down into his pain
Let's let all go
Let's die.
… And we did.

After an unknown time all came to an end
The process was complete
She lay spent against my emptied self
    both limp, expunged, deplete
The calm entered into both of us then
In the eye of the storm was peace.

We looked into one another's eyes
We saw him living there
We smiled, then laughed his liberation
    embraced once more in jubilation
We knew the cross was gift.

You're being prepared, my beloved one
Your brokenness is being made whole
It's slow and painful, this exorcism
He's allowing you long plateaus
    and falls

So that you'll remember well the demon
So that you will cherish forever the freedom
    He'll lavish on others through you.

He's honing the edge of his instrument
He's refining now your soul
He's passing you through the fire of his love
He's transforming you into gold.
He's cementing your knowledge of your need of him
He's obligating you too
He demands a great deal
    from those he has healed
He'll never let go of you
You're his.

A Final Word
ANGER, FORGIVENESS, AND HEALING

I alluded earlier to the profound experience of forgiveness that occurred simultaneously and inseparably from the healing transformation of my mind at the moment of my dramatic turning point. I believe this theme is worthy of further exploration, because I have come to understand the central importance that forgiveness holds for the spiritual journey.

Forgiveness is about letting go of anger, the anger that generally is the surface cover concealing deep hurt. It doesn't matter whether the hurt inflicted on one person by another is real or imagined, or whether it was intended or unintended. What matters is the presence of hurt in one's heart and the disappointment and loss, the experience of rejection and abandonment, the wounding of trust, which accompanies it. It is much easier to feel angry than to feel hurt, for pain is painful whereas anger is, to a certain degree and for at least a limited time, somewhat satisfying to the human psyche. Consequently our natural tendency is to cover up hurt with anger. Anger armors one against further hurt as it creates the illusion of invulnerability.

But anger also blocks spiritual growth. It blinds and distorts our perceptions. It poisons the streams deep within us, intercepts the flow of love and compassion, drives us on to vengeance and hatred. So it must be dealt with, or worked through, before spiritual growth can continue. Anger unacknowledged or unrecognized, repressed within the mind, never disappears but rather assumes a distorted form in the emotional life and continues to exert a powerful influence, usually as depression, which is simply anger turned inward against ourselves. The reader will recognize the obvious example in my own story of the hidden irrational anger toward my mother playing a major causative role in the development of my disease.

To let go of anger is to forgive. And to forgive is to let go of anger. In the letting go we must first acknowledge the underlying hurt, *experience fully the pain of it*, and finally transcend it to make allowances for the hurtful behavior on the part of the other person. In "making allowances" we generate understanding of the other and compassion begins, signaling the end of the divisiveness of rage and the birth of interconnectedness.

To forgive is divine. All forgiveness originates with God, as all that is good and right and beautiful originates with God. Perhaps, in fact, God is forgiveness, as he is love and compassion. To forgive another is to get in touch with the divine spring of forgiveness within ourselves, and in the action we discover that this spring is no paltry trickle but a veritable Niagara that floods and submerges everything indiscriminately. (No surprise there, really, for nothing about God is small or mean. He does everything in extravagant excess, in abundance.) We are astonished to find that in forgiving another we have forgiven ourselves and that the forgiveness indeed originates with God's forgiveness of ourselves. In other words, if God had not first forgiven us, we could not possibly forgive ourselves or anyone else.

To return to my own story, in my explosive spiritual rebirth that February day at the Marian Center, I knew in that profound experience of God's forgiveness that I was forgiving myself, that his forgiveness of me and my forgiveness of me were utterly inseparable. I could not experience one without the other. If God could and would wipe my fourteen-year slate of guilt clean, so too I could and would wipe it clean, *in the same moment*. I felt myself immersed and indeed drowned in this forgiveness as in a warm sea. I tasted it; I drank it in huge thirst-quenching gulps; I inhaled deeply of it; and I exhaled it. I knew that it originated from Something/Someone deep within me, from my center, from the Center who is truly my center and the center of all the universe, who pours his spirit lavishly into all of his creation. The same vital Center living and breathing at the Marian Center who opened his arms to me when I crossed its threshold five hours earlier.

Why was such deep forgiveness so essential to my healing? Have I not said elsewhere that the pervasive, enormous, and overwhelming guilt of the anorexic is at least 90 percent irrational, that it has no basis in logic or in fact? Indeed I have, but it is essential to understand that guilt is guilt. Rational or irrational, it must *all* be washed away for psychic healing to occur ... and it *is* all washed away as healing occurs. Healing is forgiveness; forgiveness is healing. Again the inseparable. Jesus intuitively knew this fact. So often in his works of healing the sick and the lame and the blind he used phrases like, "Pick up your mat and walk, *your sins are forgiven you.*" Again and again he linked healing—even from physical diseases—with forgiveness, to the amazement and often chagrin of those witnessing his miracles.

What does all of this have to do with anger? Where was the anger I let go of that day at the Marian Center during my cleansing and transforming experience of forgiveness? I too have pondered this question deeply and have arrived at some startling conclusions. My hidden anger had to do with blaming someone for all the pain I had endured through my anorexic years. Whom did I secretly blame? Not my parents, certainly, for I had fully let go of that anger during my hospitalization in 1974. Myself? Yes, partially, and therein lay the need to forgive myself. But I now believe there was someone else I blamed, and as I reexamine the content of my meditation that day I find the answer shockingly revealed: "And now I cried out ... No one is to blame! ... *I could not blame God* for my illness ... *God had permitted this condition* to develop ... not because *he hated me* and wanted to see how much I could suffer ..."

I blamed God. For most of those sick fourteen years I blamed him and was secretly angry at him. Why did he create me with a vulnerable personality? Why did he give me an alcoholic father? Why did he entrust me to parents whose marriage broke down? Why did he let me have so much difficulty acknowledging anger that I had to develop anorexia before it could surface? Why? Why? Why?

All of this was deeply unconscious, certainly, but as we have seen buried anger is all the more potent a psychic force. And of course it was irrational. Hilariously, ridiculously irrational. Had this rage surfaced into my conscious mind at any time I would have recognized this truth. But it did not, and as a subterranean poisonous force it assumed immense power. The power of a lethal disease. It was powerful enough, I now see, to prevent me from really *meaning* my prayers for healing prior to the Marian Center experience. In addressing God throughout those sick years I was like a rebellious, recalcitrant teenager addressing a parent at whom she is furious: "Just try and stop me from going out tonight (or smoking, or cutting classes). I dare you!" I was saying to God, in effect: "Make me better, God ... Just try and make me better. I dare you!"

Poor God. What a lot he had to put up with. I really did give him a run for his money. But perhaps we should not expend too much sympathy on him, for he must have known what he was getting into when he designed and executed this lunatic experiment of creating animals with spirits, free will, and his own creative potential. Animals made in his image. Foolish? Absolutely. Because the artist cannot divorce himself from his creation. God was setting himself up, making himself vulnerable to an unimaginable amount of pain when he created *Homo sapiens*. For God is nothing if not true to himself. He abides by his own rules. Having given us the power to choose he cannot rescind it, no matter how disastrous a mess we choose to make of our lives, no matter how much suffering we elect to bring upon ourselves and others and him through the willful pursuit of our own agendas. Will the experiment be ultimately successful? Will he succeed in drawing us forth, in urging us on to the ultimate goal of choosing to become fully himself, fully divine? That remains to be seen. Certainly, with a few notable exceptions, our track record to date is not an enviable one.

To return once again to my story, I finally let go of my anger at him that day at the Marian Center, thanks to his grace. I *made allowances* for him by admitting and accepting the mysterious incomprehensible ways of his love: "And now I cried out ... *No one is to blame!* ... I could not blame God ... God had permitted this condition

... because *he loves me* and wants me with him always ... It is a gift! *The illness is a gift* because it has given you the opportunity to grow ... Never before had I seen my neurosis in this light ... Somehow it changed everything."

Indeed it did change everything, as I was to discover two hours later. I forgave God, and that short time later I discovered that he had forgiven me as he healed me. Yet I could not have forgiven him if his forgiveness was not already existing within me. A true paradox. For in the experience of my healing/forgiveness I knew beyond a doubt that such forgiveness can never be conjured up or manufactured by the human spirit alone. I saw that it was a gift made freely available to me as soon as I opened myself up to receive it. God had always been ready and waiting to forgive/heal me. Indeed, in his timelessness—a concept beyond the grasp of human comprehension—he had already forgiven me even before I repented and turned to him.

But I could not accept him until I was ready to accept him, until I had suffered enough, until I had been alone enough, until I had proven to myself that I needed him, until I had exhausted my own resources. I had to endure as much pain as I *could* endure before I was capable of turning to him in an attitude of surrender and true supplication. Perhaps this is always true of the human journey into God.

I find it nothing short of fascinating that it has taken me until now—nearly ten years after my recovery and eighteen months after completing the first draft of this book—to discover this dimension to my healing, this knowledge of my anger at God. In fact, to arrive at this point I had to live through a recent period of great struggle with anger at two persons in my life, and I even had to write another book about anger and forgiveness. Yet something within me has known about it for a long time. Dr. Runions, that wise and perceptive man of God, certainly knew. His first "prescription" for me in hospital in 1974 was to read the Book of Job, a story about a man who grew angry at God. I read the book, profited from it, but failed *until now* to make the deepest connection between Job and myself. Something has drawn me to this theme for eighteen years, but it has taken me until now to plumb its full meaning for me. A slow learner, you say? As I observed before, poor God!

FORGIVENESS AND FEMININITY

There is one final insight about my healing/forgiveness that I would like to share. I have come to see the radically *feminine* nature of my experience of God's forgiveness: I had to both *open myself and become empty enough to receive* it from my God and I had to *give birth* to it myself from the center/Center of my being. Both actions are profoundly feminine, and I now believe that all authentic forgiveness has this quality. Male or female, we must get in touch with our feminine principle in order to be forgiven and to forgive ourselves and one another. Could this be one reason why forgiveness is so conspicuously absent from our patriarchal male-dominated society? Why bitterness and violence and vengeance have been and are so frequently the ruling forces in our history and economics and religion and politics?

Such questions might appear to wander from the main thrust of this discussion, yet when examined more closely perhaps they are not so far afield. Addiction in all its manifold guises (including eating disorders) is rampant[1] in Western civilization in modern times, and its incidence has been growing at an explosive rate over the past century. Could one reason for this phenomenon be that in accepting without question the dominion of male over female, that in excising the ovaries and womb from our communal body, we have cut ourselves off from the healing/liberating power of forgiveness? If so, how can we as a society end this corporate schism and return to the path of life, of shared joy and pain, of compassion that forgiveness is about? Do we want to? Or would we prefer to continue the headlong race to destruction and death that anger and hatred and hierarchical power struggles are about? And might the feminist movement be capable of leading us out of our current collective malaise of which addictive disorders are but one symptom?

Some might object to these concepts, saying: "But surely our society is becoming less male-dominated in the last thirty years, the very years when addictions and eating disorders have been escalating in incidence. Surely women's liberation and feminism have been on the rise throughout this period."

To these persons I reply that on the surface their observations are correct, yet when examined at a deeper level they are not. I am not alone in my assertion that our world is still profoundly patriarchal rather than matrifocal, has been so for countless centuries (historians tell us that patriarchy has been the ruling force in Western civilization since around 3500 B.C.), and will continue to be so for at least most of the next century. Assuming, of course, that we succeed in saving our planet from the lethal destination to which our current patriarchal road of aggressive domination, militarism, and arrogant rape of the earth appears to be leading. Even though a few women are now found in positions of power and influence in industry, commerce, and politics, I would suggest that in order to get there many of them have swallowed patriarchy whole and concentrated on developing the masculine side of their natures. Instead of following the path of subservience that our grandmothers trod without question, we now dress in business suits and strut about financial districts and offices, become competitive hustlers climbing the corporate ladder that men have erected, abort pregnancies that get in the way of our ambitions, and turn the care of our children over to daycare centers and paid servants. Such behavior does not embody the essence of femininity, to my way of thinking.

Furthermore, in hurtling ourselves willy-nilly into this violent arena of power struggles and domination over others, we have become as guilty of treating our bodies as objects as we accuse men of doing. We starve and beat our bodies into submission to a fantastic idealized shape and size promulgated by Hollywood and Madison Avenue, we paint them and adorn them and even surgically alter them to serve as instruments of our aggression, we divorce ourselves from their inherent beauty and unique function as holy vessels infused with God's own creative power. In short, we deny our own feminine/maternal nature.

And in anorexia nervosa we see the penultimate expression of this denial. As an anorexic I utterly rejected my femininity; I starved my body until my breasts and my female curves vanished and my menstrual function ceased; I pushed men away from me in abject terror of being hurt yet again. Is it any wonder that I was incapable for so long of *giving birth* to the forgiveness so essential to recovery?

I return to my earlier statement that male and female persons alike must delve within themselves to get in touch with their feminine principle in order to experience and generate forgiveness. For as humans we are *all* blessed with both masculine and feminine sides to our natures. I know many men who are more receptive and sensitive to others, more skilled at listening, more intuitive and responsive to others' needs, more creative and imaginative, more nurturing and caring, than many women in my acquaintance. And I know many women who are more analytical and logical thinkers, more driving and penetrative, more explosive and inseminative, more skilled at leadership, than many men in my acquaintance.

I believe that we must all strive to acknowledge, accept, and celebrate this reality, and that our goal must be to fully develop and integrate the two sides of our beings if we are to live as whole persons accomplishing the best of which we are capable. For both sides are needed. One is incomplete without the other. And it is possible to achieve this integration. Many humans have accomplished it: Thomas Aquinas, Teresa of Avila, Mahatma Gandhi, Albert Einstein, Mother Teresa of Calcutta, Albert Schweitzer, Martin Luther King, Jr., to name but a few. The person who achieved it in the most perfect degree to date has been Jesus Christ. He was not afraid to be feminine: listening to the poor and the broken, opening himself to their pain, seeing more than was visible to the eye, and generating within himself the forgiveness and compassion that could heal their wounds as he poured it forth unstintingly in an empowering and liberating river of mercy and love. He was not afraid to nurture, comparing himself to a vine and his followers to the branches, and at another time stating that his own body and blood must be eaten by those who chose to follow him. It would be difficult to conceive of any more powerful image of nurturing maternal care than this.

Yet he was no passive sentimental wimp either, afraid to exhibit his masculine side: He desired to penetrate and inseminate everyone in his world and ours; he demonstrated clearly that he was a fearless leader rather than a follower, breaking with tradition and the status quo of his day; he gave vent to passionate rage at times—denouncing injustice and greed, aggressively driving the moneychangers from the temple with a whip, and calling the Pharisees hypocrites and "whited sepulchers" to their faces. Small wonder that he died as he did. No human society could ever be ready to wholeheartedly accept and welcome such a challenging person as this.

As a Christian I wonder whether this accounts for why God elected to incarnate himself as a man rather than a woman: so that he could demonstrate to the society into which he placed himself—one that was at least as patriarchal as ours—how a man is capable of becoming feminine enough to give birth to forgiveness and healing. And I wonder how many of us, male and female, who profess to be Christ's disciples have the courage to do the same. For are we not called to complete his saving/healing work on earth? Have we not been instructed to follow in his footsteps, *every step of the way*? Were we not told to forgive one another "seventy times seven times"? Who among us has the faith to take his words literally? To do the work necessary to accomplish them? To open ourselves up to the only Source which could possibly empower us to do so?

And to the non-Christian I pose similar questions. What are your values and priorities as you walk the journey of your life? What do you hope to accomplish before you arrive at the grave? How much do you love this blessed planet on which you have awakened? How much responsibility for your own decisions and actions are you prepared to accept? How much value do you place on relationships with your fellow humans? Do you love truth? Beauty? Integrity? Life itself? How much courage have you found to solve the problems encountered upon your walk in life? Or do you too deny them, ignore them, run away from them, attempt to wish them away? Do you also long to bandage the wounds of our bleeding world? How far are you willing to extend yourself to accomplish this task? Are you prepared to search for the power of forgiveness in order to do so? Where will you look for it?

I formulate such questions as these in the hope that *all* of us might begin to ponder them, that together as rational creatures we may dare to carve out answers to them. For I have experienced in my illness the emptiness and death that pervades our modern world like a mushroom cloud of poisoned gas. Within myself I have known the anguish of dying and of being laid in a tomb for eight weeks before my rebirth that February day. And I see around me now a broken world apparently in the death-throes of a mortal illness. A world saturated with suffering, filled and overflowing with starving, lonely human persons, people crying out for the food of spiritual direction, people crying out for their God. I see them in my office every day voicing the symptoms that their alienated spirits express through their tension-filled bodies. I see them wandering in aimless drunken oblivion on the streets. I see them rushing about in business suits, carrying briefcases, their mouths compressed in grim lines and their eyes filled with anxious despair. I see them laughing their frantic and meaningless laughter at cocktail parties. I see them huddled about the entrances to our schools seeking chemical release from their disappointment and their pain. I see them in an angry youth joyriding at dangerous speeds and lashing out in blind acts of violence and vandalism, stretching themselves to an edge that will titillate them, relieve their boredom, provide proof that they are still alive. And I see them in my anorexic patients who at least have the courage to act out their starvation in no uncertain terms.

Yet I have hope. I believe in a God who may yet find a way to deliver us from ourselves. I believe in a humanity blessed with the seeds of divinity, blessed with the capacity for transformation, blessed with the potential to create beauty and justice and to do the work of compassion. For I have come to know that death must precede resurrection, that tears must precede laughter, that wounding must precede healing, that emptiness must precede fullness, that sin must precede forgiveness, that questions must precede answers, that night must precede dawn, that agony must precede joyful ecstasy. I have experienced this journey myself, and I continue to experience it as a lifelong process that I now embrace wholeheartedly. Perhaps the best closing testimony of hope that I can give you, my reader, is a poem expressing my decision about whether the payoff of my recovered life is worthy of the cost of my dark journey through the grave.

ECSTASY

For Him

"There are hardly any exceptions to the rule
that a person must pay dearly for the gift
of the divine fire."
Carl Gustav Jung[2]

Sometimes I feel that I can bear no more
Receiving pouring out fast as I'm able
    but he pours faster in
I am but a vessel I cry Stop! my walls will shatter
    will surely shatter
They are but human walls
    walls you have created you know them well
Stop—no don't stop—Pour! You can make them swell
    make them expand into you
Open me empty me
Then fill me with you and let me overflow
The earth is parched and in its folly does not even know
Let me be conduit, viaduct to my world
Channeling you to those in need
    there's so much need
    such grievous need
I see.

Sometimes I feel that I can bear no more
Living on the edge of ecstasy day in day out
    He leaves no place for doubt
I know the way he made it it must be—
Yet the gifts he gives are shrouded in mystery
    in holy paradox:
The more I give the more yet I receive

The emptier I can be the fuller I become
The deeper my wounding the greater my joy
In one surrender lie a triad of victories
Through my dozen dyings I achieve a hundred births
     I love his paradox
     this lunatic paradox
He's taught.

Before he caught me life was safe I knew not even lust
A living death a desert of boredom stagnant in the dust
A void I knew and did not know—he taught me how to trust.
I fled from him for centuries, no willing servant I
Created chaos in confusion, enslaved myself to empty pleasure
Sought my own will, refused to measure
Ignored his Word and spurned his treasure
     while he hung sorrowing by
and wept.

Now that you have me use me Lord though I cry out in pain
Birthing you in holy pain is all I want to do
Dancing laughing knowing growing in your spirit Lord
Burning up and out for you
     a candle with your flame
A glass reflecting you for them
     my searching suffering kin
How well I know them we are one in their wrong too I sin
Blank tablet standing in their view
     inscribed deep with your name
I am.

Committed to you now my God yet still so small and weak
But sinking deep into my weakness there I find your strength
     What crazy paradox!
Only you can give the things you ask back—these I seek
I turn to you as leaf to sun, my all to you I give
How can I ever thank you Lord for saving me from hell?

Let me be conduit, candle, glass
Come ever more in me to dwell
And one day let me drown in you as walls explode—
　　all shall be well
I'll be.

Appendix

UNCHARTED TERRITORY:
Bulimia and Compulsive
Eating Disorder

No book about anorexia nervosa would be complete without some discussion of its "sister" members of the triad of eating disorders, bulimia and compulsive eating disorder (also known as compulsive overeating). I have deliberately avoided making statements about these entities because my *personal* knowledge of them is sketchy, and this book is an intensely personal story rather than a scientific dissertation. Almost everything I know about the allied disorders is derived from books, from my work with bulimic patients, and from what I have learned by intensive observation and participation at OA meetings.

First, a definition of terms: *Bulimia nervosa* is a disorder characterized by recurrent episodes (at least once per week) of binge eating (rapid consumption of a large amount of food in a discrete period of time), each of which is terminated by abdominal pain, sleep, social interruption, self-induced vomiting, or use of laxatives or diuretics. The bulimic is aware that the eating pattern is abnormal and fears she will not be able to stop eating voluntarily once the binge starts. She experiences depression and self-loathing following the binges and has an intense fear of fatness leading to repeated attempts to lose weight by fasting and/or purging by vomiting or laxative or diuretic use.[1] Nevertheless the bulimic maintains a relatively normal body weight and the "relentless pursuit of thinness" characterizing the anorexic is not seen.

It should be noted that almost half of us with *anorexia nervosa* also binge and less frequently purge on occasion, yet the central hallmark of our disease remains the intense fear of obesity (which does not diminish as weight loss progresses) and the drive for an unrealistically low body weight. As a result, when sick we are all emaciated, having lost at least 15 percent of our original body weight and maintaining our weight at less than 85 percent of average weight for height. All of us have cessation of our menses for at least three consecutive months, due to our starvation.[2] Such is not necessarily the case in bulimia.

The diagnostic criteria for *compulsive eating disorder* are less clear, but it can probably best be viewed as recurrent episodes of binge eating followed neither by purging nor by fasting sufficient to undo the progressive weight gain caused by the bingeing. It is easy to see the similarities between this disorder and bulimia, but what may be less evident is what I have tentatively concluded from my research into OA, that compulsive eating is merely the "opposite side of the coin" from anorexia. Whereas the anorexic is driven to starve, the compulsive overeater is driven to eat. The obsessionality and the fueling by guilt, the secrecy and the destructive isolation, the terror of losing control and the spiritual fragmentation, are identical. So too is the possibility of recovery through the Twelve Steps, and it is interesting that the overeaters have recognized this so much sooner than we starvers. Perhaps the reason for that is the fact that our disease results, at least initially, in a physical appearance (thinness) that is currently socially applauded rather than ridiculed and shunned like the obesity of the overeater. This initial public approval helps us maintain our denial that we have a disease, and serves to bolster the false self-esteem that propels us on our destructive downward spiral.

All who purge, whether bulimic or anorexic, also endure this public scorn. Inducing vomiting by sticking fingers down the throat seems the ultimate "repulsive and disgusting" act, to quote the adjectives used by the furious mother of one bulimic teenager in my practice. (Her daughter, by the way, was sitting at her side in rigid silence listening to this attack on her with an expression in her eyes beyond description. It required all of my courage to continue to meet those eyes.) I must add that even we anorexics who never purge are also subjected to negative judgment and public flagellation of a different sort. For instance, one father of an anorexic, hostile sarcasm dripping from his voice, said to me, "I thought this was just some attention-seeking ploy dreamed up by spoiled little rich girls who have been given too much." His daughter lay near death in the next room as he verbalized this widely held myth. To his credit, he at least possessed the good sense to vent his rage outside of her earshot.

One thing that has become very clear to me, and that is verified in the scientific literature as well, is the fact that bulimia and compulsive overeating occur with dramatically greater frequency in Western societies than does anorexia, and that they are often overlooked or undiagnosed. Because of the absence of emaciation, bulimics and compulsive overeaters are less likely to be noticed and labeled by others. Bulimia, for example, has a reported prevalence in recent studies ranging from 2 percent of women attending a Family Planning Clinic[3] and 10 percent of female shoppers[4] to 19 percent of female college students.[5] One study even found a prevalence of 6 percent among *male* college students.[6] Extensive research in compulsive eating disorder has not been done, but tentative studies suggest that it may affect about 30 percent of obese subjects seeking treatment.[7] (It is important to note that not all compulsive overeaters are massively obese, at least in the earlier stages of their disease, nor are all obese individuals suffering from compulsive eating disorder. Similarly, not all extremely thin persons are suffering from anorexia.)

I am surprised and somewhat saddened by the fact that out of the large number of obese patients in my practice, *not one* has ever volunteered the information that she is suffering from compulsive eating disorder. Surely this striking omission is symptomatic of the profound isolation she endures in her walk. She is so accustomed to being rejected by others as a weak-willed fat slob that she cannot even speak to me of her problem. Am I just as guilty as everyone else of covert prejudice against her? Do I scorn her because she gives in to her cravings for food? Yet did I not "give in" also, every day of my fourteen sick years, to my cravings for starvation and control? Now that I am becoming more knowledgeable about compulsive overeating, am able to connect it with my own disease, and am acquainted with OA, I am becoming more receptive and intuitive with the compulsive eaters lurking in their lonely corridors in my practice and am learning to ask the questions that allow them to share their pain with me.

The astonishing prevalence figures quoted above contrast with a reported prevalence for anorexia of from 0.7 percent of women shoppers[8] to 1–4 percent of female high school and college students.[9] Perhaps the relative rarity of anorexia accounts for why the disease is shrouded in such an aura of mystery and regarded with wonderment and even fear[10] by both lay persons and professional therapists. Perhaps also that is why I have been compelled to write this book, in an attempt to end the mystique, to make the disease comprehensible, as well as to share my path to recovery with you now that it "makes sense" to me. For despite its lesser prevalence, anorexia has the highest mortality rate of the eating disorders. In the words of a clinical psychologist in my acquaintance, "Anorexics make me nervous. They can die on you right when you think you're making progress. Give me bulimics any day."

After reading the above definitions of these disorders, you might be wondering about their precision. Is anorexia really a different disease from bulimia? What about compulsive overeating? Is there really any practical value in drawing up such rigid guidelines for labeling pathology in human beings?

My answer to these questions is again yes and no. I say yes because there are some essential differences between anorexics on the one hand, and bulimics and compulsive overeaters on the other. First of all, the majority of bulimics, and possibly also compulsive overeaters who are not bulimic, have a past history of physical and/or sexual abuse, and a large number of them also suffer from alcohol or drug addictions. Such is not the case in anorexia nervosa. Alcoholism is rare in anorexics, who generally avoid alcohol because of its high caloric content. Furthermore, mind-altering drugs are viewed as symbols of human frailty (a "crutch") and are therefore abhorrent to anyone trapped in the delusion that she is Superwoman, as we anorexics are.

Second, virtually all anorexics have an identical underlying personality structure; what I term "The Good Little Girl Syndrome," characterized by an intense drive for perfection, repression of anger and other "negative" emotions, a constant seeking for the approval of others to compensate for low self-esteem, and assumption of irrational responsibility for others in that we are driven by a need to "keep everyone happy." This has been noted by psychiatrist Hilde Bruch, a world leader in the field of anorexia treatment and a pioneer in research of the disease. She observed that her anorexic patients "came from widely differing backgrounds, but when I first saw them they looked, acted, and sounded amazingly alike."[11] This remarkable similarity is not seen in bulimics and compulsive eaters, who show much greater variety in basic personality type.

Third, as mentioned earlier, bulimics are usually of fairly normal or even above-normal weight during the years of active disease and often have wild fluctuations in weight over short periods of time. This is not true of anorexics, who are all underweight during our years of active disease. After full recovery we usually maintain normal body weight and may struggle to do so in the same way that many healthy individuals in our society fight "the battle of the bulge." Compulsive eaters are, not surprisingly, all obese before they enter recovery.

Finally, the physical complications of bulimia are different from those of anorexia. Electrolyte imbalance may be even more dramatic because of the vomiting and use of laxatives and diuretics. Inflammation of the esophagus and extensive decay of the teeth caused by stomach acid, lung complications from vomiting, and permanent loss of tone in the bowel caused by the chronic use of stimulating laxatives are other difficult problems.[12] Death results from cardiac arrhythmia as in anorexia, or from suicide. (Roughly half of anorexia deaths are also due to suicide.[13]) Massive obesity from compulsive eating carries a different set of complications. Diabetes or high blood pressure may be triggered. Joint deterioration causing chronic pain is a frequent problem. Respiratory problems and heart failure may occur in the worst cases. I suspect that depression may result in suicide here as well, but could find no research in this area.

I believe it is important for everyone working with individuals suffering from eating disorders to be aware of these basic differences among them so all aspects of a person's disease may be addressed.

Yet there is a danger in categorization. All human beings are unique and complex creatures functioning within a dynamic social and environmental system. When professionals indulge their penchant for labels and diagnostic criteria, a subtle rigidity of approach may enter the therapeutic relationship, prejudices and preconceptions come into play, and the interaction between the individuals may be insidiously forced into a predetermined script lurking in the therapist's mind. Worse still, the therapist may be further propelled into his or her own disease, one that is almost universal in Western health care professionals, of treating the sick person as an object. Subject-object relationships are inherently pathological,[14] in my experience, and never give birth to the positive change seen in healthy relationships of equals participating in a mutual journey of exploration and discovery.

I therefore believe it more profitable to view the victims of eating disorders as individuals whose precise clinical picture and progression over time will be as varied as the fingerprints of the human beings involved. It is well recognized that the eating disorders form a continuum,[15] with the exact diagnosis in a given sufferer at a given time being frequently obscure. Furthermore, individuals may swing from one point on the spectrum to another.

The reader might even wonder at this point whether I suffered from combined anorexia and bulimia. How can anyone who eats three dozen gingersnaps or a quart of ice cream every day say that she is not bingeing on food? A valid question, but it must be emphasized that I maintained *rigid control* of my caloric intake at essentially all times throughout my illness. I lost weight steadily during the years when I ate gingersnaps, and I maintained a constant but well below-normal weight during the years when I ate ice cream. Nor did I experience any self-loathing or depression after ingesting my "fix" each day. Rather I felt triumphantly in control most of the time, even while another level of my psyche knew that I was *being controlled* by a demon. My reason for eating a quart of ice cream every day was very simple: It was a pleasurable and efficient way to stay in control of my caloric intake, which I carefully regulated to maintain a weight about 15 percent below my normal weight. My unconscious "bargain" with the demon was that I would do what it demanded provided it allowed me enough calories to keep my weight at this level. I could not maintain my denial if I were lying in a hospital bed. I could not pretend that my life was still manageable if I were not functioning as a successful young physician admired by all. It is true that I did binge (lose control of my caloric intake) at very rare intervals during the early years of my illness, but at no time did I purge in any fashion, so I must maintain that I was not really bulimic.

Despite my lack of personal knowledge I can be fairly certain that most bulimics and compulsive overeaters experience their disease, once it has progressed to a severe full-blown stage, in the same essential fashion as do we anorexics: as a demon that possesses their minds and drives them to do that which their healthier side does not want to do, and which they feel utterly helpless to do anything about. I make this assertion based on discussions I have had with individuals and from observing OA in action.

Bulimics sometimes fit into OA groups very well. Anorexics do not, as discussed in chapter 33. If Anorexics Anonymous is established, would it be appropriate for anorexics and bulimics to come together to seek common healing? I think this might be possible in some cases, but it would be important for the bulimics present to be in an anorexic phase of their disease in order for the healing connection to be established within the group. I am reminded of something I was told by one of my patients, possibly the sickest anorexic I have ever known, a young woman who has come very close to death three times in the last two years of her illness. During the year before I met her, she was forced into group therapy by a psychiatrist, a specialist in eating disorders, who was caring for her in hospital. The group consisted of all the anorexics and bulimics on the ward at the time. As my patient listened to others talk about their experiences of sexual abuse and alcohol addiction she felt utterly alienated and *guilty* about being there. "I wasn't raped when I was eight," she told me. "I felt as though I had no right to be sick or to be there." Needless to say, she experienced no positive growth whatsoever during this time.

The healing in Twelve-Step programs originates in the profound experience of *interconnectedness* between the members of the group. It is through learning to trust others and to trust the process itself that individuals are empowered to heal their wounds, one step at a time. It is essential never to lose sight of the fact that every addict, whether anorexic or alcoholic or bulimic or codependent, *must heal herself*, with the critical assistance of her Higher Power to provide the strength to do so. Initially she may see this Higher Power as residing outside herself (in the group or in an individual facilitator, for example), but in the fullness of recovery she will come to know the Power is also within her, filling the deepest caverns of her being, and that it is the One who has been there all along, though she could not hear its hauntingly beautiful melody before over the cacophony of her disease. I liken the Higher Power to water and myself to a fish. I swim in the water, I breathe it into myself through open gills. It flows through me and sustains me and takes me where I would go. I am not the water, yet I am of the water. It is in me, I belong in it, I am absolutely dependent on it for my survival. If I leap onto the shore where I do not belong, I will most certainly die.

Because of this requirement for deep connection if healing is to occur, it is important that Anorexics Anonymous be a relatively homogeneous group, so that the members come to discover how much we have in common. In this safe place we can begin to do our work, we can nurture ourselves and one another, we can go where we must and do what we must to conquer the enemy we share, not through brute force or greater control or willpower, but through the letting go of the illusion of control and self-sufficiency, through surrender of barricades, through the strength that is born of weakness and vulnerability.

Twelve-Step programs that work are always open to all who feel they belong there. Exclusivity is anathema to a living Twelve-Step group. So I think Anorexics Anonymous will do well to open its doors to any bulimic who feels she belongs in our midst. The division between our organization and OA will be self-regulating. Each individual will find her own niche, the place where she experiences the greatest progress in healing. Some persons might opt to attend both groups in varying proportions at different times in their lives, determined by their fluctuating needs.

This would be analogous to persons suffering from combined alcohol and drug addictions—an extremely common phenomenon in my experience. In my practice the vast majority of drug abusers are also alcoholic, and a significant minority of alcoholics are also addicted to other drugs (cocaine, sedatives, and narcotics being predominant at the present time). When these individuals move into recovery, they often attend both AA and Narcotics Anonymous for a time, but soon come to express a preference for one or the other, determined by the amount of healing they experience in the two settings.

Contact information:
Joan M. Johnston, M.D.
#405, 10830 Jasper Avenue
Edmonton, Alberta T5J 2B3
Canada

F o o t n o t e s

Foreword

1. S. Lunn, "Individual Psychotherapeutic Treatment of Anorexia Nervosa," *Acta Psychiatr Scand Suppl.* 361 (1990) 82:23–28.

Chapter 5

1. M. Sim, *Guide to Psychiatry* (London: E. & S. Livingstone, 1969), 273–80.

Chapter 13

1. J. Taylor, "Fire and Rain" (New York: EMI Blackwood Music Inc. and Country Road Music Inc., 1969, 1970).
2. A. W. Schaef, *When Society Becomes an Addict* (San Francisco: Harper & Row, 1987), 51, 88–90.

Chapter 30

1. H. B. Woolf, et al., eds., *Webster's New Collegiate Dictionary* (Springfield, MA: Merriam, 1977), 734.
2. A. W. Schaef, *Beyond Therapy, Beyond Science* (San Francisco: HarperCollins, 1992), 91.
3. M. S. Peck, *The Road Less Traveled* (New York: Simon & Schuster, 1978), 11.
4. Ibid., 221–59.
5. H.D. Thoreau, *Walden*, in *Beyond Geography: The Western Spirit Against the Wilderness*, F. Turner (New York: Viking Press, 1980), ix.
6. L. K. G. Hsu, "The Diagnosis of Anorexia Nervosa," in *The Eating Disorders*, ed. B. J. Blinder, B. F. Chaitin, and R. S. Goldstein (New York: PMA Publishing Corp., 1988), 236.

Chapter 31

1. A. W. Schaef, *When Society Becomes an Addict* (San Francisco: Harper & Row, 1987), 21.
2. P. Garfinkel and D. Garner, *Anorexia Nervosa—A Multidimensional Perspective* (New York: Brunner/Mazel, 1982), 329, 341.
3. T. R. Drews, *Getting Them Sober, Volume One* (South Plainfield, NJ: Bridge Publishing, 1980).
4. P. Leichner and A. Gertler, "The Epidemiology of Anorexia Nervosa," in *The Eating Disorders*, ed. B. J. Blinder, B. F. Chaitin, and R. S. Goldstein, (New York: PMA Publishing, 1988), 137–39.
5. N. P. Spack, "Medical Complications of Anorexia Nervosa and Bulimia," in *Theory and Treatment of Anorexia Nervosa and Bulimia*, ed. S. W. Emmett (New York: Brunner/Mazel, 1985), 5–15.
6. A. W. Schaef, *Beyond Therapy*, 31.

Chapter 32

1. *The Big Book* of Alcoholics Anonymous, 3rd ed. (New York: Alcoholics Anonymous World Services, 1976), 59–60.
2. Schaef, *Beyond Therapy*, 8.
3. M. Eckhart in *Original Blessing*, M. Fox (Santa Fe, NM: Bear & Company, 1983), 277.

Chapter 33

1. S. Orbach, "Visibility/Invisibility: Social Considerations in Anorexia Nervosa—A Feminist Perspective," in *Theory and Treatment of Anorexia and Bulimia*, ed. S. W. Emmett (New York: Brunner/Mazel, 1985), 132.
2. N. P. Spack, "Medical Complications of Anorexia Nervosa and Bulimia," in *Theory and Treatment of Anorexia Nervosa and Bulimia*, ed. S. W. Emmett (New York: Brunner/Mazel, 1985), 14.
3. A. W. Schaef, *When Society Becomes an Addict* (San Francisco: Harper & Row, 1987), 59.
4. S. Wegscheider-Cruse, "Co-Dependency: The Therapeutic Void," in *Co-Dependency: An Emerging Issue* (Pompano Beach, FL: Health Communication, 1984), 1.
5. A. W. Schaef, *Co-Dependence: Misunderstood—Mistreated* (San Francisco: Harper Collins, 1986), 21–23.

Chapter 34

1. H. Bassoe and I. Eskeland, "A Prospective Study of 133 Patients with Anorexia Nervosa. Treatment and Outcome," *Acta Psychiatr Scand*, 65 (1982): 127–33.
2. P. E. Garfinkel, D. M. Garner, and D. S. Goldbloom, "Eating Disorders: Implications for the 1990's," *Canadian Journal of Psychiatry*, 32 (1987): 624-30.
3. D. B. Herzog, M. B. Keller, M. Strober, C. Yeh, and S. Y. Pai, "The Current Status of Treatment for Anorexia Nervosa and Bulimia Nervosa," *International Journal of Eating Disorders*, 12 (1992) 2: 215–20.
4. S. Lunn, "Individual Psychotherapeutic Treatment of Anorexia Nervosa," *Acta Psychiatr Scand Suppl.* 361 (1990) 82: 23–28.
5. Ibid., 24.
6. S. Orbach, "Visibility/Invisibility: Social Considerations in Anorexia Nervosa—A Feminist Perspective," in *Theory and Treatment of Anorexia and Bulimia*, ed. S. W. Emmett (New York: Brunner/Mazel, 1985), 128.
7. A. W. Schaef, *Beyond Therapy, Beyond Science* (San Francisco: HarperCollins, 1992), 148.
8. Ibid., 30.
9. P. Leichner and A. Gertler, "The Epidemiology of Anorexia Nervosa," in *The Eating Disorders*, ed. B. J. Blinder, B. F. Chaitin, and R. S. Goldstein (New York: PMA Publishing, 1988), 131.

10. R. H. Ratnasuriya, I. Eisler, G. I. Szmukler, and G. F. M. Russell, "Anorexia Nervosa: Outcome and Prognostic Factors after Twenty Years," *British Journal of Psychiatry*, 158 (1991): 495–502.

11. L. K. G. Hsu, A. H. Crisp, and J. S. Callender, "Recovery in Anorexia Nervosa— The Patient's Perspective," *International Journal of Eating Disorders*, 11 (1992), 4: 341–50.

12. D. C. Sibley and B. J. Blinder, "Anorexia Nervosa," in *The Eating Disorders*, ed. B. J. Blinder, B. F. Chaitin, and R. S. Goldstein (New York: PMA Publishing, 1988), 247–58.

13. P. Garfinkel and D. Garner, *Anorexia Nervosa—A Multidimensional Perspective* (New York: Brunner/Mazel, 1982).

14. Ratnasuriya et al., "Anorexia Nervosa."

15. J. H. Rosenvinge and S. O. Mouland, "Outcome and Prognosis of Anorexia Nervosa," *British Journal of Psychiatry*, 156 (1990): 92–97.

16. Hsu et al., "Recovery in Anorexia Nervosa."

17. Rosenvinge, "Outcome and Prognosis."

18. K. Halmi, "Pragmatic Information on the Eating Disorders," *Psychiatric Clinics of North America*, 5 (1982): 371–77.

19. A. W. Schaef, *Co-Dependence: Misunderstood—Mistreated* (San Francisco: Harper & Row, 1987), 14.

20. *The Big Book* of Alcoholics Anonymous, 3rd ed. (New York: Alcoholics Anonymous World Services, 1976), 564.

21. Schaef, *Beyond Therapy*, 23.

22. C. P. Estés, *Women Who Run With the Wolves* (New York: Ballantine, 1992), 6–14.

23. Schaef, *Beyond Therapy*, 127–33.

24. *National Eating Disorder Information Centre Bulletin*. Toronto: National Eating Disorder Information Centre, 7 (August 1992): 3.

25. M. Fox, *A Spirituality Named Compassion* (San Francisco: HarperCollins, 1979), 79–87.

26. A. W. Schaef, *When Society Becomes an Addict* (San Francisco: Harper & Row, 1987), 112–30.

27. Schaef, *Beyond Therapy*, 208–9.

28. Fox, *Original Blessing*, 49.

29. Fox, *Spirituality Named Compassion*, 142–52.

30. Schaef, *Beyond Therapy*, 93.

31. Fox, *Spirituality Named Compassion*, 147.

32. M. S. Peck, *The People of the Lie* (New York: Simon & Schuster, 1983), 40.

33. L. Blair in Fox, *Spirituality Named Compassion*, 144.

34. D. R. Griffin, *The Reenchantment of Science: Postmodern Proposals* (Albany: State University of New York Press, 1988), xiii.

35. Schaef, *Beyond Therapy*, 197–236.

36. M. Fox, *The Coming of the Cosmic Christ* (San Francisco: HarperCollins, 1988), 13–34.

37. Schaef, *Beyond Therapy*, 298–301.

38. Fox, *Original Blessing*, 46–51.

39. W. Wordsworth, "Intimations of Immortality" in *Adventures in English Literature*, ed. R. B. Inglis, D. A. Stauffer, and C. E. Larsen (Canadian Edition: W. I. Gage and Company, 1952), 360.

40. C. S. Lewis, *The Silver Chair* (New York: Macmillan, 1953), 150.

41. Estés, *Women Who Run*, 53.

42. Schaef, *Beyond Therapy*, 128–33.

43. Fox, *Spirituality Named Compassion*, 79–80.

44. Estés, *Women*, 45.

45. Ibid., 46.

46. Ibid., 54.

47. Ibid., 56.

48. Ibid., 46.

49. Ibid., 56.

50. Ibid., 58.

51. Ibid., 56.

52. Ibid., 64–65.

53. Peck, *People of the Lie*, 37.

54. Ibid., 42.

55. Ibid., 207.

56. Schaef, *Beyond Therapy*, 6–7.

57. Ibid., 9.

58. Fox, *Original Blessing*, 11–26.

59. Fox, *Coming of the Cosmic Christ*, 181–86.

60. Fox, *Spirituality Named Compassion*, 2–14.

61. Peck, *People of the Lie*, 268–69.

62. Schaef, *Beyond Therapy*, 120.

63. Peck, *People of the Lie*, 204–5.

Chapter 35

1. M. S. Peck, *People of the Lie* (New York: Simon & Schuster, 1983), 68.

2. A. W. Schaef, *Beyond Therapy, Beyond Science* (San Francisco: Harper & Row, 1992), 132–33.

3. Ibid., 131.

4. Ibid., 133.

5. Ibid., 133.

6. A. W. Schaef, *When Society Becomes an Addict* (San Francisco: Harper & Row, 1987), 16–17.

7. Schaef, *Beyond Therapy*, 139.

8. Peck, *People of the Lie*, 208.

9. C. S. Lewis, *The Silver Chair* (New York: Macmillan, 1953), 150.

10. Schaef, *Beyond Therapy*, 33.

11. Peck, *People of the Lie*, 212–53.

12. M. Fox, *Original Blessing* (Santa Fe, NM: Bear & Company, 1983), 140–47.

13. Schaef, *Beyond Therapy*, 146.

14. Ibid., 271.

15. Schaef, *When Society Becomes an Addict*, 18.

16. Schaef, *Beyond Therapy*, 130–85.

17. Ibid., 130.

18. Ibid., 130.

19. Ibid., 180.

20. Ibid., 171–72.

21. Ibid., 275.

22. A. de Saint-Exupéry, *The Little Prince*, trans. Katherine Woods (Orlando, FL: Harcourt Brace & Company, 1943), 89.

23. M. Bodo, *Francis: The Journey and the Dream* (Cincinnati, OH: St. Anthony Messenger Press, 1988), 14.

24. S. Griffin, *Woman and Nature:* (New York: Harper Colophon, 1978), 219.

A Final Word

1. A. W. Schaef, *When Society Becomes an Addict* (San Francisco: Harper & Row, 1987), 15.

2. C. G. Jung, "Psychology and Literature," in *The Creative Process*, ed. B. Ghiselin (New York: Mentor, 1952), 221.

Appendix

1. *Diagnostic and Statistical Manual of Mental Disorders, Third Edition, Revised (DSM-III-R)*. 1987. Washington D.C.: American Psychiatric Association. Diagnostic criteria modified slightly by L. K. G. Hsu, "Classification and Diagnosis of the Eating Disorders," in *The Eating Disorders*, ed. B. J. Blinder, B. F. Chaitin, and R. S. Goldstein (New York: PMA Publishing, 1988), 237.

2. Ibid., 236.

3. P. J. Cooper and C. G. Fairburn, "Binge-Eating and Self-Induced Vomiting in the Community. A Preliminary Study," *British Journal of Psychiatry*, 142 (1983): 139–144.

4. H. G. Pope, J. I. Hudson, and D. Yurgelun-Todd, "Anorexia and Nervosa and Bulimia Among 300 Suburban Women Shoppers," *American Journal of Psychiatry*, 141 (1984): 292–94.

5. H. G. Pope, J. I. Hudson, D. Yurgelun-Todd, et al., "Prevalence of Anorexia Nervosa and Bulimia in Three Student Populations," *International Journal of Eating Disorders, 3* (1984): 45–51.

6. K. A. Halmi, J. R. Falk, and E. Schwartz, "Binge-Eating and Vomiting: A Survey of a College Population," *Psychol Med, 11* (1981): 697–706.

7. J. Gormally, S. Black, S. Daston, et al., "The Assessment of Binge Eating Severity Among Obese Persons," *Addictive Behaviors, 7* (1982): 47–55.

8. Pope, et al., "Anorexia and Nervosa and Bulimia Among 300 Suburban Women Shoppers," 292–94.

9. Pope, et al., "Prevalence of Anorexia Nervosa and Bulimia in Three Student Populations," 45–51.

10. S. Orbach, "Visibility/Invisibility: Social Considerations in Anorexia Nervosa—A Feminist Perspective," in *Theory and Treatment of Anorexia and Bulimia,* ed. S. W. Emmett (New York: Brunner/Mazel, 1985), 128.

11. H. Bruche, *The Golden Cage* (Cambridge, MA: Harvard University Press, 1978), xi.

12. N. P. Spack, "Medical Complications of Anorexia Nervosa and Bulimia," in *Theory and Treatment of Anorexia and Bulimia,* ed. S. W. Emmett (New York: Brunner/Mazel, 1985).

13. N. Butler, "An Overview of Anorexia Nervosa," in *Anorexia and Bulimia Nervosa,* ed. D. Scott (London: Croom Helm, 1988.)

14. M. Fox, *A Spirituality Named Compassion* (San Francisco: HarperCollins, 1979), 2–4.

15. W. Vandereycken, "Anorexia Nervosa in Adults," in *The Eating Disorders,* ed. B. J. Blinder, B. F. Chaitin, and R. S. Goldstein (New York: PMA Publishing, 1988), 295–304.